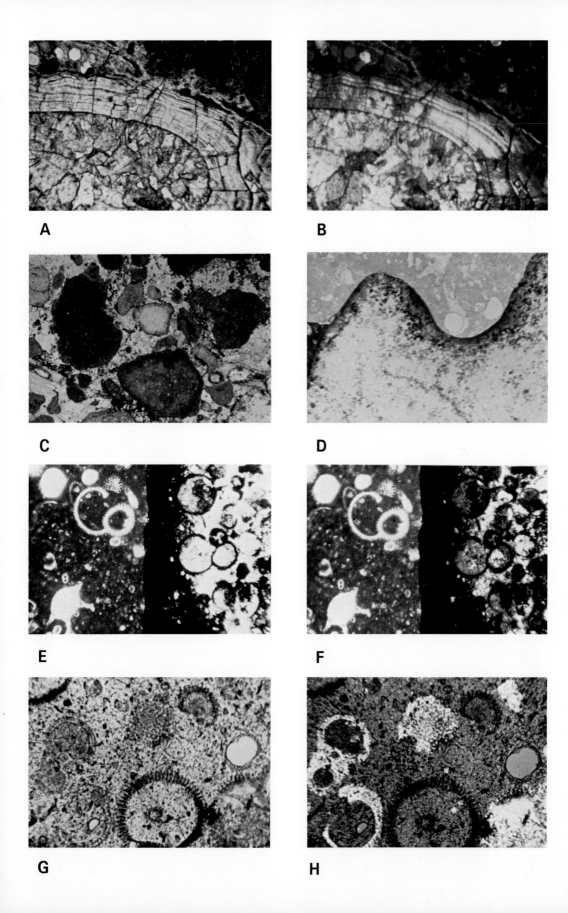

A

B

C

D

E

F

G

H

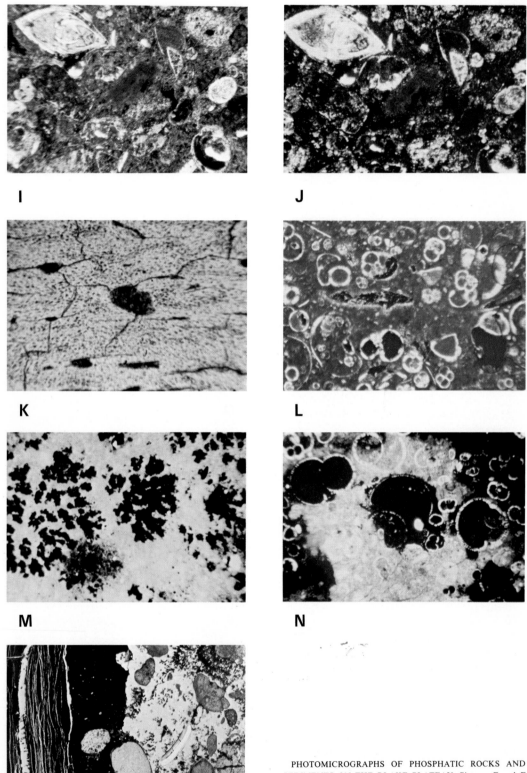

PHOTOMICROGRAPHS OF PHOSPHATIC ROCKS AND SEDIMENTS ON THE BLAKE PLATEAU. Pictures E and F are enlargements of the dark interface in D. Picture O should be oriented with dark portion at the top. For detailed explanation see Fig. 8 text, Manheim et al., page 125.

NE PHOSPHORITES—GEOCHEMISTRY,

OCCURRENCE, GENESIS

A Symposium held at the Xth International
Congress on Sedimentology in Jerusalem,
Israel, 9–14 July 1978

Edited by
Y. K. Bentor
Hebrew University, Jerusalem, Israel
and
Scripps Institution of Oceanography
La Jolla, California

Special Publication No. 29

Tulsa, Oklahoma, U.S.A.   November, 1980

A Publication of

The Society of Economic Paleontologists and Mineralogists

a division of

The American Association of Petroleum Geologists

COMPOSED AND PRINTED BY
EDWARDS BROTHERS, INC.
ANN ARBOR, MICH. U.S.A.

CONTENTS

INTRODUCTION

Y. K. BENTOR
Hebrew University, Jerusalem, Israel
and
Scripps Institution of Oceanography,
La Jolla, California

During the Xth International Congress on Sedimentology, a symposium on marine phosphorites was held in Jerusalem, Israel, 9–14 July 1978. This volume contains the papers delivered at this meeting and represents the main interests inspiring the study of phosphorites at the end of the seventies. Considerable emphasis is placed now on the geochemistry of phosphorites. The paper of Z. S. Altschuler tries to establish a world average of the trace element composition of sedimentary apatites and phosphorites and to explain its salient features, while L. Prévôt and J. Lucas investigate the trace element distribution between phosphorites and associated shales and limestones and their implication for phosphatogenesis. The papers of J. M. McArthur and Lucas et al. deal with changes in mineralogy and major and minor element chemistry of phosphorites during submarine and subaerial weathering. Two papers discuss isotope geochemical aspects, a relatively new branch of phosphorite research. Burnett et al. summarize the U- and Th-evidence for a recent age of the phosphorites of Peru, whereas Nathan and Nielsen study the S-isotopes of apatite and associated gypsum concluding that phosphorites formed during early diagenesis in a marine reducing environment.

The study of, mostly fossil, phosphorite occurrences on the present sea floor is very actively pursued at present and not less than five papers in this volume deal with it. G. F. Birch in his study of the phosphorites on the western margin of S. Africa stresses the two mechanisms of replacement and direct precipitation. P. Giresse investigates phosphorus enrichment in recent and subrecent sediments on the tropical Atlantic shelf of Africa and the climatic and oceanographic factors controlling it. F. T. Manheim's studies of the Blake Plateau phosphorites are of particular interest as they are partly related to the formation of manganese nodules. One of his conclusions is that during their formation—mainly Miocene—the Gulf Stream must at least temporarily have stopped flowing through this area. Finally, D. J. Cullen describes the submarine phosphorites of the Chatham Rise which are peculiar in some of their trace element features (U, Eu); moreover upwelling, frequently accepted as a condition of phosphorite formation, can hardly be suggested for this area.

The next five papers deal with some onshore deposits thus far less well covered in the literature. Lucas et al. describe the stratigraphy, mineralogy and major element chemistry of a phosphorite deposit in southern Turkey, and Axelrod et al. the Israeli occurrences with emphasis on the relationship between textural properties and possibilities of industrial beneficiation. I. Jarvis studies the phosphatic chalk sedimentation in the Senonian section of the Anglo-Paris Basin, an area which, during phosphatogenesis, was probably very unlike those of Recent phosphorite formation; P. Giresse describes Maastrichtian phosphorites of the Congo, attributing to them, at least partly, a deltaic origin. Boujo et al. discuss the stratigraphy and tectonic setting of Eocene phosphorites in western Senegal.

The remaining papers attack various aspects of phosphorite genesis. H. E. Gaudette and W. B. Lyons study the behavior of phosphorus during the interaction between pore water and carbonate sediments in the Bahamas, a process generally considered crucial for phosphorite formation; G. S. Odin and R. Letolle compare the environments of glauconitization and phosphatization arguing that, as glauconite genesis is now probably better understood, such a comparison might shed light on the less well understood formation of phosphorites. R. P. Sheldon, recognizing that Recent phosphorite formation might be an imperfect clue to phosphatogenesis in the past, speculates on possible long term changes in oceanic composition and circulation creating optimum conditions for phosphatogenesis. Y. Kolodny, in the final paper, draws some, mainly geochemical, conclusions concerning phosphorite genesis from the study of Recent sea floor phosphorites.

The editor hopes that the present volume might give an instructive cross-section of present ideas in phosphorite research, of the results obtained and the perplexities suffered.

SEPM SPECIAL PUBLICATION NO. 29, P. 3–18, NOVEMBER 1980

PHOSPHORITES—THE UNSOLVED PROBLEMS

Y. K. BENTOR
Hebrew University, Jerusalem, Israel
and
Scripps Institution of Oceanography
La Jolla, California 92093

ABSTRACT

The first part of this publication outlines the course of phosphorite research with emphasis on some of the major breakthroughs: the discovery of phosphate nodules on the present sea-floor, the recognition of F-carbonate-apatite as a separate mineral species, Kasakov's (1937) upwelling theory and the discovery of Recent marine phosphorites, as proven by the U-disequilibrium method.

The unsolved problems of phosphogenesis are the subject of the second part. The oceanic P-cycle is only sketchily known. The distribution of P in ocean water is much better documented, but in the absence of reliable data concerning the solubility of F-carbonate-apatite in sea water it is hard to decide, if oceanic P-concentrations reach the saturation level for apatite. Phosphorite formation seems to be connected with oceanic upwelling, but estuarine areas are another possible site. The high Mg-content of sea water seems to restrict phosphate precipitation at the present time to diagenetic processes within the sediments. Here, pH has to be relatively low and Eh strongly negative, but the optimal values are unknown. The study of trace element concentrations in phosphorites has greatly added to our understanding of their genesis, but many of these data cannot yet be interpreted. The meaning of the cyclical arrangement of phosphorite sequences alternating with high-silica rocks is not well understood. Finally, the mechanism of Recent phosphorite formation by diagenesis of siliceous oozes rich in organic matter, in areas of oceanic upwelling, seems not to be valid for many ancient phosphorites.

INTRODUCTION: AN OUTLINE OF THE HISTORY OF PHOSPHORITE RESEARCH

Phosphorites, i.e. sedimentary rocks with higher than usual phosphate contents, are present, not infrequently, in the sedimentary rock column of almost all ages since 2200 m.y.B.P. (Early Proterozoic). While most common sedimentary rocks contain a small amount of phosphate—usually in the range of 0.x%—phosphorites **sensu stricto** are much richer and can contain up to about 37% P_2O_5. The boundary between non-phosphoritic phosphate-bearing sediments and phosphorites is arbitrary, but most authors would place it at a value of 15–20% P_2O_5. The term phosphorite, as used at present, is confined to sedimentary rocks of marine origin, thus excluding igneous phosphate concentrations—mainly in low-silica alkaline ring dike complexes and carbonatite stocks (e.g. Kola Peninsula, USSR, Palabora, South Africa) and continental, including ocean island bird or bat guano deposits. Lacustrine phosphorites are very rare and have been found only in four saline lake deposits, all in the Rocky Mountain region, among them the Green River Formation in Wyoming (Love, 1964). The beds are thin and phosphate contents are low. The main phosphate mineral is apatite, but locally the rare mineral bradleyite, $Na_3PO_4 \cdot MgCO_3$, is dominant. In every case the phosphorites are related to organic-rich sediments.

During the earlier phases of sedimentological research phosphorites did not receive much attention, although small scale exploitation had started as early as 1847 in Suffolk (England). This situation did not change even when, in 1874, the *Challenger* Expedition dredged phosphorite nodules from the Agulhas Bank, South Africa (Murray and Renard, 1891). Subsequently, many similar occurrences were discovered at various parts of the present ocean floor, mostly in the vicinity of coast lines, off North Spain (Lucas et al., 1978; Lamboy, 1976), Morocco (Summerhayes et al., 1972), the Atlantic coast of southern Africa (Parker et al., 1972; Summerhayes, 1973; Summerhayes et al., 1973; see also Birch, this volume), Chatham Rise off New Zealand (Cullen, 1975; Cullen et al., 1977; Cullen, this volume), Blake Plateau (Manhein, this volume), California Borderland (Dietz et al., 1942), off Baja California (d'Anglejan, 1967, 1968) and elsewhere. For many years these occurrences were tacitly assumed by most authors to be of Recent origin because of their position on the present ocean floor, although the work of Cayeux (1934) on the nodules of the Agulhas Bank and that of Dietz et al. (1942) and Emery et al. (1949) on the phosphorites of the Californian Borderland produced convincing geological evidence for a pre-Pleistocene age of formation.

Interest in the study of phosphorites and their mode of origin rose during the 1930's mainly under the impact of the rapidly increasing use of phosphorites as industrial raw-material. About 125 million tons are, at present [1978], produced annually, of which the United States produces 40.0%, the USSR 19.8%, and Morocco 15.8%. The bulk of phosphorite goes into fertilizers and smaller amounts into detergents, water softening agents, pharmaceuticals, metal protection and gasoline additives, or serve as animal food.

The large phosphorite deposits of the world, known mostly for a long time: the Western Field of the United States in Utah, Wyoming and Idaho (McKelvey et al., 1959; Gulbrandsen, 1960; Sheldon, 1963; Cressman et al., 1964; Swanson, 1973), the Cambrian deposits of central and eastern Asia, particularly those of Karatau in the Soviet Union (Gimmelfarb et al., 1966), the Mediterranean phosphate belt, extending from Tunisia to Morocco (Salvan, 1952; Visse, 1952) and the pebble phosphates of Florida (Cathcart et al., 1952, 1953; Cathcart, 1963) were all carefully studied and mapped in much detail. The latter represents a special case, as these phosphorites are not *in situ* but were reworked, concentrated and upgraded by subaerial and submarine transport and weathering during the Pliocene from phosphorite nodules originally deposited in a dispersed form in the Miocene Hawthorn Formation (Cathcart et al., 1953). Simultaneously, many new, although mostly smaller, phosphorite deposits were discovered, e.g. in the former Spanish Sahara, the Negev, Israel, Latin America and Australia. The mineralogy and petrography of phosphorites was studied in great detail. The most comprehensive of these earlier petrographic studies are the three volumes published by L. Cayeux between 1939 and 1950. All these field and laboratory studies were made on fossil on-land deposits and the environment of their deposition could only be reconstructed indirectly by stratigraphic, petrographic and paleogeographic reasoning. The major conclusions arrived at were the following:

1) There is only one, although chemically rather variable, mineral which carries practically all the phosphorus of all phosphorites; this is F-carbonate-apatite (Deer et al., 1962). The nature of this mineral, as distinct from the common F-apatite of igneous rocks, was long debated and first proved on the basis of its characteristic X-ray diffraction pattern by Altschuler et al. (1952). Its probable crystal chemistry has since been established with some degree of confidence. A significant amount, generally 3–6% of the mineral weight, of PO_4^{-3} is replaced by CO_3^{-2}, the charge difference being partly compensated by any of a number of possible additional substitutions such as $Ca^{+2} \rightarrow Na^+$, $PO_4^{-3} \rightarrow SiO_4^{-4}$. The C^{+4}-ion of the carbonate does not fill the place of P^{+5} of the original PO_4^{-3} group but sits in the center of one of the four faces of the PO_4^{-3}-tetrahedron;

the remaining O^{-2} is partly replaced by OH^- or F^-. The substitution of PO_4^{-3} by the CO_3F^{-3}-group was first suggested by Borneman-Starynkevich and Belov (1940) and was firmly established by Smith and Lehr (1966). The apatites of some phosphorites (e.g. those of the Maastrichtian of the Congo) contain considerably less CO_3^{-2}, sometimes barely 1% (e.g. Giresse, this volume), thus approaching F-apatite in composition. This feature has, however, been attributed by several authors (e.g. McArthur, this volume; Lucas et al., this volume) to post-depositional submarine or terrestrial weathering.

Another characteristic feature of F-carbonate-apatite is its high F-content which generally exceeds the stoichiometric amount by about 10%. The excess F replaces O outside the channels of the apatite structure.

In certain phosphorites, some of them exploited (e.g. Bone Valley, Florida; Thiès, Senegal), phosphorus is not contained in F-carbonate-apatite, but in aluminous or—more rarely—ferruginous minerals such as crandallite, millesite, wavellite, strengite, phosphosiderite, and lipscombite (Lucas et al., this volume). These minerals are always secondary, formed during lateritic weathering by reactions between acid groundwater containing phosphate derived from the dissolution of the original apatite and associated aluminous (clay) or ferruginous sediments (Capedecomme, 1952, 1953; Altschuler et al., 1956; Altschuler, 1974; Slansky et al., 1964; Flicoteaux et al., 1977; Lucas et al., this volume).

2) A characteristic feature of many major phosphorite occurrences is the triple association: phosphate-chert or porcellanite-organic matter (unless later oxidized). In Cretaceous and younger deposits chert-porcellanite is derived diagenetically from diatom and radiolarian oozes, while in earlier formations—particularly the Paleozoic (e.g. Karatau [Cambrian], Phosphoria Formation [Permian]) the role of diatoms was taken largely by spongiae. As the elements involved in this trinity, P-C-Si, all have a strongly biophile character, their frequent association lends strong support to the assumption that the main step in the phosphorus concentration from the very low content of seawater—70 ppb—to a value of 15% P in a good phosphorite takes place in the biochemical cycle.

3) In regard to the environment of phosphorite deposition, conclusions were rather vague. The presence of organic matter, and frequently of pyrite, indicates a reducing environment. It seemed, furthermore, that phosphorites formed generally in zones of slow deposition: the rocks of the Phosphoria Formation were deposited at an average rate of about 1 cm/1000 yr. The phosphorites of the Parisian Basin are conspic-

uously connected with hardgrounds (Jarvis, this volume). For the Phosphoria Formation, possibly the best studied phosphorite occurrence, McKelvey and his co-workers (1953) also recognized slow deposition and thought they could distinguish between a shelf environment in which phosphorites are mainly associated with carbonates and a deeper geosynclinal environment characterized by the association phosphorite-black shales-mudstones. Whereas, in the former, phosphorite deposition apparently took place at shallow water depth, they assumed a depth of about 1000 m for the geosynclinal facies (McKelvey, 1967). The last conclusion did not fit well with the paleontological evidence (Yochelson, 1968).

4) It was recognized rather early (since Cossa, 1878) that phosphorites are able to concentrate various *trace elements* (Tooms et al., 1969). One of the most conspicuous among them is U which is generally present in phosphorites in concentrations of 50–150 ppm. No conclusions could be drawn from these observations until very recently.

In 1937, Kazakov published a pioneering paper with which the modern phase of phosphorite research might be said to have started. This paper not only proposed for the first time a comprehensive concept of phosphorite genesis, but is also one of the first attempts to explain the formation of a marine sediment in terms of the physical and chemical dynamics of the ocean. The basic idea of Kazakov was to link phosphorite sedimentation to oceanic upwelling, arguing that as deeper ocean water rises toward the surface, its temperature rises and, in consequence of the diminishing pressure, CO_2 escapes and pH increases. As the solubility of apatite is known to decrease with both increasing temperature and pH, Kazakov concluded that in the upper part of the rising current oversaturation in respect to apatite is obtained and the mineral crystallizes. According to this view, phosphorites are thus purely inorganic precipitates. Although the particular mechanism invoked by Kazakov has by now been refuted, his central idea that upwelling might be an important factor in phosphorite genesis is still very much alive (see p. 000).

The next important step in phosphorite research was the application of the U-disequilibrium method (e.g. Weatherill et al., 1967) to the age determination of sedimentary apatites. The activity-ratio of $^{234}U/^{238}U$ in sea water is not unity but is constant, all over the ocean at 1.15 ± 0.01. The activity-ratio of U taken up from the ocean water into the growing apatite lattice in the above ratio and there sequestered will then tend toward unity. As the half-life of ^{234}U is 2.47×10^5 yr., ages of up to 700,000 yr. can thus be determined. Kolodny and Kaplan (1970) measured phosphorite nodules from various parts of the present ocean floor and found their activity-ratio to be practically 1, i.e. all are older than 700,000 years, thus disproving their supposedly Recent age. For a few years it became doubtful, if sedimentary apatite is being formed at all in the present ocean (Kolodny, 1969). In 1970, however, Baturin et al. described phosphorite nodules from the Namibian shelf which they assumed, for geologic-sedimentologic reasons, to be of Recent origin and proved this assumption in 1972 by using the U-disequilibrium method for the Namibian occurrences as well as for phosphorite nodules found on the upper part of the continental slope off Peru and Chile (Baturin et al., 1972, 1974). Since then, the method has been refined by including ^{232}Th and extensively applied, mainly by Burnett and his co-workers (1977, Veeh et al., 1973, 1974; see also Burnett et al., this volume).

The recognition of oceanic areas in which phosphorites form at present, notwithstanding their small dimensions, when compared with some of the older phosphorite deposits, was a major breakthrough; it made it possible to study the conditions of their genesis by direct observation instead of deducing them by interpreting the environment of deposition of fossil deposits, now on land. Considerable effort was made to collect data on the oceanographic environment favorable for the present formation of phosphorites (e.g. Calvert et al., 1971). The two areas mentioned— the Namibian shelf and the continental slope of Peru-Chile—are still the only areas in which Recent phosphorite deposition has been observed, apart from one find of partially phosphatized sub-recent wood in the Gulf of Tehuantepec (Goldberg and Parker, 1960); additional areas of recent phosphorites, however, might be found in the future. Both areas have several features in common: they represent zones of strong upwelling and high productivity; sedimentation takes place in the oxygen-minimum zone under reducing conditions in the presence of organic matter; in both areas the phosphorite nodules are closely associated with diatomaceous oozes. The depth of deposition is moderate, 60–120 m water depth off Namibia, 200–400 m off Peru-Chile; furthermore, apatite apparently is not crystallizing in the water column above the water-sediment interface, but is probably formed within the sediment in which the organic matter is the main carrier of phosphorus. It was confidently hoped, until the last few years, that a similar regime would explain also the large economic phosphorite deposits formed in the geological past.

The Unsolved Problems

It will be obvious from the foregoing that phosphorite research has made much progress over the last 25 years. Not the least of it is the gradual emergence of a, by now widely if not universally accepted concept, according to which phosphorites are the result of diagenetic processes, taking place in a reducing marine environment, within sediments rich in organic matter. Most present phosphorite research aims to refine this picture. There are, however, numbers of problems concerning phosphorite genesis which are still hardly understood or have never been solved and others which have arisen from the modern concept itself and are challenging its universal applicability. These are discussed in the following section.

Marine Geochemical Cycle of Phosphorus

As a background to a deeper understanding of phosphorite deposition, a good knowledge of the marine geochemical cycle of phosphorus is of great importance. Unfortunately, this cycle is known only in bare outline and the quantities involved are not well established. The input of dissolved P by rivers into the ocean is estimated at about 1.7×10^{12} g/yr., individual estimates varying from 0.4–2.0×10^{12} g/yr. (Emery et al., 1955; Stumm, 1973; Lerman et al., 1975; Pierrou, 1976). Input from the atmosphere (Graham and Duce, 1979) is about 1.4×10^{12} g/yr. P. This figure contains about 0.05×10^{12} g/yr. P of anthropogenic origin. Most of this air-borne phosphorus is, however, insoluble in ocean water; the input of soluble P from the atmosphere into the ocean is estimated to only 0.22×10^{12} g/yr. P. Simultaneously, the ocean contributes about 0.33×10^{12} g/yr. P to the atmosphere, causing a yearly net loss to the ocean of 0.11×10^{12} g, almost 10% of the yearly river input. Another possible source is submarine hydrothermal activity which, although no good data are available, is generally thought to be small. With the now increasing interest in this subject better data may soon be available.

In the case of a steady-state ocean, an assumption admissible for short time-range considerations, but probably wrong for longer geological periods, oceanic sinks should equal the input into the ocean. Again the figures are known only approximately. The P-content of marine clays (~700 ppm) is very nearly the same as that of clays carried by rivers and thus does not affect the balance of dissolved P. The P-content of marine carbonates is only 400 ppm (Garrels et al., 1975; McKelvey, 1973), but in view of the large amount of carbonate precipitation in the present ocean, this sink accounts for more than 30% of all P removed from the ocean. Organic matter, even more important, accounts for more than 40%. Fish-debris, preserved in the sedimentary record accumulate probably only 2% of the total, although estimates as high as 25% have

been proferred (DeVries, 1979). Berner (1973) pointed to an additional and quantitative important sink: metalliferous sediments, mainly P-absorbing iron-hydroxides, abundant in volcanic areas of mid-ocean ridges. This sink has been estimated at 15–40% of the total (Froelich et al., 1977); this seems to be an overestimate and the figure should probably be placed nearer 12% (Froelich et al., in preparation). The sink represented by marine apatite precipitation is the most difficult to estimate in view of the restricted number of recent phosphorite samples dredged thus far. A very rough calculation of the difference between estimated total input into the ocean and the best figures for the sum of all other known sinks, shows that apatite precipitation certainly accounts for less than 10% of all sinks.

The picture emerging is thus very imprecise and is made even more complex by the existence of large cycles internal to the ocean. A flux of about 600 times the river input exists between oceanic biota and the surface water of the ocean, reducing the residence time of P in marine biota to about 50 days (against 50 years for on-land biota). The residence time of P in the surface ocean is therefore only 2.6 yr. against 50,000–100,000 yr. for the deep ocean. Morse (1979) has recently drawn attention to the very strong reflux of P from sediments into the overlying water column, mainly in shelf and slope areas, which might be tens of times greater than the total input by rivers.

The only clear result from this rather confused picture is the fact that apatite precipitation does not control the level of phosphate dissolved in the present ocean.

Dissolved Oceanic Phosphate and the Solubility of F-Carbonate-Apatite

Phosphorus is a rare trace element in ocean water which contains on the average about 70 ppb P (Gulbrandsen and Roberson, 1973). Near-surface waters are everywhere strongly depleted by biological uptake down to a few ppb and locally even less, thus frequently inhibiting biological reproduction. In the zone of organic matter regeneration, the concentration of dissolved phosphate rises sharply to values of 50–100 ppb at a depth of about 200–400 m. From here down to the ocean floor, P-contents remain constant or decline very slightly. Regional differences in the P-content of deep ocean water are conspicuous: 60–100 ppb in the Pacific and Indian Oceans, but only 35–85 ppb in the Atlantic; semi-enclosed ocean basins have frequently markedly lower P-contents; deep water of the Red Sea contains 15 ppb P and that of the Mediterranean even only 6 ppb; values are low as both seas are replenished by depleted surface water only, barriers (Tiran and Gibraltar, respectively) inhibiting the influx of P-richer deeper waters.

The dominant phosphate species in the ocean is HPO_4^{-2} which, in the critical range of pH = 7–8, accounts for 85–90% of all dissolved phosphate. About 44% of it is complexed (Gulbrandsen and Roberson, 1973).

How do these levels of P-concentration in ocean water relate to the solubility of F-carbonate-apatite? Unfortunately, this crucial question cannot be clearly answered at present. The thermodynamical data of F-carbonate-apatite being unknown, apparent solubilities have to be determined by experiment (Roberson, 1966). Because of experimental difficulties these studies have rarely been made on F-carbonate-apatite, but generally an F-apatite, OH-apatite or even amorphous Ca-phosphate. Comprehensive experiments on F-carbonate-apatite were lately been carried out by Atlas (1975, 1979). The results obtained by different authors lead to different and frequently contradictory results. It was realized that the solubility of apatites depends on a variety of factors: the exact chemical composition of the apatite, its crystal size, as well as the composition of the solvent, as Mg^{+2} and Ca^{+2} complexes affect the dissociation constants of phosphate species. Kinetics also complicate the problem as apatite precipitation is affected by the F^-, Mg^{+2} and HCO_3^--concentrations in solution. There exists even the possibility that the notion of solubility might not be applicable to apatite because secondary surface phases seem to form on the mineral creating pseudo-equilibria; at present, not even the nature of these phases is known (e.g. Atlas, 1979).

Therefore, it is evident that we cannot yet answer the question if sea water is or is not saturated with regard to F-carbonate-apatite. There is, however, some evidence that seawater is probably undersaturated: phosphatic skeletal debris (e.g. fish bone) on the sea floor are frequently corroded. Furthermore, F-carbonate-apatite can easily be precipitated from (Mg-poor) sea-water in the laboratory, but only at P-concentrations considerably above those present in natural ocean water (Nathan et al., 1972).

The situation, however, is drastically different for interstitial ocean-water, particularly of sediments rich in organic matter. As the latter is regenerated, large amounts of phosphate are liberated, as sulfate is being reduced. Additional amounts of P are added to the interstitial water by the reduction of phosphate carrying iron-oxyhydroxides. Brooks et al. (1968) and Sholkowitz (1973) found up to 7500 ppb P in interstitial waters of anoxic sediments in basins of the California Borderland. Burnett (1977) quotes a value of 1400 ppb P at a depth of 15 cm in similar sediments

of the Peru shelf and Baturin (1972) found up to 2500 ppb P in the interstitial waters within the phosphatic sediments of the Namibian shelf. Bray et al. (1973) give a value of 6200 ppb P in interstitial water in sediments of Chesapeake Bay. These are values up to 100 times those found in open ocean water and there can be little doubt that they represent oversaturation in respect to apatite. These observations give strong support to the idea that interstitial water in reducing sediments is the ideal habitat of phosphorite formation in the present ocean.

Incidentally, the observation that the bottom water overlying these sediments in the Santa Barbara Basin off California contains 330 ppb P, i.e. 4 times more than Pacific bottom water elsewhere (Sholkowitz, 1973) emphasizes the importance of phosphate reflux.

The Role of Upwelling

When Kazakov introduced the idea of upwelling into phosphorite research, he proposed a dominantly inorganic mechanism for the precipitation of apatite. This particular view has now been abandoned for a number of reasons:

(1) The rate of diffusion of CO_2 by decrease of pressure is very much lower than the velocity of upwelling currents;

(2) Supersaturation of phosphate would occur in or near the photic zone, where it would rapidly be taken up by organisms;

(3) Deep ocean water is not "rich in phosphorus" and most probably considerably undersaturated. It would indeed be a strange coincidence if the relatively small physical changes caused by upwelling in the rising water-mass would cause supersaturation. There are, in fact, many areas of upwelling in the present ocean in which no phosphorite forms today (e.g. Kolodny, in press).

(4) Martens and Harris (1970) showed in laboratory experiments that apatite precipitation is critically dependent on the Mg^{+2}/Ca^{+2}-ratio in the aqueous solution. By adding soluble phosphate to Mg-free seawater apatite crystallized readily, but by applying the same procedure to normal seawater with a Mg^{+2}/Ca^{+2}-ratio of 5.3 they obtained only an amorphous Ca-phosphate precipitate with a molar Ca/P-ratio of 1.35 (instead of 1.67 for apatite). This precipitate did not change to apatite during the eight months of their experiments, but quickly transformed to apatite when immersed in Mg-free seawater. This effect, known as the Mg-inhibition, is the result of distortion of the embryonic apatite lattice by Mg^{+2}-ions replacing Ca^{+2}, a distortion strong enough to inhibit further crystal growth.

This effect seems to rule out altogether apatite crystallization from open sea water.

The concept of inorganic precipitation of apatite from the water column in areas of upwelling seems, therefore, unrealistic at least for the present ocean. Nevertheless, the idea that upwelling plays an essential role in phosphorite genesis is still very much alive. Recent phosphorites appear to form by diagenetic reactions between organic matter-rich sediments and their interstitial water. The amount of P contained at any time in the surface water of any area is much too small to give rise to a phosphorite deposit of any considerable size. This argument takes care of the old theory (Murray and Renard, 1891) of phosphorite formation through catastrophic mass mortality. To form a large deposit high productivity has to be sustained over long periods of time. The most efficient way to do this is by upwelling of ocean water replenishing, continuously or seasonally, the depleted nutrients of the surface waters, including P. Thus, Kazakov's theory turns out to be an excellent case—not rare in science—of a correct idea proposed for the wrong reasons. Most workers today would probably agree that oceanic upwelling is an important, possibly a necessary, certainly not a sufficient factor in phosphogenesis. Two points, frequently misunderstood, should, however, be stressed. Upwelling does not supply "phosphate-rich water." Its effect is to counteract P-depletion of surface water by biological activity by providing a steady, although dilute (rarely more than 70–100 ppb) supply of P (and other nutrients). Second, upwelling does not imply the rise of water from very great depths. Thus, the source of upwelling off the Namibian coast is only about 200 m deep (Calvert and Price, 1971); in fact, water in the zone of regeneration of organic matter, just below the photic zone, is frequently slightly richer in P than deep-ocean water.

Upwelling taps the large deep-ocean water reservoir of phosphate which at the present time contains about 9×10^{16} g P, some 50,000 times the yearly input into the ocean. If potential sites of phosphorite formation are confined to zones of upwelling, this implies a very strong geographical restriction, as these zones constitute at present less than 1% of the oceanic area (Ryther, 1963). Is there any other source capable of supplying phosphorus for phosphorite formation? Some authors have pointed to estuaries to which P would be supplied by rivers: Pevear (1966) for phosphorites in the eastern United States, Giresse (this volume) for the phosphorites of the Congo. The average amount of dissolved P in river water is only 20 ppb, about one quarter that of deep ocean water. Still concentrations of 30–120 ppb P are

found in many estuaries (Redfield et al., 1963). The decisive factor for phosphorite formation, however, is not the P-concentration but the level of productivity and conditions conducive to the preservation of organic matter in the sediments. In some estuaries, particularly those with sills, productivity rivals that found in zones of upwelling (Schelske et al., 1961) and accumulation of organic-rich sediments is not unusual in estuarine zones. Pevear (1966) calculated that in the estuary of the relatively small Altamaha River, Georgia, enough P is available to form a bottom layer of apatite, 5 m thick over the entire estuary in 1 million years. Phosphorites, therefore, could form in areas of this kind, tapping, not the deep ocean P reservoir, but continental drainage. The heavy load of suspended matter, however, carried by many rivers, would probably swamp the phosphorites deposited in their estuaries. It is certainly not coincidence that all Recent, and probably many older, phosphorite deposits formed off arid coasts.

The sequence of events: upwelling → high productivity → organic matter rich sediment → P-enrichment of interstitial water by regeneration → apatite formation answers a question, once hotly debated. A good phosphorite with 30–35% P_2O_5 represents a two-million fold enrichment in respect to seawater concentration. Is this enrichment the result of inorganic or of biological processes? Organic matter containing (on a dry basis) 1% P represent already an enrichment by a factor of 140,000. From here to the final phosphorite a further enrichment by a factor of only 10–15 occurs; this is the result partly of chemical and partly of mechanical enrichment through winnowing by gentle bottom currents separating the relatively heavy apatite (specific gravity: 3.18 g/cm^3) from the other much lighter mineral particles. Thus, biological concentration of P is by far the dominant factor in phosphogenesis.

The enrichment factor of P in phosphorites seems, at a first glance, very high. It is, thus, interesting to note that some other much more common elements frequently show equally high enrichment factors in sediments. Si in a pure chert represents a concentration from seawater by a factor of 250,000 and a marine iron ore 28×10^6 times an Fe-concentration. In all three cases, the enrichment mechanism might, in fact, be similar.

The Mg-Inhibition—Primary Apatite Precipitation Versus Replacement

If the Mg-inhibition presents a serious hurdle for apatite crystallization from open-sea water, this is not necessarily the case for interstitial water. These are frequently depleted in Mg^{+2} by diagenetic formation of Mg-bearing minerals, e.g. clays (palygorskite, sepiolite, glauconite, smectites). In a reducing environment, ferri-oxi-hydroxide-coatings on clay particles are reduced to pyrite, making new exchange sites for Mg^{2+}-ions available (e.g. montmorillonite). Mg^{2+} can furthermore be lost by surface-absorption on calcite (Ca-Mg-overgrowth; Sholkowitz, 1973) or on biogenic opal (Donnelly et al., 1977) or by dolomitization. It is certainly significant in this connection that palygorskite and—more rarely—sepiolite are associated with many phosphorites. Gulbrandsen (1960) pointed out that, in the Phosphoria Formation, apatite is frequently associated with dolomite, but rarely with calcite. This is true for many other phosphorite deposits (e.g. Karatau [Kholodov, 1973]), but not for those of the Mediterranean-Middle Eastern belt.

Mg-depletion through dolomitization raises a difficult problem. Dolomitization requires a Mg^{2+}/Ca^{2+}-ratio above that of seawater, apatite formation a ratio well below that of seawater. The common association apatite-dolomite thus does not represent a true paragenesis the two minerals having formed under different conditions. The mechanism of these required strong fluctuations in the Mg^{2+}/Ca^{2+}-ratio is not evident.

Still, a depletion of the Mg^{2+}/Ca^{2+}-ratio from the ocean water value of 5.3 to a value of 0.2, i.e. by a factor of 26, as required by the experiments of Martens and Harris is very drastic. Nathan and Lucas (1976) have shown, however, that the Mg^{2+}/Ca^{2+}-ratio critical for crystallization of apatite is pH-dependent and increases with decreasing pH to a value of 0.85 for a pH of 7.0. At higher values of Mg^{2+}/Ca^{2+} only amorphous Ca-phosphate precipitated. Such a material has never been found in nature. Sedimentary apatite crystals, however, are extremely small and mostly submicroscopic; they are generally recognized only by their X-ray diffraction pattern. By this procedure amorphous Ca-phosphates could easily be overlooked. It is conceivable that amorphous precursors of apatite do exist in nature and places of Recent apatite formation off the coasts of Namibia, Peru and Chile would be suitable places to look for them.

The Mg-inhibition seems to be closely related to an old problem in phosphorite research: primary deposition of apatite versus replacement. Ames (1959) showed in a series of classical experiments that calcite powder through which a dilute phosphate solution is percolated at room temperature easily converts into apatite. There is ample evidence that this process—phosphatization—operates in nature, e.g. phosphatization of foraminiferal and other shells is widespread. Ever since Ames' experiments, replacement of calcite

(or aragonite) as a mode of apatite formation has been stressed by many authors, and some, including Ames (1959, 1960), have gone so far as to claim this as the only mode of sedimentary apatite formation. Two comments seem appropriate:

(1) Ames stated that the conversion of calcite to apatite takes place by PO_4^{-3} replacing CO_3^{-2} in the calcite lattice. This seems an impossibility as in the calcite lattice with its triangular CO_3^{-2} groups there is just not enough room to introduce the tetrahedral PO_4^{-3}-groups. Moreover, the Ca^{2+}-distribution in the calcite lattice is entirely different from that in apatite where part of the Ca^{2+}-ions occurs in 9-fold coordination. It is, therefore, not surprising that Nathan and Lucas (1972) obtained the same result by using other Ca-minerals such as gypsum and also produced textural evidence that apatite crystallized not within the gypsum crystals but in their solution cavities.

(2) The controversy primary crystallization versus replacement, is largely an artificial one. In both cases the system has to be saturated in respect to apatite; for replacement to occur the original Ca-mineral has at the same time to be unstable.

It is here, that the Mg-inhibition intervenes. The dissolution of calcite or gypsum decreases the Mg^{2+}/Ca^{2+}-ratio facilitating apatite precipitation. This might also explain the fact that in Ames experiments apatite formation ceased only when the amount of P in solution decreased below 90 ppb, whereas in the absence of dissolving calcite or gypsum considerably higher P-concentrations seem to be needed for apatite formation.

An interesting side-result of the experiments made by Nathan and Lucas with gypsum is the observation that the resultant apatite did not carry sulfate, while in most sedimentary apatites a small but variable amount of SO_4^{-2} replaces PO_4^{-3}. The sulfate-content of apatites (see Nathan et al., this volume) has sometimes been interpreted as an indication of the degree of salinity in the environment of deposition of apatite, high values indicating an evaporitic environment. This assumption seems now open to doubt.

Primary and replacement formation of apatite occur both in nature and sometimes in the same deposit. Phosphatized foraminiferal and molluscan shells are common in many ancient phosphorites. Manheim et al. (1975) reported replacement of Pleistocene foraminiferal tests off Peru, whereas Burnett (1977) described from the same deposit free growth of euhedral apatite crystals on a silica substratum (see also Birch, this volume). The way in which diagenetic apatite forms by reaction between interstitial water and sediments and the factors controlling its different modes of formation still need to be understood.

pH and Eh-Conditions

The role of pH and Eh in phosphorite formation is known only in bare outline. In areas of Recent apatite deposition pH-values in the interstitial water of less than 7.5 have persistently been measured: 7.2–7.4 for Namibia (Baturin et al., 1970), 7.4 for Peru (Manheim et al., 1975). These relatively low values could be significant. Conditions favorable for apatite precipitation generally also favor the precipitation of $CaCO_3$. Seawater is so much richer in the components of the latter, that on simultaneous precipitation calcite or aragonite would swamp apatite. Although the stability of apatite decreases with decreasing pH it is still stable at pH = 7.0, while the carbonates would generally be unstable below pH = 7.5. A pH below 7.5 would also increase the critical Mg^{2+}/Ca^{2+}-ratio for apatite crystallization.

Recent apatites form in reduced sediments. Thus, Baturin et al. (1970) measured an Eh of −210 mV in the phosphoritic sediments off Namibia and Burnett et al. (this volume) quote values as low as 0.2 ml/l dissolved O_2 in the bottom water off Peru and Chile. Impingement of the oxygen-minimum layer on the ocean floor seems to be a condition of apatite formation. There are, however, indications that too strongly negative Eh-values do not, and probably should not, always prevail during apatite formation. In many places phosphorites are associated with glauconite, a mineral considered to form in a mildly reducing environment (for the relationship of glauconite and phosphorite see Odin and Létolle, this volume). It seems significant in this connection that, as found by Burnett et al. (this volume), phosphorites form presently on the Peru-Chile continental slope not throughout the entire breadth of the oxygen-minimum belt but preferentially at its upper and lower boundary (water depth of 100 m and 400 m respectively). It is along these boundaries that Eh-oscillations are most likely to occur. The whole subject is, at present, insufficiently understood, but some additional evidence can be obtained from a study of the trace elements present in all apatites.

The Evidence of Trace Elements in Apatite

Apatites are capable of concentrating considerable amounts of various trace elements (Cossa, 1878, Swaine, 1962, Tooms et al., 1969; Gulbrandsen, 1966; Altschuler et al., 1967; Kholodov, 1973; Calvert, 1976; see also Altschuler, Prévôt and Lucas, McArthur, this volume). As pointed out by Tooms et al., the trace element pattern is a function of two factors: a crystal-chemical one, the capability of the apatite lattice to accept foreign ions, and a geochemical one, the availability of these elements in the environment of apatite formation. A good example of an element easily available, but not accepted by apatite is iodine (Shishkina et al., 1973). In a sediment, rich in organic matter, it is plentiful, but because of its large ionic size it is rejected by apatite as it cannot be accommodated in the channels of its structure which contain the F-ions. On the other hand, there are many elements which, if present in the environment, are readily accepted into the lattice and thus might provide clues for the mode of apatite formation. Only a few of them are discussed here briefly.

(1) *Ce.*—The most characteristic feature of the REE-pattern of ocean water, including interstitial water, is the negative Ce-anomaly Ce*, defined as the amount actually present divided by the amount of Ce to be expected on the basis of the abundance of the neighboring elements La and Nd (after standardization to chondrite). The low value of Ce* = 0.16 in sea water was explained by Goldberg et al., 1963, as caused by the preferential uptake of Ce^{4+} into manganese nodules. On apatites from the Phosphoria Formation, from Florida and from Morocco Ce*-values between 0.24 and 0.44 were measured by Altschuler et al. (1967). The point has been stressed that those values refer to apatite separated from phosphorite; measurements on whole phosphorite have much less meaning as the associated, partly land-derived, detrital minerals generally show a value of Ce* ~ 1. The low values of Ce* in apatite from phosphorites reflect the influence of deep-ocean water. The Ce-anomaly measures, in fact, the ratio between river water influx into the ocean, not yet equilibrated with deep ocean water, and upwelled ocean water in the environment of sedimentary apatite formation. The low values obtained by Altschuler for Permian, Eocene and Mio-Pliocene apatites provide support for the assumption that these were also formed in areas of oceanic upwelling, although for the Florida phosphorites this remains in doubt.

(2) *Eu.*—Magmatic apatites show strong negative Eu-anomalies because of prior preferential uptake of Eu^{2+} by calcic plagioclase. Sedimentary apatites, on the contrary, show a very erratic Eu-behavior. Some (Karatau, USSR; California Borderland, Chatham Rise and fossil fish detritus) exhibit strong to weak negative anomalies (for the Chatham Rise, see Cullen, this volume), others have no anomaly at all (off Namibia, Mid-Pacific seamounts), wheras still other areas (Blake Plateau, Agulhas Bank) show medium to strong positive anomalies (Tooms et al., 1969). Eu in seawater is three-valent and shows no anomaly. The variations in marine apatites certainly have a meaning, but it cannot be deciphered at present.

(3) *U.*—In seawater, dissolved U is present in the hexavalent state, mainly as a uranyl-carbonate complex (Starik et al., 1957; Burton, J. D., 1975). In strongly reducing marine sediments, however, the element is also precipitated as U^{4+} (Kolodny and Kaplan, 1973). In marine apatites, U occurs usually in both oxidation states, although in strongly varying proportions (Altschuler et al., 1958; Kolodny et al., 1970). The presence of U^{4+} in most apatites can only be explained by their formation in a strongly reducing environment. Once incorporated into the apatite lattice, however, U^{4+} can still undergo oxidation to U^{6+}, by radio-active decay (Kolodny et al., 1970) and by weathering (Altschuler et al., 1958; Clarke and Altschuler, 1958; Burnett et al., 1977). Moreover, additional U^{6+} can be taken up from ground- or river-water (Altschuler et al., 1958). In a general, but rather irregular way, the U^{6+}/U^{4+}-ratio increases, as shown by Altschuler (1974), with age and degree of weathering. Because of these post-depositional changes, superimposed on the original ratio, the interpretation, in individual cases, is thus frequently difficult.

(4) *Other heavy metals.*—Apatites frequently concentrate heavy metal ions such as Ag, Cd, Zn, Pb, Mo, Y, Sr, Se as well as lanthanons (Altschuler, this volume). Many of these elements are also enriched in organic matter, emphasizing thus again its close relationship to phosphorites.

Cyclicity and Episodicity of Phosphorite Formation

Many phosphorites exhibit partly rhythmical laminations and cyclical arrangements on every scale from thin-section to field section (Sheldon, this volume); moreover, they show a marked episodicity throughout geological time (Cook et al., 1979; Sheldon, this volume). Some of the most basic problems of phosphorite genesis are connected with these features.

(1) *Small-scale lamination and cyclicity*—Most of the older phosphorite deposits show pronounced lamination on a time scale of probably a few years to a few hundred years with thin laminae of phosphorites alternating with others of shale, mudstone, carbonate or chert. These alternations result from local changes, e.g., the shifting of river mouths or of morphological features on the shallow sea-bottom, slight changes in the direction and strength of currents, small-scale temperature oscillation, variations in the amount of rainfall on the nearby land and a variety of similar causes. The perfect preservation of the laminae in these organic-rich sediments is additional proof that phosphorite deposition took place in an anoxic environment.

(2) *Medium-scale cyclicity*—Many phosphorite occurrences are associated with chert units. In a typical sequence phosphorite beds, usually associated with shale or carbonate layers, alternate repeatedly with chert units. The phosphorite-containing, as well as the chert units, are usually meters to tens of meters thick and thus probably represent each a time span of deposition of several 100,000 to a few million years. Thus, three to four major chert units, including the Rex Chert, occur within the Phosphoria Formation; spongolites and phtanites are associated with the Karatau phosphorites, Kazakhstan (Kholodov, 1973); in many places within the North-African and Middle Eastern belt, phosphorite layers, up to 3 m thick, alternate repeatedly with chert units of similar thickness (Mishash Flint of Israel).

The association chert—phosphorite is by itself not surprising; both are essentially biogenic sediments formed in zones of high productivity. What is less clear are the causes of their cyclical deposition which certainly contain an important clue for phosphorite formation but have so far not received much attention. These cycles can certainly not be explained by segregation after deposition. If they were the result of simultaneous deposition of phosphate-carrying and of siliceous sediments, the formation of a siliceous phosphorite or at the most a phosphorite containing chert nodules or an alternation of thin phosphorite and chert laminae would be expected. Both types of phosphorite occur (Israeli Negev, Karatau and elsewhere) but are rare. Chert units poor in phosphate alternating with phosphorite units poor in silica, each meters or tens of meters thick, however, cannot be explained by such a mechanism.

Could it be that this cyclicity reflects rhythmic, eustatic or tectonic, changes in water depth at the place of deposition? All Recent phosphorites form at shallow depth; the maximum for Peru-Chile is 400 m, but most are shallower, and the same seems to be the case for older phosphorites. What happens during deposition in shallow water has been well documented by Baturin (1971) for the instructive case of the Recent phosphorites off Namibia. He distinguishes four stages in the diagenetic evolution of phosphorites, from the original barely phosphatic diatomaceous ooze to the final hard phosphorite nodules. During this evolution P_2O_5-contents increase from 5.10% to 32.74% whereas SiO_2-contents decrease from 49.18% to 0.15% (see also Price and Calvert, 1978). A similar, albeit less drastic, change was observed by Baturin (1971) for the Recent phosphorites off Chile. Under these circumstances, a silica-poor phosphorite is being formed. The elimination of amorphous silica from the sediment is not surprising, as it has been calculated (Heath, 1974) that only 2% of all the opaline silica formed in the ocean is finally incorporated into sedimentary rocks. The preservation of silica in sediments is, among other factors, a function of the rate of deposition. Off Namibia, it is low and silica is therefore almost quantitatively dissolved. In the Monterey Formation, which contains many phosphorite layers, however, the sedimentation rate was high: 25 m/10^3 years (Ingle, 1973) and here even the delicate diatom frustules are preserved. Similarly, about 600 m of diatomaceous ooze was laid down in the Bering Sea during the last 4–5 m.y. (Hein et al., 1978).

Let us assume now that water depth increases and with it the path of P-bearing organic matter formed near the ocean surface and settling at the ocean floor. Many authors (e.g. Sholkowitz, 1973) have shown that P is readily released from decaying organic matter, considerably quicker than C; in the Bay of Maine the C/P-ratio in particulate matter increases from 112 at the ocean surface to 325 at a water depth of 100 m (quoted by Sholkowitz, 1973). Baturin (1971) found a C/P-ratio of 68 in Recent diatom ooze off Namibia against a ratio of 25 in living diatoms. If the distance to the ocean floor is too large, little or no organic phosphorus will reach the bottom. Thus, Baturin et al. (1970) attributed the absence of phosphorite in the classical euxinic sediments of the Black Sea, at least partly, to its great depth of more than 2000 m. The more robust of the opaline tests, however, can sink to much greater depth without being dissolved. Under favorable circumstances a siliceous ooze is then deposited to be later transformed into porcellanite or chert. Such an idea of oscillating water depth could also explain Yochelson's (1968) finding in the Phosphoria Formation of a rich benthonic fauna in layers interbedded with highly bituminous ones. These layers would have been deposited during intervals in which the bottom water was aerated. For many Proterozoic and Cambrian phosphorites of Asia and Australia deeper marine conditions during the deposition of the cherty units than during formation of the underlying phosphorites have in fact been deduced on sedimentologic-paleontologic grounds (Cook and Shergold, 1978). The phosphorite-chert cyclicity is a very important problem meriting a more thorough study.

(3) *Long-period episodicity or is the present the key to the past?*—It was probably inevitable that, when less than 10 years ago, the first phosphorites were discovered which could be proven to form at the present time and their environment of formation was studied, the hope was generally expressed that it would be possible to interpret the large older phosphorite deposits, now on land, by assuming a similar environment and similar mechanisms of formation. These hopes have largely been disappointed (Bentor, 1979).

First, there are marked differences in texture between Recent and ancient phosphorites. The former occur, generally, as hard irregular bodies ("nodules") centimeters to decimeters across, generally with a fine concentric layering, or as soft structureless masses. Pre-Miocene phosphorites have variable textures (Cayeux, 1939, 1941, 1950; Trueman, 1971), but hard nodules are rarely, if ever, found in them. The vast majority of them consists of pellets, small structureless spherical, elliptical or irregular apatitic bodies, generally less than 1 millimeter across, set in a calcareous, clayey, sandy or phosphatic fine-grained matrix. They form layers frequently continuous over long distances and have, because of the abundance of pellets, a sandy appearance. Sand-sized phosphate grains, however, are rare in Recent phosphorites.

Second, there is a difference in mineral paragenesis. Recent and Miocene phosphorites on the sea floor generally show coating or interlayers of Mn-oxides (Dietz et al., 1942; Manheim et al., this volume) and are very frequently associated with glauconite. Both features are rare in the older phosphorites.

There is also a difference in the lithological association. Recent phosphorites are not accompanied by carbonates, older ones frequently are.

Older phosphorites formed mostly in areas of slow deposition and represent condensed sections (Jarvis, Odin and Létolle, this volume); areas of Recent phosphorite formation are distinguished by higher rates of deposition.

Modern phosphorites form at the continental shelf or upper continental slope, and those off Namibia under stable tectonic conditions; ancient phosphorites show a much larger variety of environmental setting, including deposition in epicontinental seas, sometimes at greater distance from the coasts (Jarvis, this volume), and are frequently syntectonic (Bentor, 1953).

Moreover, there are many indications that the two types of phosphorites formed by different mechanisms. Recent ones seem to form exclusively by diagenetic processes below the sediment-water interface. The finely laminated character of many older phosphorites makes their formation on the sea floor much more likely. This conclusion is strengthened by the frequent occurrence, in older phosphorites (e.g. Phosphoria, Karatau, Israel), of beds made up almost exclusively of apatitic oolites, which must be considered to have formed floating above the sediment-water interface.

Finally, there is a major difference in the size of the deposits. The Phosphoria deposit contains about 7×10^{17} g P. Under present conditions, more than the total annual P-influx into the ocean would have to be precipitated continuously for a period of 10 m.y. within one area, 0.17% of the present total ocean floor, to form a deposit of this size.

The differences just outlined might not apply to all ancient phosphorites. Thus, some Cambrian deposits (e.g. India, Santa Ram, personal communication) have textures similar to the Recent ones and might have formed under similar conditions. But they apply certainly to most of the ancient phosphorites.

Two conclusions seem inescapable:

(1) There were periods in the geological past more favorable for phosphorite formation than the present one, during which phosphorites accumulated at a much vaster scale than now.

(2) The mechanisms of apatite precipitation acting at present might also have been operative periodically in the past, but additional mechanisms, not realized at the present time, seem to have been important.

These conclusions are supported by the long-period episodicity of phosphorite formation, on the order of entire geological periods, i.e. over many tens of millions of years, which can be observed in the geological record (Cook et al., 1979; Sheldon, this volume). The late Proterozoic, Early Cambrian, the Ordovician, Permian, Late Cretaceous-Eocene and Miocene stand out as times of enhanced phosphorite deposition, whereas barely any phosphorites of Silurian-Devonian, Triassic or Oligocene age have been found thus far.

Looking for different mechanisms means looking for a different ocean, a not unlikely proposition, as the present ocean is certainly not typical for the ocean during most of the past.

The Carbonate Compensation Depth in the critical equatorial belt of the Pacific is now about 1 km deeper than 40–50 m.y. ago; at present carbonates are accumulating there at a depth of 4.5 km over some 12° of latitude, but no carbonate sediments formed there 40–50 m.y. earlier (Berger, 1978). This restriction of carbonate sedimentation in the deep ocean might have been partly compensated by an enhanced one in wide-spread epicontinental seas. It is, however, unlikely that they cancelled each other out entirely. As carbonates are, at present, one of the major sinks of oceanic phosphate, any diminution of carbonate precipitation over the whole ocean would have made more P available for apatite precipitation.

Earlier phosphorites, just as Recent ones, are generally associated with organic-rich sediments. But at many periods in the past, these were much more widespread at the ocean floor than at present. During the Cretaceous, a time of extensive phosphorite formation, euxinic conditions occured not only in the deeper parts of epicontinental seas (Frush and Eicher, 1975), but also in many parts of the deep ocean (Fischer and Arthur, 1977; Schlanger and Jenkyns, 1976). There was a broad oxygen minimum layer affecting a large portion of the water column (Kauffman, 1979). Similar, possibly less widespread, reducing conditions seem to have existed in the ocean during other periods of large-scale phosphorite deposition, e.g., Cambrian and Permian.

Fischer and Arthur (1977) have studied past variations in oceanic circulation. In this respect again, the present ocean is not representative for the past. Its global circulation is probably much faster than during most of the geologic past because of the larger temperature differences between the ice-fed high latitude ocean waters and those of the warm equatorial regions. The deep ocean water flowing toward the equator is the main phosphorus reservoir of the ocean. The longer the time interval between high latitude sinking and equatorial upwelling, the more will these waters be enriched in phosphorus sinking down from the biosphere. On upwelling, these waters could probably support a higher than present productivity and could conceivably be saturated in respect to apatite under the physical conditions of the near-surface. Thus, apatite could possibly precipitate above the water-sediment interface.

The Cretaceous is again a good example. During this period deep ocean bottom water had probably nowhere a temperature much below 15° C (Bowen, 1966). Under these conditions, deep ocean circulation would be controlled not by temperature but by salinity differences (Berger, 1970); ocean water would be expected to sink in the subtropical belt and to rise in high latitude (Berger, in press). For the Paleogene, there is evidence of open ocean overturn (Haq et al., 1977). Cretaceous deep sea black shales in the North Atlantic have been interpreted as being deposited in a stagnant ocean basin (Lancelot et al., 1972).

It seems to follow that, as far as phosphorite formation is concerned, a simplistic actualism does not work. Phosphorite deposition in the past probably took place in a number of ways, only one of which is operative at the present time. The study of alternative mechanisms, in relation to conditions in the ocean, different from the present ones, is an important task for future phosphorite research.

CONCLUSIONS

During the last 20 years remarkable progress has been made in our understanding of marine phosphorite genesis, but the number of problems still unsolved has not diminished. A consensus is emerging as to the mode of formation of Recent phosphorites. Their study and that of the oceanic environment favoring their accumulation will certainly continue. An interesting facet of this research is a better understanding of the chemical evolution phosphatic sediments undergo from the first ghost-like phosphorus concentrations to the formation of the mature phosphorite combined with research on the mechanism of apatite growth.

Many new phosphorite deposits have lately been discovered or become better known. This applies particularly to deposits of late Pre-Cambrian to Middle Cambrian age, centered on, but not confined to, central and eastern Asia. Additional deposits, although probably of smaller size, certainly still await discovery.

Geochemical studies of apatite and phosphorite will have to continue. This applies to both, major elements, such as the substitution of PO_4^{-3} by SiO_4^{-4}, SO_4^{-2}, CO_3^{-2} and other groups, and trace elements. The major aim should be an increased understanding of the genetical and environmental meaning of this chemical variability. In this connection, increasing emphasis might well be put on isotope studies, a relative newcomer in phosphorite research.

An important task of the future is a comprehensive study of the relationship between phosphorites and other associated lithologies, mainly siliceous rocks and possibly—as recently emphasized by Cook et al. (1979)—marine iron ores. These relationships should be interpreted in terms of paleo-oceanographic conditions.

Even as we approach an understanding of Recent phosphorite genesis, it becomes increasingly clear that older phosphorites had additional modes of formation. These mechanisms will have to be studied in their relationship to paleo-environments, a task requiring a close collaboration between sedimentologists, geochemists and paleo-oceanographers.

ACKNOWLEDGMENTS

The author wishes to express his thanks to Dr. Z. S. Altschuler, the United States Geological Survey, Reston, Va; Dr. W. C. Burnett, the Florida State University; Dr. K. O. Emery, Woods Hole Oceanographic Institution and Dr. M. Kastner, Scripps Institution of Oceanography, La Jolla, who critically read the manuscript and suggested valuable improvements.

REFERENCES

ALTSCHULER, Z. S., 1974, The weathering of phosphate deposits—environmental and geochemical aspects: Environmental Phosphorus Handbook, John Wiley, N.Y., Chapt. III, p. 33–96.

ALTSCHULER, Z. S., CISNEY, E. A., BARLOW, J. H., 1952, X-ray evidence of the nature of carbonate-apatite: Bull. G.S.A., v. 63, p. 1230–1.

ALTSCHULER, Z. S., JAFFE, E. B., CUTTITTA, F., 1956, The aluminum-phosphate zone of the Bone Valley Formation, Florida, and its uranium deposits: U.S.G.S. Prof. Pap. 300, p. 495–504.

ALTSCHULER, Z. S., CLARKE, R. S., AND YOUNG, E. J., 1958, Geochemistry of uranium in apatite and phosphorite: U.S.G.S. Prof. Pap. 314-D, p. 45–90.

ALTSCHULER, Z. S., BERMAN, S., CUTTITTA, F., 1967, REE in phosphorites—geochemistry and potential recovery: U.S.G.S. Prof. Pap. 575-B, p. 1–9.

AMES, L. L., 1959, The genesis of carbonate-apatite: Econ. Geol., v. 54, p. 829–841.

AMES, L. L., 1960, Some cation substitutions during the formation of phosphorite from calcite: Econ. Geol., v. 55, p. 354–362.

ATLAS, E. L., 1975, Phosphate equilibria in sea water and interstitial waters: Ph.D. Dissert. Oregon State Univ., Corvallis, 154 p.

ATLAS, E. L., 1979, solubility controls of carbonate-fluorapatite in seawater: Rep. on the Marine Phosphatic Sediments Workshop, Honolulu, 1979, ed. W. C. Burnett and R. P. Sheldon, p. 18–20.

BATURIN, G. N., 1971, Formation of phosphate sediments and water dynamics: Oceanology, v. 11, p. 372–376.

BATURIN, G. N., 1971, Stages of phosphorite formation on the ocean floor: Nature Phys. Sc., v. 232, p. 61–62.

BATURIN, G. N., 1972, Phosphorus in interstitial waters of sediments on the South West Africa Shelf: Oceanology, v. 12, p. 849–855.

BATURIN, G. N., 1978, Phosphorites in the ocean: Ac. Sc. USSR, Moscow, 231 p. (in Russian).

BATURIN, G. N., KOCHENOV, A. V., PETELIN, V. P., 1970, Phosphorite formation on the shelf of S.W. Africa: Lith. and Min. Res., v. 3, p. 266–276.

BATURIN, G. N., KOCHENOV, A. V., SENIN, Y. M., 1971, Uranium concentration in Recent ocean sediments in zones of rising currents: Geoch. Int., v. 8, p. 284–286.

BATURIN, G. N., MERKULOVA, K. I., CHALOV, P. I., 1972, Radiometric evidence for recent formation of phosphatic nodules in marine shelf sediments: Marine Geol., v. 13, p. M37–M41.

BATURIN, G. N., AND KOCHENOV, A. V., 1974, U-content of oceanic phosphorites: Lith. and Min. Res., no. 9, p. 124–129. (English: p. 99–103, vol. 9).

BATURIN, G. N., MERKULOVA, K. I, CHALOV, P. I., 1974, Absolute dating of oceanic phosphorites by disequilibrium uranium: Geokhimia, no. 5, p. 801–807. (English: Geochemistry v. 11, 568–574).

BENTOR, Y. K., 1953, Relations entre la tectonique et les dépôts de phosphates dans le Neguev Israelien: 19th Int. Geol. Congress, Algier, 1952, XI, p. 93–101.

BENTOR, Y. K., 1979, Modern phosphorites—not a sure guide for the interpretation of ancient deposits: Rep. Marine Phosphatic Sediments Workshop. Ed: W. C. Burnett and R. P. Sheldon, Honolulu, 1979, p. 29.

BERGER, W. H., 1970, Biogenous deep-sea sediments: Fractionation by deep sea circulation: G.S.A. Bull., v. 81, p. 1385–1402.

BERGER, W. H., 1978, Sedimentation of deep sea carbonate: Maps and models of variations and fluctuations: J. Foram. Res., v. 8, p. 286–302.

BERGER, W. H., in press, Impact of deep sea drilling on paleo-oceanography: 2nd Maurice Ewing Symposium. Ed. M. Talwani, W. Hay and W. B. F. Ryan, A.G.U. 1979.

BERNER, R. A., 1973, Phosphate removal from sea water by adsorption on volcanogenic ferric oxides: E.P.S.L., v. 18, p. 77–86.

BORNEMAN-STARYNKEVICH, I. D., AND BELOV, N. V., 1940, Isomorphic substitutions in carbonate-apatite: C. R. Ac. Sci. USSR, v. 26, p. 804–806.

BOWEN, R., 1966, Paleotemperature Analysis: Elsevier, Amsterdam, 265 p.

BRAY, J. P., BRICKER, O. P., TROUP, B. N., 1973, Phosphate in interstitial water of anoxic sediments: Oxidation effects during sampling: Science, v. 180, p. 1362–1364.

BROOKS, R. R., PRESBY, B. J., KAPLAN, I. R., 1968, Trace elements in the interstitial waters of marine sediments: Geochim. Cosmochim. Acta, v. 32, p. 397–414.

BURNETT, W. C., 1977, Geochemistry and origin of phosphorite deposits from off Peru and Chile: G.S.A. Bull., v. 88, p. 813–823.

BURNETT, W. C. AND GOMBERG, D. N., 1977, Uranium oxidation and probable subaerial weathering of phosphatized limestone from the Pourtales Terrace: Sedimentology, v. 24, p. 291–302.

BURNETT, W. C., AND VEEH, H. H., 1977, Uranium-series disequilibrium studies in phosphorite nodules from the W. coast of S. America: Geochim. Cosmochim. Acta, v. 41, p. 755–764.

BURTON, J. D., 1975. Radioactive nuclides in the marine environment: Chemical Oceanogr., v. 3, p. 91–191.

BUSHINSKI, G. I., 1964, On shallow water origin of phosphorite sediments, in Van Straaten, L. M.J.V., ed., Deltaic and Shallow Marine Deposits; Elsevier, Amsterdam, p. 62–70.

BUSHINSKI, G. I., 1966, The origin of marine phosphorites: Lith. & Min. Res., v. 3, p. 292–311.

BUSHINSKI, G. I., 1966, Old phosphates of Asia and their Genesis: Akad. Nauk SSSR, Geol. Inst. Translations, v. 149, p. 1–192.

CALVERT, S. E., 1976, The mineralogy and geochemistry of near-shore sediments: Chemical Oceanogr. Ed. Riley & Chester, v. 6, Acad. Press, p. 187–280.

CALVERT, S. E., AND PRICE, N. B., 1971, Upwelling and nutrient regeneration in the Benguela Current, October, 1968: Deep-Sea Res., v. 18, p. 505–523.

CAPEDECOMME, L., 1952, Sur les phosphates alumineux de la région de Thiès (Sénégal): C.R. Ac. Sc. Paris, v. 235, p. 187–189.

CAPEDECOMME, L., 1953, Etude minéralogique des gîtes phosphatés de la région de Thiès (Sénégal): XIX Congr. Int. Géol. Alger, 1952, XI, II, p. 103–118.

CATHCART, J. B., 1963, Economic geology of the Plant City Quadrangle, Florida: U.S.G.S. Bull. 1142-D, 56 p.

CATHCART, J. B., BLADE, L. V., DAVIDSON, D. F., KETNER, K. B., 1953, The Geology of the Florida land pebble phosphate deposits: 19th Int. Geol. Congress, Algiers, Sec., v. 11, p. 77–91.

CAYEUX, L., 1934, The phosphate nodules of Agulhas Bank: Ann. S. African Mus., v. 31, p. 105–136.

CAYEUX, L., Les Phosphates de Chaux sédimentaires de France: Serv. de la Carte Géol. de la France, Paris, Vol. I, 1939, 350 p; Vol. II, 1941, 309 p; Vol. III, 1950, 358 p.

CLARKE, R. S. JR., AND ALTSCHULER, Z. S., 1958, Determination of the oxidation states of uranium in apatite and phosphorite deposits: Geochim. Cosmochim. Acta, v. 13, p. 127–142.

COOK, P. J., AND McELHINNY, M. W., 1979, A reevaluation of the spatial and temporal distribution of sedimentary phosphate deposits in the light of plate tectonics: Econ. Geol., v. 74, p. 315–330.

COOK, P. J., AND SHERGOLD, J. H., 1978, Proterozoic and Cambrian phosphorites of Australia and Asia—a progress report: The Fertilizer Raw Material Resources Workshop, East-West Resource System Institute, August 1978.

COSSA, 1878, "Sur la diffusion du Cerium, du lanthane et du didyme," extract of a letter from Cossa to Sella, presented by Frény: C. R. Ac. Sc., Paris, v. 87, p. 378–388.

CRESSMAN, E. R. AND SWANSON, R. W., 1964, Stratigraphy and petrology of the Permian rocks of SW-Montana. U.S.G.S. Prof. Pap. 313-C, p. 275–569.

CULLEN, D. J., 1975, Petrology, distribution and economic potential of phosphorite deposits on Chatham Rise, E of New Zealand: N.Z.O.I. Oceanogr. Summary no. 8, 6 p.

CULLEN, D. J., AND SINGLETON, R. J., 1977, The distribution of submarine phosphorite deposits on Central Chatham Rise, E. of New Zealand: N.Z.O.I. Oceanogr. Field Rep. no. 10, 24 p.

D'ANGLEJAN, B. F., 1967, Origin of marine phosphorites off Baja California, Mexico: Mar. Geol., v. 5, p. 15–44.

D'ANGLEJAN, B. F., 1968, Phosphate diagenesis of carbonate sediments as a mode of in situ formation of marine phosphorites, observations in a core from the E. Pacific: Canadian J. Earth. Sci., v. 5, p. 81–87.

DAVIDSON, C. F., AND ATKIN, D., 1953, On the occurrence of uranium in phosphate rock: 19th Int. Geol. Congr. Algier, Sect XI, p. 13–31.

DEER, W. A., HOWIE, R. A., AND ZUSSMAN, J., 1962, Rock-forming minerals, v. 5, p. 323–338, John Wiley.

DeVries, T., 1979, Preservation of fish debris in Recent sediments: Rep. on the Marine Phosphatic Sediments Workshop, Honolulu, 1979. Ed. W. C. Burnett and R. P. Sheldon, p. 23–24.

Dietz, R. S., Emery, K. O., Shepard, F. R., 1942, Phosphorite deposits on the sea floor off S. California: Bull. G.S.A., v. 53, p. 815–847.

Donnelly, T. W. and Merill, L., 1977, The scavenging of magnesium and other chemical species by biogenic opaline deep-sea sediments: Chem. Geol., v. 19, p. 167–186.

Emery, K. O., 1960. The Sea off California, p. 68–76. John Wiley.

Emery, K. O., and Dietz, R. S., 1949, Submarine phosphorite deposits off California and Mexico: Cal. J. of Mines and Geol., v. 46, p. 7–15.

Emery, K. O., Orr, W. L., Rittenberg, S. C., 1955, Nutrient budgets in the ocean, *in* Essays in the Natural Sciences in Honor of Captain Allen Hancock, p. 299–309, U.S.C.

Fischer, A. G., and Arthur, M. A., 1977, Secular variations in the pelagic realm: Soc. Ec. Paleont. and Mineral. Spec. Publ. 25, p. 19–50.

Flicoteaux, R., Nahon, D., Paquet, H., 1977, Genèse des phosphates alumineux à partir des sédiments argilo-phosphatés du Tertiaire de Lamlam (Sénégal): Sci. Géol. Bull. 30, v. 3, p. 153–174.

Froelich, P. N., Bender, M. L., and Heath, G. R., 1977, Phosphorus accumulation rates in metalliferous sediments on the East Pacific Rise: E.P.S.L., v. 34, p. 351–359.

Frush, M. P., and Eicher, D. L., 1975, Cenomanian and Turonian foraminifera and paleoenvironments in the Big Bend region of Texas and Mexico, *in* The Cretaceous system in the western interior of North America, W.G.E. Caldwell, ed: Geol. Ass. Canada Spec. Pap. 13, p. 277–301.

Garrels, R. M., Mackenzie, F. T., Hunt, C., 1975, Chemical cycles and the global environment: William Kaufman, Inc.

Gimmelfarb, B. M., and Tushina, A. M., 1966, Principal phosphorite ore deposits of the Karatau: Lithol. and Min. Res., v. 4, p. 483–495.

Goldberg, E. D., Koide, M., Schmidt, R. A., Smith, R. H., 1963, REE-distribution in the marine environment: J. Geoph. Res., v. 68, p. 4209–4217.

Goldberg, E. D., and Parker, R. H., 1960, Phosphatized wood from the Pacific sea floor: G.S.A. Bull. v. 71, p. 631–632.

Graham, W. F., and Duce, R. A., 1979, Atmospheric pathways of the phosphorus cycle: Geochim. Cosmochim. Acta, v. 43, p. 1195–1208.

Gulbrandsen, R. A., 1960, Petrology of the Mead Peak phosphatic shale member of the Phosphoria Formation at Coal Canyon, Wyoming: U.S.G.S. Bull. 1111C, p. 71–146.

Gulbrandsen, R. A., 1966, Chemical composition of phosphorites of the Phosphoria Formation: Geochim. Cosmochim. Acta, v. 30, p. 769–778.

Gulbrandsen, R. A., and Roberson, C. E., 1973, Inorganic phosphorus in seawater: Environmental Phosphorus Handbook, John Wiley, Chapter 5, p. 117–140.

Haq, B. U., Premoli-Silva, I., and Lohmann, G. P., 1977, Calcareous plankton paleobiogeographic evidence for major climatic fluctuations in the early Cenozoic Atlantic Ocean: J. Geoph. Res., v. 82, p. 3861–3876.

Heath, G. R., 1974 Dissolved silica and deep-sea sediments, *in* Studies in Paleo-Oceanography. Ed. W. W. Hay. S.E.P.M. Spec. Publ. 20, p. 77–93.

Hein, J. R., Scholl, D. W., Barren, J. A., Jones, M. G. and Miller, J., 1978, Diagenesis of late Cenozoic diatomaceous deposits and the formation of the bottom simulating reflector in the Southern Bering Sea: Sedimentol. v. 25, p. 155–181.

Ingle, J. C. Jr., 1973, Summary comments on Neogene biostratigraphy, physical stratigraphy and paleo-oceanography in the marginal north-eastern Pacific Ocean, *in* Initial Rep. of the Deep Sea Drilling Proj., Kulm, L. D. et al., eds., v. 18, p. 949–960.

Kauffman, E. G., 1979, Cretaceous, *in* Treatise on Invertebrate Paleontology. Ed. R. A. Robison and C. Teichert, Part A: Introduction, p. A418–A487.

Kazakov, A. V., 1937, The phosphorite facies and the genesis of phosphorites, *in* Geol. Investigations of Agricultural Ores. Trans. Sci. Inst. Fertilizers and Insecto-Fungicides, v. 142, p. 95–113.

Kholodov, V. M., 1973, Trace element distribution in the Kurumsak-Chulaktau Deposits of Karatau. English translation: Geoch. Intern., v. 10, p. 795–802.

Kolodny, Y., 1969, Are marine phosphorites forming today?: Nature, v. 224, p. 1017–1019.

Kolodny, Y., in press, Phosphorites, *in* The Sea. Vol. VII. E. C. Emiliani, ed.

Kolodny, Y., and Kaplan, I. R., 1970, Uranium isotopes in sea floor phosphorites: Geochim. Cosmochim. Acta, v. 34, p. 3–24.

Kolodny, Y., and Kaplan, I. R., 1973, Deposition of uranium in the sediment and interstitial water of an anoxic fjord: Proc. Symp. Hydrogeoch. and Biogeochem., Tokyo, v. 1, p. 418–442.

Lamboy, M., 1976, Géologie marine et sous-marine du plateau continental au Nord-Ouest de l'Espagne—Genèse des glauconies et des phosphorites: Ph.D. Thesis, University of Rouen, 285 p.

Lancelot, Y., Hathaway, J. C., Hollister, C. D., 1972, Lithology of sediments from the western North-Atlantic, Leg XI, Deep Sea Drilling Project: Init. Repts. Deep Sea Drilling Project 11, p. 901–949. U.S. Gov. Print. Off., Washington, D.C.

Lerman, A., Mackenzie, F. T., and Garrels, R. M., 1975, Modelling of geochemical cycles: Phosphorus as an example: G.S.A. Mem. 142, p. 205–218.

Love, J. D., 1964, Uraniferous phosphatic lake beds of Eocene age in intermontaine basins of Wyoming and Utah: U.S.G.S. Prof. Pap. 474E, 66 p.

Lucas, J., Prévôt, L., Lamboy, M., 1978, Les phosphorites de la marge N de l'Espagne, Chimie, Minéralogie, Genèse: Oceanogr. Acta, v. 1, p. 55–72.

Manheim, F. T., Rowe, G. T., Jipa, D., 1975, Marine phosphorite formation off Peru: J. Sed. Petr., v. 45, p. 243–251.

Martens, C. S., and Harris, R. C., 1970, Inhibition of apatite precipitation in the marine environment by Mg-ions: Geochim. Cosmochim. Acta, v. 34, p. 621–625.

McConnell, D., 1973, Apatite. Springer, N.Y.-Wien, 111 p.

McKelvey, V. E., 1967, Phosphate Deposits: U.S.G.S. Bull. 1252-D, 21 p.

McKelvey, V. E., 1973, Abundance and distribution of phosphorus in the lithosphere: Environ. Phosph. Handbook, p. 13–31.

McKelvey, V. E., Swanson, R. W., Sheldon, R. P., 1953, The Permian Phosphoria deposits of western United States: 19th Int. Geol. Congr. Algier, Section XI, p. 45–64.

McKelvey, V. E., Williams, J. S., Sheldon, R. P., Cressman, E. R., Cheney, T. M., and Swanson, R. W., 1959, The Phosphoria, Park City and Shedhorn Formations in the western phosphate field: U.S.G.S. Prof. Pap. 313A, 47 p.

Morse, J. R., 1979, Fluxes of phosphate from ocean floor sediments: Rep. on Marine Phosphatic Sediments Workshop, Honolulu, 1979. Ed: W. C. Burnett and R. P. Sheldon, p. 22.

Murray, J., and Renard, A. F., 1891, Voyage of H.M.S. "Challenger" during the years 1873–1876: Rep. on Deep Sea Deposits, Chapt. VI, Part III, p. 378–391.

Nathan, Y., and Lucas, J., 1972, Synthèse de l'apatite à partir du gypse: application au problème de la formation des apatites carbonatées par précipitation directe: Chem. Geol., v. 9, p. 99–112.

Nathan, Y., and Lucas, J., 1976, Expériences sur la précipitation directe de l'apatite dans l'eau de mer; implications dans la genèse des phosphorites: Chem. Geol., v. 18, p. 181–186.

Parker, R. J., and Siesser, W. G., 1972, Petrology and origin of some phosphorites from the South African continental margin: J. Sed. Pet., v. 42, p. 434–440.

Pevear, D. R., 1966, The estuarine formation of United States Atlantic coastal plain phosphorites: Econ. Geol. v. 61, p. 251–256.

Pierrou, U., 1976, The global Phosphorus Cycle, in B. H. Svensson and R. Soderlund, SCOPE Rep. 7, Ecological Bull. Stockholm, v. 22, p. 75–88.

Price, N. B., and Calvert, S. E., 1978, The geochemistry of phosphorites from the Namibian Shelf: Chem. Geol., v. 23, p. 151–170.

Redfield, A. C., Ketchum, B. H., and Richards, F. A., 1963, The Influence of Organisms on the Composition of Sea-water: The Sea, vol. 2, ed: M. N. Hill, p. 26–77. Interscience, New York.

Rittenberg, S. C., Emery, K. O., Orr, W. L., 1955, Regeneration of nutrients in sediments of marine basins: Deep-Sea Res., v. 3, p. 23–45.

Roberson, C. E., 1966, Solubility implications of apatite in sea water: U.S.G.S. Prof. Pap. 550-D, p. D178–D185.

Ryther, J. H., 1963, Geographical Variation in Productivity, in The Sea, Vol. 2, ed: N. M. Hill, p. 347–380. Interscience, New York.

Salvan, H., 1952, Phosphates, in Géologie des gîtes minéraux marocains. Serv. Géol. Maroc, Notes et Mémoires 87.

Schelske, C. L., and Odum, E. P., 1961, Mechanisms maintaining high productivity in Georgia estuaries: Proc. of the Gulf and Caribbean Fisheries Inst., 14th Ann. Session, p. 75–80.

Schlanger, S. O., and Jenkyns, H. C., 1976, Cretaceous oceanic anoxic events: causes and consequences: Geol. Mijnb., v. 55, p. 179–184.

Starik, I. E., and Kolyadin, L. B., 1957, The occurrence of uranium in ocean water: Geochemistry, v. 3, p. 245–256.

Sheldon, R. P., 1963, Physical stratigraphy and mineral resources of Permian rocks in W. Wyoming: U.S.G.S. Prof. Pap. 313-D, p. 49–273.

Shishkina, O. V., and Pavlova, G. A., 1973, Iodine in the phosphorite nodules and bone phosphate of Recent shelf deposits: Geokhimia, p. 1573–1527. (English: p. 1161–1165).

Sholkowitz, E., 1973, Interstitial water chemistry of the Santa Barbara basin sediments: Geochim. Cosmochim. Acta, v. 37, p. 2043–2073.

Slansky, M., Lallemand, A., Millot, G., 1964, La sédimentation et l'altération latéritique des formations phosphatées du gisement de Taïba (Sénégal): Bull. Serv. Carte Géol. Als.-Lorr., v. 17, p. 311–324.

Smith, J. P., and Lehr, J. R., 1966, An X-ray investigation of carbonate-apatites: J. Agric. Food Chem., v. 14 (4), p. 342–349.

Stumm, W., 1973, The acceleration of the hydrochemical cycle of phosphorus: Water Res., v. 7, p. 131–144.

Summerhayes, C. P., 1973, Distribution, origin and economic potential of phosphatic sediments from the Agulhas Bank, S. Africa: Trans. Geol. Soc. S. Africa, p. 271–277.

Summerhayes, C. P., Birch, G. F., Rogers, J., Dingle, R. V., 1973, Phosphate in sediments off S.W. Africa: Nature, v. 243, p. 509–511.

Summerhayes, C. P., Nutter, A. H., Tooms, J. S., 1972, The distribution and origin of phosphate in sediments off N.W. Africa: Sed. Geol., v. 8, pp. 3–28.

SWAINE, D. J., 1962, The trace element content of fertilizers: Commonwealth Bureau of Soils, Technical Communication, v. 52, Herpenden, England, 306 p.

SWANSON, R. W., 1973, Geology and phosphate deposits of the Permian rocks in Central Western Montana: U.S.G.S. Prof. Pap. 313-F, p. 779–833.

TOOMS, J. S., SUMMERHAYES, C. P., CRONAN, D. S., 1969, Geochemistry of marine phosphate and manganese deposits: Ann. Rev. Oceanogr. Mar. Biol., v. 7, p. 49–100.

TRUEMAN, N. A., 1971, A petrological study of some sedimentary phosphorite deposits: Bull. Austr. Min. Dev. Lab., v. 11, 71 p.

VEEH, H. H., BURNETT, W. C., SOUTAR, A., 1973, Contemporary phosphorite on the continental margin of Peru: Science, v. 181, p. 844–845.

VEEH, H. H., CALVERT, S. E., PRICE, N. B., 1974, Accumulation of uranium in sediments and phosphorites of the SW African shelf: Marine Chem., v. 2, p. 189–202.

VISSE, L., 1952, Genèse des gîtes phosphatés du SE algéro-tunisien: 19th Int. Geol. Congr. Alger Monogr. Rég., Algérie 27.

WETHERILL, G. W., AND TILTON, G. R., 1967, Geochronology: Res. Geochem., v. 2, p. 1–28.

YOCHELSON, E. L., 1968, Biostratigraphy of the Phosphoria, Park City and Shedhorn Formations: U.S.G.S. Prof. Pap. 313-D, p. 571–660.

YOUNG, R. A., 1967, Dependence of apatite properties on crystal structural details: Transac. N.Y. Ac. Sc. II, 29, v. 7, p. 949–959.

SEPM SPECIAL PUBLICATION No. 29, P. 19–30, NOVEMBER 1980

THE GEOCHEMISTRY OF
TRACE ELEMENTS IN MARINE PHOSPHORITES
PART I. CHARACTERISTIC ABUNDANCES
AND ENRICHMENT*

Z. S. ALTSCHULER
U.S. Geological Survey
956 National Center
Reston, VA 22092

INTRODUCTION

The need for a contemporary evaluation of the trace element contents of marine phosphorites has both economic and scientific dictates. The current by-product production of uranium and rare earths from phosphoric acid, and the application of rare earth geochemistry to problems of ore and mineral genesis are, respectively, instances of such need, and demonstrate, as well, the economic utility of geochemical studies.

The substantial enrichment of a variety of trace elements in marine phosphorites has been widely documented and discussed since the early determinations of rare earths in Nassau phosphates by Cossa in 1878. The U.S. Department of Agriculture has presented many fine and still authoritative chemical appraisals of deposits known and exploited early in this century (Hill, Marshall and Jacob, 1932; Jacob et al. 1933) and created a bank of representative samples for additional surveys of individual elements such as those on arsenic (Tremearne and Jacob, 1941), molybdenum and rare earths (Robinson, 1948) and selenium (Rader and Hill, 1936). A critical analysis of the trace element geochemistry of phosphorites was published by Krauskopf in 1955, and Swaine in 1962 assembled virtually all of the extant determinations. Kholodov (1963) and Tooms, Summerhayes and Cronan (1969), and Calvert (1976) have published extensive interpretive reviews. Kholodov's review is based on new Russian data, Tooms et al. is based on Swaine's assemblage, and Calvert critically examines new data on sea-floor nodules. Gulbrandsen (1966) contributed an important body of data, evaluating and discussing the composition of a major regional deposit, the Phosphoria Formation.

Surprisingly, however, an average marine phosphorite composition, comparable to those for shales, or coal, or manganese nodules, has not been established. Swaine's comprehensive survey, being intentionally all-inclusive, is too eclectic in its assemblage of insular continental and marine rocks, its grouping by geography rather than by formation and in its inclusion of low-grade and altered rocks, to serve for abundance data. Furthermore, the older data were dominantly from only four major provinces, the Permian Phosphoria, the Ordovician of Tennessee, the Mio-Pliocene of Florida and the Eocene of North Africa, and were derived by methodologies which, for many elements, have been superseded or improved.

Sources of Data

The recent publication of a number of excellent regional summaries of geology and analytical data on phosphorites of the Phosphoria (Gulbrandsen, 1966), the Georgina Basin (deKayser and Cook, 1972, and Cook, 1972), and the Karatau (Kholodov, 1973), as well as surveys of individual elements and groups in marine phosphorites, obviates many of the above difficulties. To these analyses I have added a number of unpublished averages of major deposits based mainly on analyses of phosphate concentrates from two or more large-scale prospecting or production composites. This group includes the averages for the Tennessee brown-rock deposits, the Oulad-Abdoun basin of Morocco, the Pungo River Formation of North Carolina, and the Bone Valley Formation of Florida. A third group consists of comprehensive analytical surveys of many samples, those of Chaikina and Nikolskaya (1970) for the Belkinsk and Tamalyk deposits of Siberia, and Cathcart (1976) for the Bambui group of Minas Geraes. A final group of averages was also made by the author from smaller numbers of samples, culled from the literature or U.S. Geological Survey files. The entire assemblage of averages, representing 18 different basins, offers sufficient scope in geologic time, diversity of geologic setting, and geographic coverage, to assure the representativeness that is implicit in a world average or a tabulation of abundances. The data are presented in Table 1.

*Publication authorized by the Director, U.S. Geological Survey.

TABLE 1.—AVERAGE TRACE ELEMENT CONTENTS OF MAR[...]

		1	2	3	4	5	6	7	8
		Tamalyk Krasnoyarsk	Belkinsk Altai Sayan	Bambui Gp. Minas Geraes	Battle Cr. Fm., Georgina Basin	Battle Cr. Fm., Georgina Basin	Karatau, Kazakhstan	"Brown Rock" Tenn.	Alborz Mts.
Region		Siberia	Siberia	Brazil	Australia	Australia	U.S.S.R.	USA	Iran
Geologic Age		pre-C	pre-C	pre-C	Camb.	Camb.	Camb.	Ord./Tert.	Dev.
No. averaged () No. composites []		(38)	(33)	(14)[a]	(17)	(7)	(5–10)	(2+1[])	(3)
Element	Detection Limit								
Ag	0.1	1			3.8	1.6	210	tr	.4
As[c1]		7.8	5.7				15	15	
B[6]	10 or 30			10^6				14[c]	—
Ba	3	500	3000	1440[b]	604	130		400	370
Be	0.7	6	3	3			4	2	1
Cd[c]	10	30						—	
Ce	70			—				235	235
Co[1]	1	—		10	5	35		5[c]	9
Cr	1	90	50	50	110	48	55	27	20
Cu	0.3	300	3	30	43	30		30	60
Ga	1			10			2	8	3
Hg[c]									
La	30			50	8			—	170
Li[4]	30				6	10	3		
Mn	0.7	100	200	4200[b]	480	7540		1700	3350
Mo[2]	3	10	2.6	—	7	175	5	1.2[c]	335
Ni	2	200		30	21	9		30	35
Pb	1	30	40	20	40	170		23	180
Se[c3]	0.8			—				—	
Sc	1			10				8	30
Sn	3	5		—				—	—
Sr	2	300	300	300	745	100	790	570	90
Ti	2	500	400	1000	300	1670			270
U[c]	300			30					
V	1	70	60	150[b]	110	23	17	30	18
Y	2	100		100	1100	87	215	63	235
Yb	1			6[b]				4	23
Zn	100	2500	80	—	125	764		—	—
Zr	3			70				210	65

a = Most frequently reported value   c = Chemically determined, U.S. Geol. Survey Lab. Altschuler unpublished, except as otherwise noted.
b = Arithmetic average   — = Not detected

Table 1. Sources and Descriptions

1—Siliceous and clayey phosphorites, Altai-Sayan geosyncline; Chaikina and Nikolskaya (1970), Analyst: Siber. Acad. Sci.

2—Calcareous phosphorites, Altai-Sayan geosyncline; Chaikina and Nikolskaya (1970), Analyst: Siber. Acad. Sci.

3—Silty and clayey pelletal phosphorites, intra-cratonic basin, P_2O_5: 19–35%; Cathcart (1976), Analyst: U.S. Geol. Survey Lab.

4—Cherty and calcareous pelletal phosphorites, intra-cratonic basin, P_2O_5: 8–37%, mostly 24–37%; de Keyser and Cook (1972), Analyst: Austr. Mineral Development Lab.

5—Silty aphanitic phosphorites, intra-cratonic basin, P_2O_5: 13–38%; de Keyser and Cook (1972), Analyst: Austr. Mineral Development Lab.

6—Dark, granular and oolitic phosphorites, cherty and dolomitic, in a sequence of black shales and dolomites of the Lesser Karatau geosyncline. Averages of 5–10 specimens, except for Cr(1), Mo(1), and Li(3); P_2O_5: 26–32%; Kholodov, V. M., 1973; Analyst: Instit. of Geol. Sciences, U.S.S.R.

7—Residually concentrated pelletal phosphorite, Ordovician carbonate platform, decalcified during late Tertiary to Recent, P_2O_5: 11, 27, 29%, samples include one production composite; W. D. Carter (unpublished), Analyst: U.S. Geol. Survey Lab.

8—Phosphorite sandstones, quartzose and ferruginous, in sequence of phosphatic black shales, sanstones and limestones, platform setting, P_2O_5: 24–28%; Aval, Namin et al., 1968, Analyst: U.S. Geol. Survey Lab.

9—Phosphatic pebbles and cements from nearshore, quartzose sandstones and siltstones of the mid-Paleozoic platform; Neptune Range. P_2O_5 greater than 26%; Cathcart and Schmidt, 1977; Analysts: U.S. Geol. Survey Lab.

10—Dark pelletal phosphorites, muddy and calcareous, associated with black chert, shale and limestone of the geosyncline, P_2O_5 greater than 10%, Patton and Matzko (1959), Analyst: U.S. Geol. Survey Lab.

[1] Sources as follows: Anal. 1, 2, and 6: Blisskovskiy et al. (1968); Anal. 7, 15, and 18: Tremearne and Jacob (1941).

[2] Analyses 2 and 6 after Blisskovskiy (1969); Anal. 7 and 11 after Clark and Hill (1958).

[3] Detection limits and values as per Rader and Hill (1936) as follows: Anal. 7: 1 sample; Anal. 15: 3 samples; Anal. 14: 4 samples. Anal. 18 i[...]

[4] Chemically determined lithium by Paul Greenland, U.S. Geol. Survey, as follows: Anal. 15: av. of 2 composites; Anal. 18: av. of 5 composites.

[5] Average of 3 prospecting composites by neutron activation.

[6] Augmented by chemical data from Rader and Hill (1938) as follows: Anal. 7: av. of 6 samples; Anal. 11: av. of 8 samples; Anal. 18: av. o[...]

[7] Augmented by chemical data from Clark and Hill (1958) as follows: Anal. 7: av. of 3 samples; Anal. 11: av. of 9 samples.

9	10	11	12	13	14	15	16	17	18
Dover -andstone, Pensacola Mts.	Slope Lisbourne Gp., Alaska	Phosphoria Fm., N. Rocky Mts.	La Caja Fm., Concepcion del Oro	Kyzyl Kum Uzbekistan	Mishash Fm. Hamakhtesh haQatan	Oulad Abdoun Basin	Monterey Fm., Calif.	Pungo Riv. Fm., N. Car.	Bone Valley Fm., Florida
Antarctica	USA	USA	Mexico	U.S.S.R.	Israel	Morocco	USA	USA	USA
Dev.	Miss.	Perm.	Jurassic	Cret.	Campan.	Eocene	Miocene	Miocene	Pliocene
(4)	(4)	(60)[a]	(8)	(5)	(3)	(4[])	(5)	(2[])	(8[])
1	4	3	1.6	2	1	7	1.3	—	1.4
80		40				15			12
	30	13[c]	3.8		35		13	30	18[c]
400	190	100	130	200	135	100	720	75	56
8.5	—	—	.8	2	0.7	3	1.8	3	2
		40[c]				10[c]	200	20[c]	16[c]
250									255
		2[c]							
5	—	2	3	7	20[c]	—	5		4.5(2)
175	400	1000	45	7	265	300	220	175	60
10	350	100	40	2	36	150	25	60	13
		—	—				12		—
						.055[c]		.085[c]	.025[c]
110	300	300	104	200	45	300	65	150	106
						3.6[c]			3.1[c]
750	30	30	190	2000	17[c]	8	130	10	230
4	27	19[c]	7	2	17	—	38	7	2.8
45	250	100	43	7	73	20	70	13	9
90	50	—	12	7	90[c]	—	—	20	55
		13				4.8			2.6
18	15	10	6		5	2.5	12	7	6
6	15	—	—		—	10	—	5	—
650	750	1000	1010	70	1200[c]	1500	1900	5000	1400
900	40	1000	295		110[c]	200	1200	750	405
260		90[b]				105	140		140
65	240	300	220	7	195[c]	70	160	25	70
	300	300	136	20	70	700	120	300	235
	40	10	7		5	30	5	15	12
	50	300	300	70	280	215[c5]	200	200	180(95)
120	15	30	50	20	17	30	100	50	130

1—Dark pelletal shaly phosphorites, average of the Retort (20) and Meade Peake (40) phosphatic shale members of the Phosphoria, associated with black chert, shale and carbonates of the Permian geosyncline, P_2O_5: 23–37%; Gulbrandsen, 1966, Analyst: U.S. Geol. Survey Lab, Altschuler (unpublished).

2—Gray, calcareous, pelletal phosphorites, in a sequence of offshore cherty and silty limestones of the Mexican geosyncline, Zacatecas Prov., Rogers, deCserna et al., 1956, P_2O_5: 20–26%; Z. S. Altschuler (unpublished), Analyst: U.S. Geol. Survey Lab.

3—Phosphatic sandstones and shales, near shore deltaic and littoral sediments, P_2O_5: >10%; Kapustyanskii (1964), Analyst: Inst. of Geol. Sciences, U.S.S.R.

4—Calcareous pelletal and bone phosphorite, associated with limestones and cherts of carbonate platform, P_2O_5: 22–33%; U.S. Geol. Survey (unpublished). Uranium value is average of 14 samples of P_2O_5 in excess of 20%, in Mazor, 1963.

5—Clayey pelletal phosphorites, associated with limestones, cherts and clays of carbonate platform; composite samples of mining production in four localities, representing 10,000 tons, P_2O_5: 33%; Z. S. Altschuler (unpublished), Analyst: U.S. Geol. Survey Lab.

6—Dark pelletal shaly phosphorites, associated with radiolarian chert and organic-rich bentonitic shales of Tertiary geosyncline, P_2O_5: 15–20%; H. Gower (unpublished), Analyst: U.S. Geol. Survey Lab. Zn and Cd values are averages of two determinations.

7—Pelletal phosphorites, quartzose and clayey, associated with limestones, sands, and silts of estuarine and near shore coastal plain platform; average of two composites: concentrates from prospecting composites of entire mined zone in two areas; P_2O_5: 30–33%; Z. S. Altschuler (unpublished), Analyst: U.S. Geol. Survey Lab.

8—Pebbly and pelletal phosphorite from sandy and clayey phosphorites reworked from phosphatic limestones and dolomites of the Hawthorn carbonate platform; average eight composites: four pebble and four pellet concentrates composited from one week's production at each of four mining localities in Land Pebble Field, representative of approximately 100,000 tons, P_2O_5: 30–35%; Z. S. Altschuler (unpublished), Analyst: U.S. Geol. Survey Lab.

based on 6 samples in Robbins and Carter (1970).

9 samples.

TABLE 2.—AVERAGE CONTENTS OF RARE EARTHS AND
SCANDIUM IN SEDIMENTARY MARINE APATITE[1]
(ALL DATA IN PPM)

	Average	Range	Average Shale[4]
La	133	25–300	45
Ce	104	14–160	91
Pr	21	3–40	10.7
Nd	98	18–200	41.4
Sm	20	3–51	7.2
Eu	6.5	1–20	1.4
Gd	12.8	4–20	6.0
Tb	3.2	1–6	1.0
Dy	19.2	2.5–40	5.8
Ho	4.2	1–8	1.6
Er	23.3	2–70	3.8
Tm	1.2	0.4–2	0.6
Yb	12.6	2–24	3.6
Lu	2.7	0.5–7	0.7
Y[2]	275*	40–610*	38.4
Total Ln	461	77–860	220
Total RE	736*	117–1470*	258
Sc[3]	2	0.3–5.8	

[1] Sources and analyses: Average of 13 analyses of chemically separated rare earths, as follows: Phosphoria Fm., Ida.: 1 locality; Bone Valley Fm., Fla.: 2 localities plus 1 large scale composite; Oulad-Abdoun Basin, Mor.: 2 large scale composites; Georgina Basin, Austr.: 3 localities; Pungo Riv. Fm., N. Car.: 4 large scale composites. Ida., Mor., and Fla. analyses by quantitative spectroscopy of chemical separates (Altschuler et al., 1967); Australian analyses by semi-quant. spectroscopy of chemical separates (Cook, 1972); N. Carolina analyses by INAA, values for Pr, Gd, Ho and Er by interpolation (Altschuler and Stinnes, unpublished).

[2] Average of 9 analyses. Y not determined on N. Carolina samples.

[3] Average of 6 analyses. Sc not determined on Australian or N. Carolina samples.

[4] Average of 3 published determinations of composite of 36 European Paleozoic shales (Herrmann, 1970).

*Average Y of 610 ppm by semi-quant. spec. of untreated samples, assumed for pelletal phosphorites, Georgina Basin (Cook, 1972). Y average may therefore be too high due to unusually high Australian average.

Data Selection and Treatment for Regional Averages

All the analyses represent bedded marine phosphorites except for the Tennessee "brown rock" deposits, which are residually concentrated from bedded marine deposits. The generalized petrography and the geologic setting are given for each deposit, and the tenor in P_2O_5 is cited or inferred for most of them (see list of sources, Table 1).

All of the analyses are "complete" analyses or analyses of groups of elements. Most are of dominantly phosphatic rocks, containing more than 20 percent P_2O_5, and thus equivalent to more than 50% in apatite content. For a few of the averages in which a small number of analyses were available, an analysis as low as 10 percent P_2O_5 has been included, but even this is equivalent to 27% apatite in the rock, assuming a reasonable norm of 37 percent P_2O_5 in marine carbonate-

fluor-apatite. The published averages of the Tamalyk and Belkinsk deposits lacked P_2O_5 information but were described as rich phosphorites, and the analyses averaged from the Kyzyl Kum and Brooks Range deposits were described as having more than 10 percent P_2O_5.

The data averaged in Table 1 were obtained, in most instances, from semi-quantitative spectrographic analyses, except for As, Cd, Hg, Se, and U which were determined chemically. The data on Au and Th in Table 3 are by neutron activation. The analyses of Bi are by radio-isotope dilution. The data on rare earths are by neutron activation or quantitative spectroscopy after rigorous chemical separation (Table 2).

In all, three bodies of data and their respective averages are presented here: Table 1 presents spectrographic and chemical analyses of 28 elements in the form of regional or formational averages for 18 rich phosphorites. Table 4 presents the mean of these formational averages. Table 2 presents an average of quantitative rare earths (lanthanons and yttrium) and scandium determinations on 13 apatite concentrates from five major marine phosphorites. Table 3 gives quantitative chemical data on contents of gold, bismuth, and thorium in large-scale apatite composites from four major marine phosphorites. The abundances in tables 2 and 3, being of pure apatite rather than whole phosphorite, are therefore not included in table 4.

The following procedures were used in calculating the average for each deposit (table 1) and the average of averages, or the grand mean, which comprises the abundance tabulation (table 4). For determinations reported as "trace" or "not detected," a value equal to one half of the detection limit was assumed, using the detection limits of the U.S. Geological Survey laboratories, as these applied in all but a single instance. Except for tin, none of the abundance evaluations could have been seriously affected by this procedure. For published analyses of which a modal average was originally presented (analyses No. 3, 9 and 11 table 1), if an element's distribution was pronouncedly bi-modal the data were recalculated and averaged. For analysis No. 9, all of the data were averaged. For a few elements which are particularly insensitive to spectrographic determination (see footnotes, table 1), chemical data on significant composites, or groups of samples from the literature, were added to the compilation.

If one of the 18 regional averages was clearly aberrant or anomalous for a particular element the abundance for that element was calculated in two ways, with and without the anomalous average. Anomalies were so identified if the distribution was otherwise seriate and clustered and the "anomalous" value was more than twice

TABLE 3.—CONTENTS OF AU (IN PPB), BI AND TH (IN PPM) IN REPRESENTATIVE SEDIMENTARY MARINE APATITE FROM FOUR MAJOR FIELDS

	Phosphoria Fm. N. Rocky Mts.	Oulad Abdoun Basin, Morocco	Pungo Riv. Fm. N.C.	Bone Valley Fm. Fla.	Tentative Average Marine Apatite
Au[1]	0.5	2.6	0.7	1.8	1.4 ppb
Bi[2]	0.07	0.05	0.017	0.12	0.06 ppm
Th[3]	11.0	3.5	6.0	6.0	6.5 ppm

[1] Fire Assay and Neutron Activ. Anal., J. J. Rowe and F. W. Brown, U.S.G.S. Lab.; Phosphoria Fm.: 1 mining composite; Morocco: Av. of 2 prospecting composites; N. Car.: Av. of 2 prospecting composites; Fla.: Av. of 2 production composites.

[2] Neutron Activ. Anal., E. Y. Campbell and Paul Greenland, U.S.G.S. Lab.; Phosphoria Fm.: 1 mining composite; Morocco: 1 prospecting composite; N. C.: Av. of 2 prospecting composites; Fla.: Av. of 5 production composites.

[3] Neutron Activ. and chem. Anal., U.S.G.S. Lab.; Phosphoria Fm. Av. of 4 samples. (3 by wet chem., Gulbrandsen, 1966); Morocco: Av. of 2 prospecting composites; N. Car.: 1 prospecting composite; Fla.: Av. of 4 samples (3 from Altschuler Clarke and Young, 1958) and 3 production composites.

the next highest value. The highest values for silver, cadmium, molybdenum, and zinc are obviously aberrant. They may be errors or instances of mineralization. In either case, they require segregation. The anomalies for barium, chromium and strontium, though not as striking, are nevertheless clearly deviant and so far outside their respective distributions as to significantly alter their mean abundances.

Trace Element Abundances in Average Marine Phosphorite

The trace element abundances are presented in table 4. For a number of elements two values

TABLE 4.—AVERAGE TRACE ELEMENT ABUNDANCES IN MARINE PHOSPHORITE (BASED ON 18 REGIONAL AVERAGES, DATA IN PPM EXCEPT FOR HG)

	Detection Limit	Average Phosphorite	Number Averaged	Range of Averages	Median Phosphorite
Ag	0.1	2/15	15	ND-7/210	1.5
As		23	8	6–80	15
B	30	16	11	ND-35	13
Ba	3	350/500	17	56-1450/3000	200
Be	0.7	2.6	16	ND-8.5	2.5
Cd	10	18/40	8	ND-40/200	18
Co	1	7	15	ND-35	5
Cr	1	125/172	18	7-400/1000	75
Cu	0.3	75	17	2-350	36
Ga	1	4	9	ND-12	2
Hg ppb		55	3	25-85	55
La	30	147	13	ND-300	110
Li	30	5	6	3-10	4.3
Mn	0.7	1230	17	8-7540	200
Mo	3	9/37	18	ND-38/175, 335	6
Ni	2	53	16	7-250	33
Pb	1	50	17	ND-180	30
Sc	1	11	12	5-18	10
Se		4.6	6	ND-13	3.7
Sn	2	3	13	ND-15	ND
Sr	2	750/980	18	70-1900/5000	750
Ti	2	640	15	40-1670	405
U		120	7	30-260	105
V	1	100	18	7-300	70
Y	2	260	16	20-1100	175
Yb	1	14	11	4-40	10
Zn	100	195/325	16	ND-764/2500	190
Zr	3	70	13	17-210	50

TABLE 5.—CONCENTRATIONS OF TRACE ELEMENTS IN MARINE PHOSPHORITES RELATIVE TO SHALE
(DATA IN PPM)

	Average Shale[1]	Average Phosphorite[2]	Enrichment Factor[3]	Normal Abundance	Depletion Factor
Ag	0.07	2	Ag 30		
As	13	23		As	
B	100	16			B 6
Ba	580	350		Ba	
Be	3	2.6		Be	
Cd	0.3	18	Cd 60		
Co	19	7			Co 3
Cr	90	125		Cr	
Cu	45	75		Cu	
Ga	19	4			Ga 5
Hg ppb	400	55			Hg 7
La	40	147	La 4		
Li	66	5			Li 13
Mn	850	1230		Mn	
Mo	2.6	9	Mo 4		
Ni	68	53		Ni	
Pb	20	50	Pb 2		
Sc	13	11		Sc	
Se	0.6	4.6	Se 8		
Sn	6	3			Sn 2
Sr	300	750	Sr 2		
Ti	4600	640			Ti 7
U	3.7	120	U 30		
V	130	100		V	
Y	26	260	Y 10		
Yb	2.6	14	Yb 5		
Zn	95	195	Zn 2		
Zr	160	70			Zr 2

[1] From Turekian and Wedepohl, 1961.
[2] From Table 4.
[3] An element is considered "enriched" if its abundance is at least 2× that of shales, and "depleted" if its abundance is 1/2 or less. Abundances between these limites are classed as "normal," following Tooms et al., 1969.

are given, a high value (to the right of the slash mark, /) which utilizes all the averages in table 1, and a lower, and preferred value, which excludes any of the aforementioned anomalous averages. The range of averages is presented in the same manner so that the excluded anomaly may be identified, and the range may be expressed in two ways.

The average abundances and the ranges displayed in table 4 are to be construed as the characteristic values of formations, or deposits of phosphorite, but not as the abundances of pure marine apatite, or the ranges of concentration which would obtain from individual small samples. It is the author's conviction that phosphorite, in its most common granular, ovular and pelletal forms, is characteristically (though not exclusively) reworked and concentrated by wave and current action (Altschuler, 1965). Consequently, even relatively small samples represent natural composites derived from areas of primary or diagenetic fixation larger than the individual sample

site. Therefore, to achieve truly definitive ranges one would have to sample singular entities—individual pebbles, ovules, phosphatized shell casts, fragments of bone or precipitated layers. Yet this, in turn, poses a dilemma, for a phosphorite, like all polymineralic clastic sediments, is a collectivity in which the non-phosphatic components may either dilute or augment a particular element's abundance. In summary, table 4 presents the characteristic or normative abundances and ranges of concentration, and the extreme abundances and ranges, of marine phosphorite as a class of rocks.

Elements Enriched in Marine Phosphorite

From Tables 5 and 2 it can be seen that the marine phosphorites, as a class, are characteristically enriched, relative to shales, in a large group of trace elements. The evaluation of the degree to which a group of elements is concentrated or depleted in a particular group of rocks may be motivated by such concerns as environmental pollution, by-product recovery, or the search for geochemical indicators of depositional environment or mode of origin. Accordingly, relative enrichment has generally been evaluated against a variety of bases, most commonly crustal abundance. Whereas crustal abundances are the appropriate comparative norm for evaluating large classes of rock or major aspects of the geochemical cycle, it is felt that the special attributes differentiating phosphorite from other marine rocks may best be discerned by comparison to the general category of marine rocks. Therefore, the element abundances of average phosphorite are compared to those of average shale. Moreover, shales, as the most common surficial rock, are clearly a superior basis for evaluating environmental stress due to phosphorite occurrence or utilization.

The influence of the particular norm chosen for evaluation of the elements enriched in phosphorites is forecefully illustrated in the examples of arsenic and boron, which both show enrichment in marine shales in contrast to their crustal abundances. Compared to crustal abundances arsenic and boron would be found to be enriched in phosphorites. Compared to shales, however, arsenic is found to be normal, and boron is revealed to be depleted in phosphorites, though the former is usually listed as enriched and the latter as normal.

The elements enriched in phosphorite, listed in order of degree of enrichment, are Cd (60x), U (30x), Ag (30x), Y (10x), Se (8x), Yb (5x), Mo (4x), La (4x) and Sr, Pb and Zn (each 2x). Except for Ce all other lanthanons also fall in this group (see table 2). The elements found to be depleted in phosphorite are Li (13x), Ti (7x), Hg (7x), B (6x), Ga (5x), Co (3x) and Sn and Zr (each 2x). The elements of normal abundance in phosphorites are seen to be As, Ba, Be, Ce (from table 2), Cr, Cu, Mn, Ni, Sc and V. Based on Swaine's data for phosphates of a variety of origins, and using the norm of crustal abundances, Tooms et al. (1969) arrive at somewhat different groupings, notably in finding As, Cr and Sn to be enriched, and Ba, Cu, Mn and Ni to be depleted.

It is clear that with more data these assessments of average concentration may be changed. It is nevertheless instructive to evaluate and list the degrees of enrichment, as those elements greatly enriched or depleted are most probably correctly classified, particularly in view of the conservative treatment of aberrant values.

Behavior of Coherent Elements: Zn and Cd; The Rare Earths.—This ordering of the degree of enrichment provides yet additional insight into the special selectivity of phosphorites as sinks for certain elements which are normally members of coherent pairs or groups. Zinc and cadmium, both enriched in phosphorite, are such a pair. Cadmium is virtually never found independently in common rocks, and, in most large classes of rock, the abundance of zinc exceeds that of cadmium by a factor of several hundred (Zn/Cd = xoo). In phosphorites, as revealed in the enrichment factors in table 5, as well as in the raw data of table 1, cadmium is differentially enriched over zinc, very substantially. The ratio of Zn/Cd is generally in the neighborhood of 10. There seems little doubt that this is an instance of crystallo-chemical favorability, as the ionic radii of Cd and Ca are almost identical, whereas the Zn ion is almost 20 percent smaller. Whereas Zn and Cd both substitute in apatite, Cd is preferentially fixed. Admittedly, zinc and cadmium are not fixed solely in apatite in all phosphorites. Sphalerite has been found in some phosphatic shales of the Phosphoria Formation, which contain unusually high zinc concentrations, and very high zinc contents, such as those reported in the Tamalyk phosphorites (2500 ppm, table 1) and the Georgina basin phoscretes, (commonly 1000–3000 ppm, deKayser and Cook, 1972) may be attributable to sphalerite formation, in addition to substitution in apatite. In the Georgina basin, the occurence of zinc-bearing manganese minerals may be equally indicated by the very high content of manganese. Aberrantly high cadmium without comparable increase in zinc (200 ppm Cd in California phosphorites) is probably due to solid solution in apatite.

Fractionation among the rare earth elements is similarly reflected in the enrichment values derived by comparison to shale abundances. Averages for total rare earths in shales generally fall between 200 and 300 ppm (Ronov, Balashov, Migdisov, 1967; Herrmann, 1970) and the comparable figure for phosphorites is 700 ppm total R. E. (Semenov, Kholodov and Barinski, 1962; see also table 2). Thus one would expect uniform two- to threefold enrichment for the individual rare earth elements in phosphorites, assuming coherence within the group. We may note that the enrichments of La (4x) and Yb (5x) conform reasonably to expectation for semiquantitative analyses; however, the apparent tenfold enrichment of Y reveals a preferred uptake with respect to the lanthanons. One may question such distinctions based on semi-quantitative spectrographic data, as the rare earths vary in their detectability by this method. However, the enhanced enrichment of Y is firmly established by quantitative analyses of beneficiated sedimentary apatite concentrates from large and representative prospecting composites (table 2 and table 6) which reveal yttrium to constitute 20 percent, or more, by weight of the total rare earths. By contrast

TABLE 6.—CHARACTERISTIC AND POSSIBLY TYPIFYING GEOCHEMICAL RATIOS FOR MARINE APATITE AND PHOSPHORITE

	1	2	3	4	Average Marine Phosphorite		Average Shale[1]
	Phosphoria Fm., N. Rocky Mts.	Oulad Abdoun Basin, Morocco	Pungo Riv. Fm., N.C.	Bone Valley Fm., Fla.	from Anal. 1-4,	from Table 4	
Zn/Cd[3]	7.5	22.	10.	12.	14.	10.	300.
Th/U[3]	0.12	0.025	0.09	0.05	0.07	0.055	3.2
Ce/La[2]	0.54	0.64	1.21	0.81	0.80		2.1
Y/RE[2]	0.34	0.32		0.19	0.28		0.15
Y/La[2]	1.6	2.15		1.36	1.7	1.8	0.85

[1]Based on Turekian and Wedepohl (1961) for Zn, Cd, Th and U; average of Herrmann (1970) and Haskin and Haskin (1966 in Herrmann, 1970) for Y, Ce and La.
[2]Based on averages of large composite samples for analyses 2, 3 & 4, and a single sample for analysis 1. All analyses are of apatite concentrates rather than whole rock. Analyses, 1, 2, and 4 by quantitative spectroscopy of chemically separated rare earths (Altschuler et al., 1967); analysis 3 by INAA (Altschuler and Stinnes, unpublished). Y not determined.
[3]Based on chemical analyses for Cd, Th, and U (see tables 1 & 3) and spectrographic analyses for Zn (see table 1).

yttrium is only 12–15 percent of the rare earths in average shale (Ronov et al. 1967; Herrmann, 1970). The inherent cerium deficiency of sedimentary marine apatite has been described earlier (Altschuler, Berman and Cuttitta, 1967). This is another striking instance of differentiation within a coherent group. Although all other rare earths are enriched in phosphorite, cerium is "normal." It is an attribute reflecting fixation from seawater which is notably deficient in cerium (Goldberg et al., 1963; Hogdahl, 1967). It is now equally clear that marine apatite is also preferentially enriched in yttrium, albeit slightly, and that this enrichment is likewise a reflection of precipitation or fixation from a seawater source, as the rare earth distribution patterns for seawater show a marked enrichment of yttrium (Hogdahl, 1967).

Thus the two dominant features of rare earth differentiation in seawater, the deficiency in cerium and the excess of yttrium, are each reflected in marine apatite as a class. The degree to which individual deposits display these features is modified by the contributions of terrestrial waters to their basins of deposition. It is equally clear that the contributions of terriginous debris, as well as of major authigenic components other than apatite (notably Mn oxides, glauconite, carbonates) may mask these affects in whole rock analyses of phosphorites, as noted earlier (see Altschuler, Berman and Cuttitta, 1967, for comparisons of separated marine apatite with impure phosphorite and shales).

Fixation in Apatite.—Of the elements enriched in phosphorites, Cd, U, Y and lanthanons, Sr, Pb, and Zn are known, or may be presumed on crystallochemical grounds, to substitute for calcium in apatite. These elements generally are more concentrated in purified marine apatite than in "impure" phosphorites. The substitution of tri- and quadrivalent elements is readily tolerated in

apatite due to the possibility and frequency of even greater substitutions of a compensatory nature: $-Na^{+1}$ for Ca^{+2} and SiO_4^{-4} for PO_4^{-3}. Such coupled substitutions as Ce^{+3} for Ca^{+2}, compensated by Na^{+1} for Ca^{+2} and by SiO_4^{-4} for PO_4^{-3}, are well established at major levels of concentration in the britholite group of apatites (both Ce and Y substituted apatites). Moreover, the levels of sodium and silicate in marine sedimentary apatite are more than sufficient to supply the required valence compensation for such species as U^{+4} and REE^{+3}.

Fixation in Other Phases.—The contents of the remaining elements enriched in phosphorites, Ag, Se and Mo, have been attributed to organic complexing or absorption, along with As, Ni, V, Zn and Cr (Krauskopf, 1956) and Cu, Cd and Sb (Gulbrandsen, 1966). The basis of this attribution is the well established enrichment of most elements in this group in bituminous shales, and the finding in the Phosphoria Formation, that these elements are most concentrated, as a group and individually, in samples which are significantly richer in organic matter (Gulbrandsen, 1966). In some of these samples, however, this would equate to an improbably high metal content in the organic matter (15–45 percent by weight, see table 1, Gulbrandsen, 1966; Calvert, 1976 for similar comments). Furthermore, many of the elements of this largely chalcophile group occur as sulfides or coprecipitate within pyrite in organic-rich sediments (Fleischer, 1956). Therefore, it is equally likely that the association with organic matter simply reflects the dependence of the generation of H_2S, and of consequent metallic sulfides, on the reducing regime induced by an excess of organic accumulation over available oxygen. Thus, arsenic and molybdenum are found in pyrite and secondary hydrous iron oxides in Russian phosphorites (Blisskovskiy, 1968, 1969), and arsenic is associated with secondary iron oxides in the altered phases of the Bone Valley Formation (Stow, 1969). Very high contents of zinc and cadmium in organic-rich zones of the Phosphoria Formation are attributed to sphalerite, whereas phosphorites with normal contents of zinc and cadmium are not found to contain sphalerite (Desborough, 1977). High contents of lead are similarly attributed to sulfides by Blisskovskiy (1969a) who proposed that the normative lead is fixed by adsorption on the marine apatite. There is very little evidence regarding the hosts for the normative contents of V, Ni, and Cr in phosphorites. Vanadium is often greatly enriched in slightly phosphatic, organic-rich shales, associated with rich phosphorites, but V is strikingly diminished in rich phosphorites and in marine carbonate-fluor-apatite (Gulbrandsen, 1966; Blisskovskiy, 1969). Both V and Cr may be concentrated in iron oxides and clays, at high concentrations. Blisskovskiy (1969) finds V and Cr to be enriched in hydrous iron-oxides in weathered phosphorites of the Seybrinsk region. Krauskopf (1956) has postulated the fixation of Cr as a reduced hydroxide, $Cr(OH)_3$, in organic-rich phosphorites. As Gulbrandsen (1966) has noted, many elements in phosphorites may have more than one form of occurrence. Investigations by microprobe and scanning microscopy will undoubtedly provide new insights.

Gold, Bismuth and Thorium.—Little is known of the elements Au, Bi and Th in phosphorites. Table 3 presents quantitative chemical data on representative apatite separates from four major fields. Based on these, Au and Th appear to be normal in rich phosphorites relative to shales, and Bi appears to be enriched. Enrichment of Bi may be due to substitution in apatite, as the Bi^{+3} ion (I.R. = 0.93Å) is close to Ca^{+2} (I.R. = 0.99Å) in size, and Bi has been shown as a minor substituent of hydrothermal apatite (Clark, 1965), and bismuth silicate-apatites have been synthesized (Engel, Gotz and Eger, 1979). Bismuth may occur in sulfide and sulfosalt minerals, as well. Thorium is discussed later in the text.

Impact of Weathering

It is clear that the granularity which characterizes many phosphorites abets drainage and ground-water alteration, and that many apparently unaltered phosphorites have been leached of organic matter and pyrite, sustaining loss of color, oxidation of Fe^{+2} to Fe^{+3}, and of U^{+4} to U^{+6}, leading to both leaching and secondary uptake of such uranium (see data in Altschuler, Clarke and Young, 1958; Kolodny and Kaplan, 1960; McArthur, 1978). Stow (1969) has shown loss of pyrite and dark color, and the remobilization of arsenic to secondary iron oxides, due to weathering in the Bone Valley Formation. Thus, the present form and concentration of an element may not reveal its primary manner of fixation. This argument has been extended by McArthur (1978) who suggests, largely from chemical comparisons, that all deposits of marine apatite initially share a uniform minor element composition, which becomes modified post-depositionally by ground-water alteration. This argument presupposes that marine apatite has a singular and very narrow range of fixation and diagenetic history, a position in conflict with the diverse body of minerals and rocks with which primary marine apatite is found.

Trace Elements Depleted or Normal in Phosphorite

The elements depleted in phosphorite (B, Co, Ga, Hg, Li, Sn, Ti and Zr) fall mainly in two categories. Some occur in relatively stable and insoluble minerals—Ga in clays, Zr in zircon, Ti in ilmenite and rutile—and are therefore richer in highly detrital shales than in largely chemogenic phosphates. Others possess ionic radi (Li and Co) or anionic configurations (BO_3) which are not accommodated in the apatite structure. The depletions of Hg and Sn are not understood. Each may substitute in apatite, though their presence seems most readily explained by organic complexing, as both are known to be notably concentrated in carbonaceous matter.

Ba, Ni, Se and V, among the "normal" group, are other elements whose ions or anions are too small or too large for incorporation in marine apatite. Ba apatites have been synthesized, and vanadate apatites are known. However, as Ba^{+2} and $(VO_4)^{-3}$ are much larger respectively than Ca^{+2} and PO_4^{-3} they readily form chlor-apatite structures, but are not accommodated in the carbonate fluor-apatite structure. That barium shows little correlation with strontium in phosphorites is not surprising, as strontium is readily accomodated in marine apatite and barium is excluded. Barite is found in the Alborz mountains samples reported in table 1 (Altschuler, Analyses and Petrology, in Aval et al., 1968).

Tooms, Summerhayes and Cronan (1969) find a general correspondence between relative elemental abundances in seawater and those in phosphorites. However, based on wider sampling, restriction to marine phosphorite, and comparison with shale rather than crustal abundances, less correspondence is found in this study. Thus Li, Sn and B, though enriched in seawater, are depleted in phosphorites. Cr, Pb, Sc, Y and all lanthanons, though relatively depleted in seawater, are enriched in phosphorite (Ce excepted). Moreover, Ba, Cu, Mn, Ni and V, listed as impoverished in seawater, (Tooms et al., 1969) have normal abundances in phosphorite.

Geochemical Ratios Characterizing Marine Phosphorite

Table 6 presents a group of ratios which clearly differentiate marine apatite, and therefore rich marine phosphorite, from shales, as well as from sandstones and limestones. Each of the ratios is based on a pair, or group of elements which normally is coherent for a major part of the geochemical cycle. Thus, a substantial departure in the value of this ratio in marine apatite from that in shales, or other major sediments, represents a distinction peculiar to phosphate accumulation. In the instance of the Zn/Cd ratio, the distinction is imparted by the capacity for ionic substitution within apatite. In the rare earth and thorium/uranium ratios, the distinction is imparted by seawater and maintained by the capacity for coupled substitutions.

The ratio Th/U is particularly interesting. In felsic and intermediate igneous rocks this ratio is generally 3–4. Major portions of igneous uranium and thorium are leachable in acid, and are found to be largely "interstitial"—absorbed on surfaces of grains and fractures (Brown and Silver, 1956; Larsen and Gottfried, 1961). Moreover more thorium than uranium is leachable (Phair in Larsen, 1957). The non-leachable uranium and thorium are largely contained in the accessory minerals, zircon, titanite, apatite, epidote and monazite, occuring either as inclusions or independent grains. These generally have higher contents of uranium and thorium than their parent rocks, and zircon, apatite and titanite are disproportionately richer in uranium.

Despite the greater leachability of thorium than uranium from primary rock, the Th/U ratio of seawater shows a profound reversal and has been variously reported to range from 0.002 to 0.0001 (Baranov and Kristianova, 1959). This is attributed to the readiness with which uranium may be oxidized to the hexavalent $(UO_2)^{+2}$ cation complex, and transported as a soluble phase, probably as a uranyl carbonate complex. In contrast, the solely tetravalent Th^{+4} ion is readily coprecipitated with oxidate minerals like iron and manganese oxides, and with clays, and is, therefore, readily concentrated in secondary phases and weathering products. Thus, average detrital shales and sandstones display Th/U ratios like those of igneous rocks, ranging from 2.5 to 4.0 (Vinogradov and Ronov, 1956; Turekian and Wedepohl, 1961); whereas bauxites (Adams and Richardson, 1960), deep-sea red clays (El Wakeel and Riley, 1961) and weathered, red and yellow clays (Adams and Weaver, 1958) often yield higher ratios. Limestones that are not rich in detritus have lower contents of uranium (2.2 ppm) and thorium (1.7

ppm) than shales and are more particularly depleted in thorium, yielding Th/U ratios in the range of 0.5–1.0 (Baranov, Ronov and Kunashova, 1956; Adams and Weaver, 1958; Turekian and Wedepohl, 1961). Mid-oceanic atoll limestones, which are virtually detritus-free, do show very low Th/U ratios (0.06–0.002, Sackett and Potratz, 1963). These facts make all the more startling the characteristic values of phosphorites [120 ppm U (table 1); 6.5 ppm Th (table 3); Th/U = approximately 0.06 (table 6)]. It has been shown that young and unaltered marine apatite contains dominantly tetravalent uranium (Altschuler, Clarke and Young, 1958). Therefore the substitution of the available Th^{+4} and U^{+4} ions in marine phosphate may be presumed to be equally auspicious, as each of these ions is virtually identical in size to the Ca^{+2} ion. In fact, Th^{+4}, being slightly closer to Ca^{+2} in ionic radius, might be favored. However, uranium is 70 times more abundant in phosphorites than it is in limestones, whereas thorium is only 5 times more abundant. The general enrichment of both U and Th in phosphorite compared to another calcium-bearing marine precipitate, limestone, must be due in large measure to the adaptability of the apatite structure to coupled and compensating replacements, possibly SiO_4^{-4} for PO_4^{-3}, the same feature that permits the enrichment of rare earths in marine and igneous apatite. The more limited relative enrichment of thorium in marine apatite, creating an unusually low and distinctive Th/U ratio in the order of 0.05.–07, may be attributed to the general paucity of thorium in seawater. A similar explanation must govern the very low Th/U ratios of mid-ocean atoll limestones, unique among limestones in this respect.

Median Values and Element Distribution Patterns

A tabulation of median values, hence a median phosphorite, is included in table 4 for comparison with the average, or mean phosphorite. Significantly, most of the median values are lower than the mean values. For a number of the elements medians and mean values are essentially the same (Be, Cd, Hg, Li, Sc, Sr and Zn). None of the elements have median values larger than mean values, reflecting a universal tendency of skewness toward the lower values, or a prominent mode in the lower range.

Those elements with median values which are appreciably lower than mean values display pronounced log-normal tendancies, and are skewed toward the low range and non-seriate in the high range, as in the examples of Mn, Cu, Pb and Mo,—or, they are prominently bi-modal with the dominant and skewed mode in the lower range, as in the examples of Ba, Cr, V and La. Such distributions may reflect two or more modes of fixation, such as sulfide and apatite precipitation (possibly affecting As, Cd, Cu and Pb), the fixation of manganese in carbonates as well as in apatite, the occurence of lanthanum in detritus as well as in apatite, or the fixation of vanadium by organic matter and mineral phases.

The two major groups of elements, however, do not display two contrasting groups of distribution. Thus, in the group with coincident medians and means, scandium is skewed, strontium tends to be normal, and zinc is tri-modal. Geometric means were not calculated, as, given the diversity of distributions, the geometric mean offers no greater assurance of defining the central tendency. In addition, as semiquantitative spectrographic data are characterized by large increases in analytical variance at the extremes of the range, geometric mean data probably would be misleading. Reliance was placed, instead, on the aforementioned treatment of the anomalies and the presentation of dual averages for elements with singular anomalies. The fact that the characteristic averages (without the anomalies) always equalled or exceeded the medians confirms the assumption that this treatment is not too censored at the high end.

The non-seriate and bi-modal distributions that characterize so many of the elements very likely reflect the contributions from phosphorites of two major and distinct environments, those of the stable shelf or platform, and those of the geosyncline. Thus the prior suggestion, of two or more sources or modes of fixation for elements such as As, Cd, Cu, Mo and V, may, in turn, be linked to this environmental distinction for the reason that organic matter, finer detritus, and metallic sulfides accumulate more readily in geosynclinal than in shallow open shelf or platform sediments. These questions will be explored in detail in a forthcoming paper.

REFERENCES

ADAMS, J. A. S., AND RICHARDSON, K. A., 1960, Thorium, uranium and zirconium concentrations in bauxite: Econ. Geology, v. 55, no. 8, p. 1653–1675.
———, AND WEAVER, CHARLES, E., 1958, Thorium-to-uranium ratios as indicators of sedimentary processes: Example of geochemical facies: Am. Assoc. Pet. Geol. Bull., v. 42, no. 2, p. 387–430.
ALTSCHULER, Z. S., 1965, Precipitation and Recycling of Phosphate in the Florida Land-Pebble Phosphate Deposits: U.S. Geological Survey Prof. Paper 525-B, p. B91–B95.
———, BERMAN, S., AND CUTTITA, F., 1967, Rare earths in phosphorites—Geochemistry and potential recovery: U.S. Geol. Surv. Prof. Paper 575-B, p. B1–B9.
———, CLARKE, R. S., AND YOUNG, E. J., 1958, Geochemistry of Uranium in Apatite and Phosphorite: U.S. Geological Survey Prof. Paper 314-D, p. 45–90.
AVAL, M. M., NAMIN, M. S., AND GHASIMPUR, R., 1968, Upper Devonian phosphate, in Recent Phosphate Discoveries in Iran: Geol. Survey Iran, Report no. 10, 79 p.
BARANOV, V. I., AND KHRISTIANOVA, L. A., 1959, Radioactivity of the waters of the Indian Ocean: Geochemistry (English translation), no. 7, p. 765–769.
———, RONOV, A. B., AND KUNOSHOVA, K. G., 1956, On the geochemistry of dispersed thorium and uranium in clays and carbonate rocks of the Russian Platform: Geochemistry (English translation), no. 2, p. 123–139.
BLISSKOVSKIY, V. Z., 1969, Molybdenum, chromium and vanadium in phosphorites: Geochemistry Inter. no. 9, p. 878–887.
———, 1969a, Geochemistry of lead in phosphorites: Geol. Rud. Mestorozhd., v. 11, 2, p. 95–97 (in Russian).
———, ROMANOVA, L. V., SMIRNOVA, A. I., AND YEDAKOVA, L. M., 1968, Arsenic in phosphorites: Geochemistry Inter., no. 6, p. 592–602.
BROWN, H., AND SILVER, L. T., 1956, The possibilities of obtaining long range supplies of uranium, thorium, and other substances from igneous rocks: U.S. Geol. Survey Prof. Paper, 300, p. 91–95.
CALVERT, S. E., 1976, The mineralogy and geochemistry of near-shore sediments, in Chemical Oceanography (Ed. by R. P. Riley and R. Chester), v. 6, 2nd ed., p. 187–280. Academic Press, London.
CATHCART, J. B., 1974, Geology and mineralogy of phosphate rock in the Bambui Group near Cédro Abaete and vicinity, Minas Gerais, Brazil: U.S. Geol. Survey Open-File Report 74-219, 59 p.
———, AND SCHMIDT, D. L., 1977, Middle Paleozoic sedimentary phosphate in the Pensacola Mts., Antarctica: U.S. Geol. Survey Prof. Paper 456-E, 18 p.
CHAIKINA, M. V., AND NIKOLSKAYA, YU. P., 1970, Distribution of minor elements in Siberian phosphorites: Akad. Nauk S.S.S.R., Sibir. Otdel., Geologia i Geofizika, no. 2, p. 132–137 (in Russian).
CLARK, A. H., 1965, The mineralogy and geochemistry of the Ylogarvi Cu-W deposit, Southwest Finland: Bismuth-bearing apatite: C. R. Soc. Géol. Finlande, XXXVII, p. 195–199.
CLARK, L. J., AND HILL, W. L., 1958, Occurrence of copper, zinc, molybdenum and cobalt in phosphate fertilizers and sewage sludge: Jour. Official Agric. Chem., v. 41, p. 631–637.
COOK, P. J., 1972, Petrology and geochemistry of the phosphate deposits of Northwest Queensland, Australia: Econ. Geol. v. 67, p. 1193–1213.
COSSA, 1878, "Sur la diffusion du cerium, du lanthane et du didyme" extract of a letter from Cossa to M. Sella, presented by M. Fremy: Acad. Sciences [Paris] Comptes rendus, v. 87, p. 378–388.
DE KEYSER, F., AND COOK, P. J., 1972, The geology of the Middle Cambrian phosphorites and associated sediments of north-west Queensland: Australia Bur. Mineral Resources, Geology Geophysics Bull. 138, 79 p.
DESBOROUGH, G. A., 1977, Preliminary report on certain metals of potential economic interest in thin vanadium-rich

zones in the Meade Peak Member of the Phosphoria Formation in western Wyoming and eastern Idaho: U.S. Geol. Survey, Open-File Report 77-341.

EL WAKEEL, S. K., AND RILEY, J. P., 1961, Chemical and mineralogical studies of deep sea sediments: Geochim. et Cosmochim. Acta, v. 25, p. 110–146.

ENGEL, G., GOTZ, W., AND EGER, R., 1979, Über bismuthaltige Silicatapatite ungewöhnliche Oxidapatite: Z. anorg. Chem. 449, p. 127–134.

FLEISCHER, MICHAEL, 1956, Minor elements in some sulfide minerals: Econ. Geol. 50th Anniv. Vol. p. 970–1024.

GOLDBERG, E. D., KOIDE, M., SCHMITT, R. A., AND SMITH, H. V., 1963, Rare earth distribution in the marine environment: J. Geophys. Res. v. 68, p. 4209–4217.

GULBRANDSEN, R. A., 1966, Chemical Composition of Phosphorites of the Phosphoria Formation: Geochim. Cosmochim. Acta, v. 30 no. 8, p. 769–778.

HERRMANN, A. G., 1970, Yttrium and lanthanides, *in* Handbook of Geochemistry (Ed. K. H. Wedepohl): v. 11/2, 39, p. 57–71. Springer Verlag, Berlin.

HILL, W. L., MARSHALL, H. L., AND JACOB, K. D., 1932, Minor metallic constituents of phosphate rock: Indus. Eng. Chemistry, v. 24, p. 1306–1312.

HØGDAHL, OVE, 1967, Distribution of the rare earths in sea-water: Prog. Rept. no. 4, to NATO, Central Instit. for Ind. Res., Blindern, 34 p.

JACOB, K. D., HILL, W. L., MARSHALL, H. L., AND REYNOLDS, D. S., 1933, The Composition and Distribution of Phosphate Rock with Special Reference to the United States: U.S. Department of Agriculture Technical Bulletin 364, 90 p.

KAPUSTYANSKI, I. D., 1964, Rare elements in phosphorites and phosphatized Cretaceous formations of Kul'dzuk-Tau Mt., Kyzyl-Kum: Nauchny Trudy Tashkent, Gos. Univ. no. 249, Geol. no. 21, p. 230–239 (in Russian).

KHOLODOV, V. N., 1963, On Rare and Radioactive Elements in Phosphorites: Akad. nauk Inst. Mineral. Geokgm. Kristallokhim. Redk. Elem., Tr., v. 17, p. 67–108 (in Russian).

———, 1973, Trace-element distribution in the Kurumsak-Chulaktau deposits of Karatau: Geochemistry Inter. v. 7, p. 795–803.

KOLODNY, Y., AND KAPLAN, I. R., 1960, Uranium Isotopes in the Sea-Floor Phosphorites: Geochim. Cosmochim. Acta, v. 34, p. 3–24.

KRAUSKOPF, K. B., 1955, Sedimentary Deposits of Rare Metals: Econ. Geol., 50th Anniv. Vol., p. 411–463.

LARSEN, E. S., 3d, 1957, Distribution of uranium in igneous complexes: U.S. Geol. Survey TEI-700, p. 249–253.

———, AND GOTTFRIED, DAVID, 1961, Distribution of uranium in rocks and minerals of the Mesozoic batholiths in western U.S.: U.S. Geol. Survey Bull. 1070-C, p. 63–103.

MAZOR, E., 1963, Notes concerning the geochemistry of phosphorus, fluorine, uranium and radium in some marine rocks in Israel: Israel Jour. of Earth Sci., v. 12, p. 41–52.

MCARTHUR, J. M., 1978, Systematic variations in the contents of Na, Sr, CO_2 and SO_4 in marine carbonate-fluorapatite and their relation to weathering: Chem. Geology, v. 21, p. 89–112.

PATTON, W. W., AND MATZKO, J. J., 1959, Phosphate deposits in Alaska: U.S. Geol. Survey Prof. Paper 302-A, 16 p.

RADER, L. F., AND HILL, W. L., 1936, Occurrence of selenium in natural phosphates, superphosphates and phosphoric acid: Jour. Agr. Res., v. 51, p. 1071–1083.

———, 1938, Determination and occurrence of boron in natural phosphates, superphosphates and defluorinated phosphate rocks: Jour. Agr. Res., v. 57, p. 901–916.

ROBBINS, C. W., AND CARTER, D. L., 1970, Selenium concentrations in phosphorous fertilizer materials: Proc. Soil Sci. Soc. Am., v. 34, p. 506–509.

ROBINSON, W. O., 1948, The presence and determination of molybdenum and rare earths in phosphate rock: Soil Sci., v. 66, p. 317–322.

ROGERS, C. L., DECSERNA, E. T., AND ULLOA, SALVADOR, 1956, General geology and phosphate deposits of Concepcion del Oro district, Zacatecas: Mexico, U.S. Geol. Survey Bull. 1037-A, 102 p.

RONOV, A. B., BALASHOV, YU. A., AND MIGDISOV, A. A., 1967, Geochemistry of rare earth elements in the sedimentary cycle: Geochem. Int. v. 4, p. 1–17.

SACKETT, W. M., AND POTRATZ, H. A., 1963, Dating of carbonate rocks by ionium-uranium ratios, *in* subsurface geology of Eniwetok Atoll: U.S. Geol. Survey Prof. Paper 260-Bb, p. 1053–1066.

SEMENOV, E. I., KHOLODOV, V. N., AND BARINSKII, R. L., 1962, Rare Earths in Phosphorites: Geochem., v. 5, p. 501–507.

STOW, S. H., 1969, The occurrence of arsenic and the color-causing components in Florida Land-Pebble phosphate rock: Econ. Geol. v. 64, p. 667–671.

SWAINE, D. J., 1962, The Trace Element Content of Fertilizers: Commonwealth Bureau of Soils, Technical Communication, no. 52, Herpenden, England, 306 p.

TOOMS, J. S., SUMMERHAYES, C. R., AND CRONAN, D. S., 1969, Geochemistry of Marine Phosphate and Manganese Deposits: Oceanogr. Mar. Biol. Ann. Rev., v. 7, p. 49–100.

TREMEARNE, T. H., AND JACOB, K. D., 1941, Arsenic in natural phosphates and phosphate fertilizers: U.S. Dept. Agric. Tech. Bull., no. 781, 32 p.

TUREKIAN, KARL K., AND WEDEPOHL, KARL HANS, 1961, Distribution of elements in some major units of the Earth's crust: Geol. Soc. Am. Bull., v. 72, p. 175–192.

VINOGRADOV, A. P., AND RONOV, A. B., 1956, Evolution of the chemical composition of clays of the Russian Platform: Geochemistry (English trans.), no. 2, p. 123–139.

SEPM SPECIAL PUBLICATION No. 29, P. 31–39, NOVEMBER 1980

BEHAVIOR OF SOME TRACE ELEMENTS IN PHOSPHATIC SEDIMENTARY FORMATIONS

LILIANE PRÉVÔT AND JACQUES LUCAS
Centre de Sédimentologie et Géochimie de la Surface (CNRS)
Laboratoire de Géologie de l'Université Louis Pasteur de Strasbourg
1, Rue Blessig, 67000 Strasbourg, France

ABSTRACT

From analyses of sedimentary phosphorites of various origins, either carried out at the Center of Sedimentology and Geochemistry of Strasbourg, or gathered from literature, the authors have tried to derive general rules on the behavior of trace elements in these rocks. Sr, Ba, V, Ni, Cr were especially examined. Trace elements witness the history of the rock; they corroborate the biologic origin of phosphorus concentration by characteristics common to all deposits.

INTRODUCTION

Unweathered sedimentary marine phosphorites of Cretaceous and younger age (including Recent ones), are remarkably uniform as to the composition of their apatite (generally carbonate-fluor-apatite) as well as to the mineral assemblages present. Thus, the major element composition of these rocks provides but few clues to their mode of origin.

It is, however, well-known that apatites readily act as hosts for numerous trace elements which are also likely to occur as substitutions in carbonates and clays, two groups of minerals frequently associated with apatite in phosphorites. The abundance of trace elements in phosphorites has been discussed by several authors (Gulbrandsen, 1966; Tooms et al., 1969; Cook, 1972; Altschuler, 1967, 1973); but the study of all rocks of the phosphatic series, i.e. of phosphorites as well as of the associated limestones or dolomites, clays and cherts, might be more indicative of the genesis of phosphorite deposits.

To limit the scope of our work, we have concentrated on trace elements most frequently found in phosphorites, with the exception of U and the REE, and on a rapid survey of the data in the literature concerning them (Swaine, 1962; Tooms et al., 1969). After mineralogical determination by X-ray analysis, the samples were chemically analyzed by the direct reading spectrometric method (quantometer). The general scheme of this method is described by Besnus and Lucas (1968) and Besnus and Rouault (1973). Fluorine was analyzed by the specific electrode method. The results are shown in fig. 1. As the world-wide mean values might not be too significant because of their generality, we have portrayed not the values themselves but the variations observed by comparing the amount of each element in the earth crust, in sea-water, calcitic limestone and phosphorites.

The elements shown in line I of fig. 1 are concentrated in both sea water and phosphorites, as compared with their crustal abundance. The variation between sea water and phosphorites, however, is not always the same, B and Sr being lower in phosphorites, while Zn is about equally distributed and U is enriched in phosphorites. As for the calcium carbonates, they are poorer than sea water in the content of all these elements.

Line II shows the behavior of Cr, Pb, REE and V. All show a very low concentration in sea-water relative to both crust and phosphorites. They are more concentrated in phosphorites than in the crust, whereas for $CaCO_3$ the opposite is true. The elements in line III, finally, are more concentrated in the crust than in either phosphorites or carbonates.

The main differences between phosphorites and carbonates appear in triangles 3, 4, 5 and 6, where the concentration arrows point toward the phosphorite pole, but, at least for Zn, U, Cr, REE and V, away from the carbonate pole.

Distribution and Behavior of Elements

We shall now briefly* examine the distribution and behavior of some important elements based on the results of about one thousand analyses of onshore and offshore marine phosphorites of Cretaceous and younger age. A preliminary paper on trace elements presented two years ago at the Second Symposium on the Origin and Distribution of the Elements (Prévôt et al., 1977) was already based on the analyses of about 500 samples from marine phosphoritic series of Morocco, Senegal,

---

*More details are given in Prévôt and Lucas (1979).

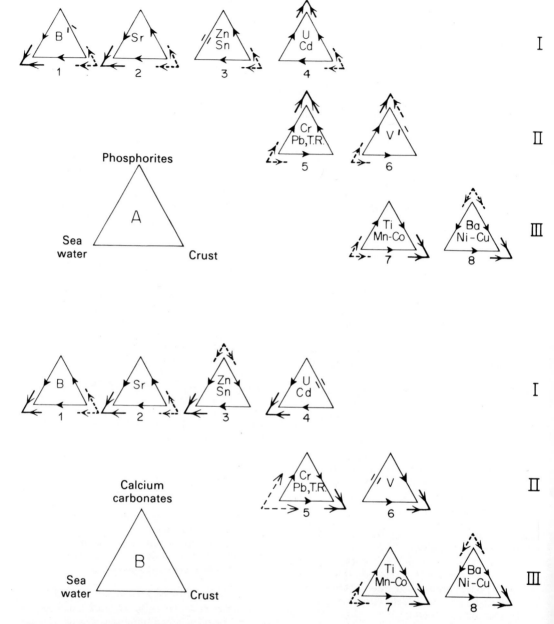

Fig. 1.—Relative variations in trace element concentrations between sea water, crust and (A) phosphorites or (B) calcium carbonates, after data gathered by Tooms et al. (1969) and the chemical composition of an average carbonate given by Rösler (1972). Arrows represent the direction of enrichment. [The concentration factor for sea water is 1/10,000.]

Israel and the continental margin off northern Spain. This paper should be usefully consulted for the geographical and stratigraphical situation of the sections studied, and for their short descriptions. In the meantime, the number of analyses has doubled, most of the new ones concerning the Moroccan deposits (fig. 2), from where all those of table I originate. Most of the samples from Morocco are from the Ganntour deposit, the geology of which was studied by Boujo (1976). This Moroccan deposit, consisting of pelletal phosphorites, can be considered to be an au-

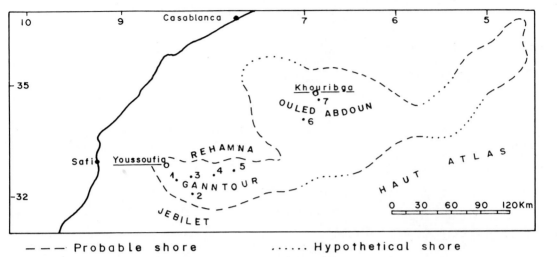

Fig. 2.—Location map. 1: D3; 2: D8; 3: RVI; 4: El 0.; 5: BG; 6: OF; 7: RII.

tochthonous formation, affected only by local reworking. It was deposited in a long narrow gulf, having only one communication with the ocean to the west, and extending over 100 kilometers. The phosphatic series, in which more or less argillaceous phosphorites, cherts, and calcium carbonates (limestones and/or dolomites) alternate, reflects a rythmic sedimentation which lasted from the Maastrichtian to the beginning of the Lutetian. Its always strongly reduced thickness varies from 180 meters at Youssoufia in the west to 100 meters at the Tessaout in the east. Another important character is the distinction between the northern uplifted fringe where light phosphorites with calcite (and dolomite) crop out and a "drowned" zone where the series, entirely situated under the ground water level, contains only dark phosphorite with dolomite.

Sr.—As is well-known, Sr is strongly concentrated in phosphorites (table 1). Our analyses gave values around 1000 ppm in good agreement with the determinations of Gulbrandsen (1966) on the Phosphoria Formation. Whatever the composition of the phosphorite, Sr always correlates positively with P_2O_5 (fig. 3), rarely with calcite and never with Al_2O_3. Thus, there can be no doubt that this element is preferably associated with the apatite. Sr and P_2O_5 are, however, not strictly proportional. The sample highest in P_2O_5 is not necessarily always also the richest in Sr.

The source of the Sr in apatites does not seem to raise a problem, as Sr accompanies phosphorus in sufficient amounts, e.g., in sea water. The relation between the two elements is even closer, if one believes the hypothesis that apatite forms by transformation of biological calcium carbonate;

it is well-known that phosphorus concentrates in soft parts of microorganisms and in bones of macroorganisms and strontium in tests and shells which can contain up to 1 percent Sr (Kulp et al., 1952). During weathering, strontium is quickly lost to the apatite lattice (Lucas et al., this special publication) and even to the phosphorite.

Two diagrams are particularly instructive: Selja and Bengrir (fig. 3). The clusters of points are bounded by a limiting line. By simplifying in the extreme the complexity of a history resulting from the mobility of calcium carbonates, some clues can be deduced from these diagrams, based on the following plausible assumptions:

—phosphorus epigenizes carbonates, preferentially aragonite;
—phosphatization preserves the strontium of the replaced carbonate (aragonite or calcite);
—calcitization of aragonite proceeds with loss of strontium;
—apatites are formed by early diagenesis within a carbonatic mud, the carbonates of which are mostly aragonitic tests;
—the instable aragonite tends to calcitize;
—phosphatization and calcitization of aragonite compete with each other.

Points situated on the limiting line correspond to the maximum of strontium aragonite can transmit to the epigenizing apatite. The cluster of points No. 1 corresponds to a lack of phosphorus for the epigenizable calcium carbonate; the apatite formed uses as much strontium as possible. The points at the very top of the cluster No. 2 correspond to phosphorites containing small amounts of calcium carbonate; they may picture the result of the antagonism between phospha-

TABLE 1.—COMPARISON OF MEAN TRACE ELEMENT CONTENTS BETWEEN DOMINANTLY CALCITIC OR DOLOMITIC SAMPLES (CARB.) AND DOMINANTLY PHOSPHATIC SAMPLES (PHOSPH.) IN SEVEN MOROCCAN LOGS. (FOR LOCATION SEE FIG. 2).

Sample locality	Dominant phase	Number of samples	P_2O_5	CaO	MgO	F	Sr	Ba	V	Ni	Cr	Zn	Cu
Drill-hole 3	Carb.	18	2.53	24.12	13.47	—	233	44	96	50	147	67	34
(Ganntour)	Phosph.	27	16	31.54	3.69	1.97	988	64	42	41	192	210	22
Drill hole 8	Carb.	22	3.09	20.48	11.82	—	159	48	51	27	119	74	39
(Ganntour)	Phosph.	16	18.55	31.70	2.38	2.21	1002	83	191	64	298	249	56
Recette VI trench	Carb.	19	3.14	29.35	6.17	—	185	37	69	38	108	151	25
(Ganntour)	Phosph.	26	15.72	32.76	2.38	1.87	1025	111	62	42	217	213	29
El Ouata pit	Carb.	19	2.08	26.28	15.32	—	166	29	72	44	71	158	52
(Ganntour)	Phosph.	25	24.79	46.47	0.84	2.75	1199	107	71	48	214	144	44
Exploration Channel Bengrir	Carb.	8	2.46	27.18	16.33	—	230	36	174	72	101	554	50
(Ganntour)	Phosph.	12	28.9	45.02	1.18	—	1288	155	146	21	149	155	36
Oulad Fares pit	Carb.	7	5.19	47.11	4.94	—	208	36	385	57	221	598	41
(Oulad Abdoun)	Phosph.	10	29.73	46.44	0.45	—	702	100	106	41	251	244	46
Recette II pit	Carb.	20	4.97	33.63	8.42	—	260	76	297	74	178	327	30
(Oulad Abdoun)	Phosph.	15	31.83	50.42	0.63	—	617	108	74	43	219	279	40

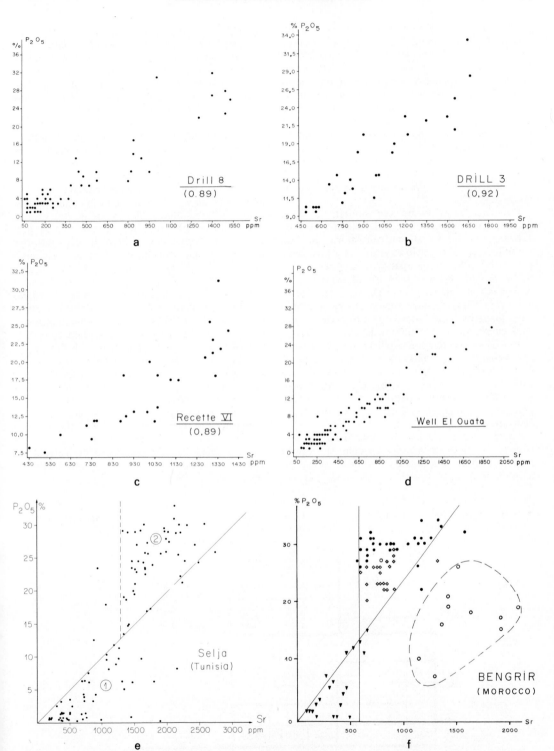

FIG. 3.—Some P_2O_5-Sr correlation diagrams. Number in brackets is correlation coefficient. a) Drill-hole 8, Morocco; b) Drill-hole 3, Morocco; c) Recette VI, Morocco; d) El Cuata pit, Morocco; e) Oued Selja, Tunisia (after Lucas, Chaabani, Prévôt, 1979); f) Bengrir, Morocco (after Wadjinny, 1979).

tization and calcitization; points nearest to the straight line correspond to direct phosphatization of aragonite; the farther the points are away from the straight line, the later phosphatization did occur, at the expense of a more and more calcitic carbonate, i.e. less and less rich in strontium. Points situated at the lower part of the cluster No. 2 correspond to a balance between these two possibilities: lack of phosphorus, or phosphatization following calcitization.

The slope of the limiting line of Selja is different from that of Bengrir. This difference may result from a difference in the strontium content of the initial aragonite.

Ba.—Ba seems to behave similar to Sr in phosphorites and in the associated carbonates (fig. 1, triangle 8), but is systematically more abundant in the former (table 1). In any case, it is positively correlated either with apatite (e.g. Recette VI: Sr-Ba = 0.61; P-Ba = 0.54 for 53 samples), or with clays, but never with carbonates (Prévôt et al., 1977). Thus, barium appears to be inherited from plankton where it is known to concentrate, as does strontium (Martin and Knauer, 1973).

V.—The close relationship between phosphates and vanadates is well-known. The behavior of V is indeed much different in phosphorites and carbonates (fig. 1, triangle 6); it is enriched in the former, where it substitutes easily for phosphorus, reaching sometimes commercial concentrations.

The average content of V varies from one site to another—between 40 and 350 ppm; the values are even more dispersed from one sample to another in a same trench or borehole, varying from 30 to 1000 ppm. Though more abundant in phosphorites, V does not show a marked regular positive correlation with any mineral of the phosphorites; yet its attraction for apatite is as clear as its affinity with the clay minerals. The best partnership of V is not with any mineral, but with other trace elements with which it forms a constant positively correlated group (table 2). These elements are V, Ni, Cr, Zn, and sometimes Cu, an association which is considered to be typical of organic matter (Krauskopf, 1955; Gulbrandsen, 1966; Cook, 1972).

Ni.—The above correlation explains that Ni, in spite of its low abundance in phosphorites (50 ppm), behaves almost like V. It is, however, a less evident substitute in apatites, which may explain its lower concentration. Its concentration increases when phosphorites contain glauconites or iron oxides (Debrabant and Paquet, 1975; Lucas et al., 1978).

Cr.—Cr is enriched in phosphorites to values of 200 to 300 ppm, and in the Phosphoria Formation even up to 1000 ppm. More abundant in the phosphorite family than in the carbonate family, it is often in positive correlation with P_2O_5 (e.g., drill-hole 8: Cr-Sr = 0.75; Cr-P = 0.83 for 53 samples; Recette VI: Cr-Sr = 0.59; Cr-P = 0.50 for 50 samples), especially in dark colored nonweathered phosphorites still rich in organic matter. Other factors are obviously interfering, as shown by the points on the right of the diagram (fig. 4). Clay is one of these factors and we can suppose that Cr, though primarily carried by apatite, is further fixed in or on clays, when these are present.

TABLE 2.—Correlation coefficients between elements of the intercorrelated group in phosphate deposits for three sections of Morocco

				D 8	D 3	R VI		
All samples →				(50)	(60)	(50)	← no. of samples	
				0.28	0.26	0.28	← lower significant correlation coefficient for P = 0.05	
phosphorites →				(16)	(27)	(26)		
				0.49	0.38	0.39		

	(V) — D8	(V) — D3	(V) — RVI	(Ni) — D8	(Ni) — D3	(Ni) — RVI	(Cr) — D8	(Cr) — D3	(Cr) — RVI
(Ni) all	0.82	0.64	0.49						
(Ni) phosph.	0.92	(0.35)	0.87						
(Cr) all	0.70	0.77	0.28	0.84	0.82	0.33			
(Cr) phosph.	0.56	0.73	0.54	0.84	0.44	0.59			
Zn all	0.75	(0.25)	0.53	0.75	0.29	0.74	0.78	0.45	0.31
Zn phosph.	0.81	0.55	0.78	0.95	(0.36)	0.82	0.71	0.43	(0.34)

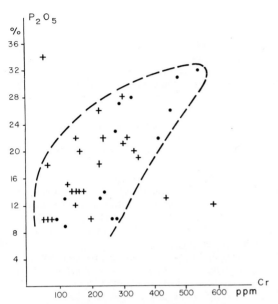

FIG. 4.—Two examples of positive P_2O_5-Cr correlation: drill-hole No. 3 (crosses) and drill-hole No. 8 (points) from Ganntour (Morocco).

Zn.—Zinc has a much more haphazard behavior. Sometimes it is more abundant in phosphorites, at other times in carbonates; correlated either with apatite or with clays, it does not show any dominant trend other than belonging to the group V, Ni, Cr, Zn.

U.—Uranium and Rare Earths should be studied along with trace elements. We have only few new data on these elements and prefer, therefore, to refer to the literature presented by Slansky (1977) for uranium and by Altschuler (1967, 1973) for uranium and Rare Earths.

Minor Elements

Some minor elements occurring in 0.x% should be briefly mentioned. K and Ti are strongly associated with clays, Na is distributed between clays and apatite, but is clearly dominantly located in the apatite lattice. Mn, though available in very low quantities, is enriched relative to its content in sea water in both phosphorites and carbonates. Its relation with phosphates is well-known, for example, in polymetallic oceanic nodules. Sulfur content in phosphorites is highly variable. The SO_3-content is 0.75 percent in Nzalet (Morocco), 1.75 percent in the Phosphoria Formation, and 3.12 percent in Abu Tartur, Egypt (Hermina, 1974). Whatever its content, its good correlation with P_2O_5 proves that at least part of it is inside the apatite lattice.

DISCUSSION

The quantity of an element in a rock and its partition between different minerals of this rock are affected by numerous factors, but depend primarily on the availability of this element in the genetic environment and on the possibilities offered to this element to find accommodation in the lattices.

McArthur (1978) believes that the environment has no influence, since phosphorites form always in the marine environment and this is assumed to be of constant composition. All apatites must have been primarily the same, becoming different only through weathering.

We do not agree with this idea. Numerous authors, such as Broecker (1974), have shown that, if sea water is relatively constant in its major components, the concentration of its trace elements may vary greatly. Moreover, numerous clues lead us to believe that phosphorites form by early diagenesis (they are synsedimentary), either within the bottom mud (Lucas and Prévôt, 1975) where interstitial water is no longer sea water, or in micro-environments where confinement may be high (Lucas et al., 1978).

On the other hand, it seems difficult to make alteration alone responsible for such different parageneses as can be observed: calcite is sometimes secondary, substituting for apatite (Lucas et al., 1979), but very often it is a primary, micritic foraminiferal mud. Dolomite, also, is often synsedimentary. How could two different carbonates accompany apatite, if the genetic environment was constant? Glauconite also often occurs beside apatite, sometimes so closely associated with it, that the micro-environment (Odin, 1975; Lamboy, 1976) of both minerals seems to have been the same, in this case one containing iron. In other cases, sulfur is abundant in the environment, so that gypsum forms.

Such parageneses are local: there are phosphorite deposits with glauconite or with sulfates, others are only calcitic or dolomitic, or both. These parageneses reflect differences in the genetic environment, depending on the supplies from the continent and from the ocean. These supplies change with place and time. Thus, the V, Ni and Cr contents of some boreholes in Morocco show variations depending more on the age than on whether the facies is dolomitic or phosphatic.

We consider it, therefore, certain that the genetic environment of phosphorite, though leading always to the same apatitic mineral (F-carbonate-apatite), can produce various accompanying minerals.

We have already pointed out that the relation of trace elements with P_2O_5 is never strictly proportional; even when the correlation is good, the scatter of the values may be significant.

Likewise, the existence in all phosphorites studied of an intercorrelated group of elements without tie with any major element or mineral phase (table 2), raises the question of the reason for this association. These elements, which have no special affinity for each other, must have been gathered by their common affinity for another substance which has in the meantime largely disappeared. The known association of such elements as V, Ni, Cr, Zn, U, with organic matter, together with the abundant signs of biological activity of macro- as well as microorganisms (Fauconnier, 1977; Doubinger, 1979), indicate that organisms, especially plankton, play an important role in the genesis of phosphorites. Some authors (Tooms et al., 1969) attribute less importance to these organisms. We think, on the contrary, that the described trace element associations show that the first trap for these elements is a biological one, becoming then biochemical. Only the final arrangement of the trapped elements in a very specific environment is chemical (Lucas and Prévôt, 1975).

A preconcentration of most trace elements characteristic of phosphorites explains why their range of concentration in phosphorites is fortuitous with respect to their range of concentration in sea water. If apatite forms by direct chemical precipitation from sea water, there should exist a relation between these two concentration ranges. Such a relation has, so far, not been found, whereas a relation between phosphorite and organic matter does appear. The rate of concentration by organisms obviously also depends on the sea water concentration, but the micro-nutrients here considered are available in sufficient quantities in sea water, so that they are not a limiting factor of organism growth. The elementary contents of plankton are difficult to determine, because they vary with the species, and even with their age and with seasons (Martin and Knauer, 1973). However, it is known that only those elements can enter organisms, which are able to form easily soluble and mobile complexes.

Palynological studies now under way show good correlations between the chemistry of phosphorites and the *Hystrichosphere* families (Prévôt et al., 1979). The species change rapidly and do not concentrate elements with the same intensity. The nature of the organic matter transporting and subsequently releasing trace elements changes with stratigraphy.

These biologically concentrated elements, released when the organic matter is decomposed, must have found in phosphorites host structures sufficiently accommodating to fix and preserve these elements. Fixation may occur by simple adsorption on minerals, mainly on clays and apatite, but is stronger when the elements enter the lattices. The complex lattice of apatite, which allows many coupled substitutions, easily accepts various elements; thus, strontium prefers this host to any other. The sites available in apatite are more or less suitable also for elements, to which clays are more attractive. It appears, nevertheless, that apatite is in many cases an intermediate host, as there might have been no clay present at the time of formation.

REFERENCES

ALTSCHULER, Z. S., 1973, The weathering of phosphate deposits. Geochemical and environmental aspects, *in* Environ. Phosphorus Handbook, Ed. J. Wiley and Sons, New York, p. 33–96.

ALTSCHULER, Z. S., 1967, Rare earths in phosphorites: U.S. Geol. Survey Prof. Pap. 575-B, p. 1–9.

BESNUS, Y., AND LUCAS, J., 1968, Dosage des éléments à l'état de traces dans les roches et les autres substances minérales naturelles: Coll. Nat. du CNRS, no. 923, édition CNRS, 1970.

————, AND ROUAULT, R., 1973, Une méthode d'analyse des roches au spectromètre d'arc à lecture directe par un dispositif d'électrode rotative: Analysis, v. 2, no. 2, p. 111–116.

BOUJO, A., 1976, Contribution à l'étude géologique du gisement de phosphate crétacé-éocène des Ganntour (Maroc occidental): Mém. Sci. Géol. Strasbourg; no. 43, and Notes et Mémoires du Serv. géol. Maroc, no. 262.

BROECKER, W. S., 1974, Chemical oceanography. Ed. Harcourt B. J., U.S.A., 214 p.

COOK, P. J., 1972, Petrology and geochemistry of the phosphate deposits of northwest Queensland, Australia: Econ. Geol., v. 67, p. 1193–1213.

DEBRABANT, P., AND PAQUET, J., 1975, L'association glauconites-phosphates-carbonates (Albien de la Sierra de Espana, Espagne méridionale): Chem. Geol., v. 15, p. 61–75.

DOUBINGER, J., 1978, Dinokystes et Acritarches des sédiments phosphates de Ganntour (Maroc): Sci. Géol. Bull., v. 31, p. 3.

FAUCONNIER, D., 1977, Les Dinoflagellés de l'Albien et du Cénomanien inférieur du Bassin de Paris. Répartition stratigraphique et relations avec la nature du dépôt: Thèse (Doctorat d'Univ.) Orléans, 229 p.

GULBRANDSEN, R. A., 1966, Chemical composition of phosphorites of the Phosphoria Formation: Geochim. et Cosmochim. Acta, v. 30, p. 769–778.

HERNINA, M., 1974, Abu Tartur phosphorite deposit, western desert, Egypt: Geol. Surv. Mining Author. Paper 61, p. 1–10.

KRAUSKOPF, K. B., 1955, Sedimentary deposits of rare metals: Econ. Geol., 50th Ann. Vol., p. 411–463.

KULP, J. L., TUREKIAN, K., AND BOYD, D. W., 1952, Strontium content of limestones and fossils: Bull. Geol. Soc. Am., v. 63, p. 701–716.

LAMBOY, M., 1976, Géologie marine et sous-marine du plateau continental au Nord-Ouest de l'Espagne. Genèse des glauconies et des phosphorites: Thèse Université Rouen, 285 p.

LUCAS, J., AND PRÉVÔT, L., 1975, Les marges continentales pièges géochimiques; l'exemple de la marge atlantique de l'Afrique à la limite Crétacé-Tertiaire: Bull. Soc. Géol. Fr., (7) XVIII, v. 4, p. 496–501.

———, PRÉVÔT, L., AND LAMBOY, M., 1978a, Les phosphorites de la marge nord de l'Espagne. Chimie, minéralogie, genèse: Oceanol. Acta, v. 1, p. 107–118.

———, CHAABANI, F., AND PRÉVÔT, L., 1979, Phosphorites et évaporites: deux formations de milieux sédimentaires voisins étudiées dans la coupe du Paléogène de Foum Selja (Metlaoui, Tunisie): Bull. Sci. Géol. Strasbourg, v. 32. (in press).

———, PRÉVÔT, L., ATAMAN, G., AND GÜNDOĞDU, N., 1979, Etude minéralogique et géochimique de la série phosphatée du sud-est de la Turquie (Mazidagi-Mardin): Sci. Géol. Bull., v. 32. (in press).

MCARTHUR, J. M., 1978, Systematic variations in the contents of Na, Sr, CO_3 and SO_4 in marine carbonate-fluorapatite and their relation to weathering: Chem. Geol., v. 21, p. 1639–1653.

ODIN, G., 1975, Les glauconies: constitution, formation, âge: Thèse d'Etat, Paris, 250 p.

PRÉVÔT, L., LUCAS, J., NATHAN, Y., AND SHILONI, Y., 1977, Distribution of trace elements in marine phosphorites, in Origin and distribution of the elements, Proceedings of the Second Symposium, Paris-UNESCO, Ed. Pergamon, p. 293–304.

———, AND LUCAS, J., 1979, Comportement de quelques éléments traces dans les phosphorites: Sci. Géol. Bull., v. 32 (in press).

———, LUCAS, J., AND DOUBINGER, J., 1979, Une correspondance entre la composition chimique et le contenu palynologique d'une série phosphatée sédimentaire: Sci. Géol. Bull., v. 32. (in press).

RÖSLER, H. J., AND LANGE, H., 1972, Geochemical tables. Elsevier Ed.

SLANSKY, M., 1977, Répartition et possibilités de concentration de l'uranium dans les phosphates sédimentaires: Rapport au Intern. Atomic Energy Agency Advisory Committee Meeting on Uranium Deposits in Africa, Lusaka, 1977, 10 p.

SWAINE, D. J., 1962, The trace element content of fertilizers: Commonwealth Bureau of Soils, Techn. Commun. no. 52, Herpenden, England, 306 p.

TOOMS, J. S., SUMMERHAYES, C. P., AND CRONAN, D. S., 1969, Geochemistry of marine phosphate and manganese deposits: Oceanogr. Mar. Biol. Ann. Rev., v. 7, p. 49–100.

WADJINNY, A., 1979, Etude sédimentologique de la série phosphatée de Bengrir (Ganntour, Maroc): Thèse 3ème cycle, Strasbourg.

SEPM Special Publication No. 29, p. 41–51, November 1980

DIFFERENT ASPECTS OF PHOSPHORITE WEATHERING

JACQUES LUCAS,[1] RENÉ FLICOTEAUX,[2] YAACOV NATHAN,[3] LILIANE PRÉVÔT[1]
AND YAACOV SHAHAR[4]

[1] Laboratoire de Géologie de l'Université Louis Pasteur et Centre de Sédimentologie et Géochimie de la Surface (CNRS), 1 Rue Blessig, 67000 Strasbourg, France.
[2] Laboratoire de Sédimentologie Continentale de l'Université de Marseille III, Rue Henri Poincaré, 13397 Marseille Cedex 4, France.
[3] Geochemistry Division, Geological Survey of Israel, Malkei Israel St. 30, Jerusalem, Israel.
[4] Geology Department, Ben Gurion University of the Negev, Beer-Sheba, Israel.

ABSTRACT

Several examples of phosphorite weathering (Morocco, Senegal, Israel), are studied. Weathering of phosphorites is shown to begin by loss of CO_2 from the carbonate-fluor-apatite, which tends toward a fluor-apatite; dolomite loses its Mg, then calcite is leached. When calcium carbonates are eliminated, calcium apatite transforms to aluminum- or iron-phosphates.

Four cases are studied, two of slight weathering by J. L. and L. P., one of intense weathering in an aluminous environment by R. F. and one of intense weathering in an environment rich in iron by Y. N. and Y. S.; the discussion is by all authors.

The Sidi Daoui Deposit, an Example of Slight Weathering
(El Mountassir, 1977; Lucas et al., 1979c)

The Sidi Daoui deposit is a subhorizontal tabular sedimentary rock body, cut by a slightly sloping topographic paleosurface (fig. 1). Along the topographic surface, this disposition induced the development of a weathering zone of several meters which affected the different facies of the phosphatic series. On weathering, the phosphorites turned red and were enriched in clay, whatever their original composition. It is easy to compare the "non-weathered" with the weathered facies (table 1).

The non-weathered phosphorite is pelletal with an unconsolidated matrix. It consists of apatite, calcite and dolomite, which are often silicified, and minor amounts, about 1 to 5 percent, of clay. The apatite is a fluor-carbonate-apatite with 4.5 to 6 percent CO_2 in the lattice; the CaO/P_2O_5 ratio is 1.56 and the F/P_2O_5 ratio is 0.12 (table 2). The clay minerals are smectite, Mg- and Fe-montmorillonites and some palygorskite (attapulgite).

As the phosphorite turns red, its mineralogy changes: CO_2 in apatite decreases to between 1.5 and 4.5 percent; the CaO/P_2O_5 ratio decreases to 1.30 and the mineral is depleted in both strontium and fluorine. This is a trend towards fluorapatite. Calcite is partially dissolved, as can be seen under the microscope, and X-ray analysis reveals a poor crystallinity. Dolomite, depleted in magnesium, shows a trend to dedolomitization. Clay minerals are poorly crystallized smectites and mixed-layer clays; palygorskite disappears

and kaolinite appears. The relative amount of clay increases.

A geochemical study brings confirmation and precision to these mineralogical changes. Some positive correlation coefficients (table 3) increase in the rubefied facies: those of the elements in clay minerals, showing that weathering is accompanied by relative clayification; and that of the couple Ca-P, indicating the diminished influence of calcite. Other correlation coefficients lessen: Mg-L.O.I., confirming dedolomitization; P-Sr, indicating that strontium tends to evacuate the apatite. The vanadium, nickel, chromium and zinc contents increase.

The Taïba Deposit, Another Example of Slight Weathering
(Menor, 1975; Lucas et al., 1979b)

This example represents a case of more advanced weathering. The Taïba deposit consists of three different facies types surrounding each other (fig. 2). A limestone center (1) is bordered by a phosphatic belt (2), which is itself fringed by a sandy-clayey formation (3) called "Feral." Each of these formations is clearly separate, geographically as well as mineralogically. Though they succeed one another laterally, there are no progressive transitions. The limestone does not contain any phosphate; the phosphorite does not contain any calcite; it is nevertheless possible to find locally a mixed facies in which phosphate and limestone occur together. The phosphate formation is divided into two parts: heterogeneous ore with blocks of chert overlain by homogeneous less silicified and more regular ore. Phosphorites

N W   S E

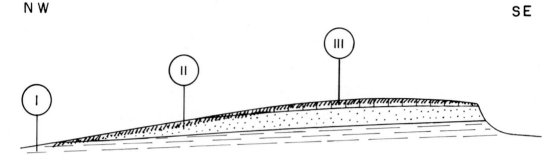

FIG. 1.—Schematic cross section of the Sidi Daoui deposit. I—Senonian; II—Phosphorite Formation; III—Lutetian limestone cover.

consist of an association of pellets, pseudo-oolites often with diffuse edges, nodules which are slightly bigger (1 cm), phosphatic microfossils, and coprolites in a clayey or phosphatic cement. Numerous dissolution figures and signs of compaction can be observed in the field as well as under the microscope. This series shows no or few signs of redeposition, but was reworked by diagenetic dissolution and recrystallization.

From numerous chemical analyses (Table 4) and from the CO_2-content values, which were either calculated by the Gulbrandsen method or measured directly (Table 5), it can be seen that

the apatite is mainly a fluor-apatite with 1 percent CO_2, a CaO/P_2O_5-ratio of 1.30 and a F/P_2O_5-ratio of 0.09 to 0.10. But in limy samples all these values increase; apatite is close to carbonate-fluor-apatite. Carbonate is only calcite; dolomite is absent. Clay minerals are montmorillonite and kaolinite; the former is Fe-rich and Mg-poor. Though palygorskite is abundant in the underlying marls (marnes de Lamlam), it is absent in the phosphate formation. Trace elements are less abundant in carbonate-free phosphorites than in those containing carbonate. Most of the trace elements are associated with clay minerals and

TABLE 1.—AVERAGE CHEMICAL COMPOSITION OF STANDARD (60 SAMPLES) AND WEATHERED (84 SAMPLES) FACIES.

	Non-Weathered Facies (60 samples)			Weathered Facies (84 samples)	
Element	Mean	Standard Deviation	Element	Mean	Standard Deviation
SiO_2	6.32	7.5297	SiO_2	10.38	8.1242
Al_2O_3	.89	.9877	Al_2O_3	3.21	2.1333
MgO	1.17	2.5670	MgO	.63	.5349
CaO	44.61	10.7570	CaO	44.62	7.2625
Fe_2O_3	.45	.4350	Fe_2O_3	1.48	.9211
MnO	.00	.0062	MnO	.02	.0114
TiO_2	.06	.0686	TiO_2	.15	.0963
Na_2O	.23	.1333	Na_2O	.28	.1713
K_2O	.09	.0822	K_2O	.31	.2206
L.O.I.	12.23	9.6796	L.O.I.	6.79	4.5929
P_2O_5	24.38	9.1122	P_2O_5	28.11	7.4531
Sr	690.42	413.6262	Sr	535.63	314.6788
Ba	64.18	31.9526	Ba	61.67	21.4934
V	48.90	61.6293	V	159.39	126.8747
Ni	53.16	63.1503	Ni	81.18	63.1516
Co	1.02	.1302	Co	1.01	.1111
Cr	234.07	144.8901	Cr	339.47	174.2579
B	2.00	.0000	B	2.32	1.5408
Zn	171.14	104.1844	Zn	233.47	154.0414
Ga	1.02	.1325	Ga	1.29	.8766
Cu	47.50	17.1733	Cu	48.54	21.3764
Pb	1.05	.2216	Pb	1.11	.6287
Sn	1.73	.4459	Sn	2.00	.0000
Cd	.00		Cd	.00	

Major elements in percent, trace elements in ppm. Means exclude values outside the intervals of ±2 average standard deviations.

TABLE 2.—CHARACTERISTICS OF THE TWO TYPES OF APATITES OF SIDI DAOUI.

Apatites	a(Å)	c(Å)	mean CaO / P₂O₅	mean F / P₂O₅	%CO₂ calculated (Gulbrandsen method)	
non-weathered facies	9.323 to 9.348	6.880 to 6.900	1.54	>0.12	>4.5	Carbonate-fluor-apatite
weathered facies	9.351 to 9.392	6.870 to 6.890	1.29	<0.12	<4.5	Fluor-apatite

TABLE 3.—SOME SIGNIFICANT CORRELATION COEFFICIENTS (X 100)

	non-weathered	weathered		non-weathered	weathered
Si-Al	67	74	Ca-P	58	**68**
Mg	*34*	**87**	Sr	**64**	42
Fe	55	**73**	Fe-Ti	**84**	72
Ti	69	**83**	K	57	**88**
K	57	**76**	Ni	**71**	33
Al-Mg	*67*	59	Ti-K	70	**80**
Fe	85	**96**	Ni	63	65
Ti	**96**	81	Na-Sr	41	**63**
K	69	**90**	P-Sr	**74**	33
Ni	*71*	37	V-Cr	49	*69*
Mg-Ti	*62*	**70**	-Ni	**63**	38
K	51	**64**	Ni-Zn	70	**74**
Pf	52	42	Ni-Cr	37	**60**

67 indicates that the correlation coefficient is not corroborated by the diagram.

and phosphatic Eocene to Oligocene deposits, and from the phosphatization of Oligocene or more recent detrital deposits (Brancart and Flicoteaux, 1971; Flicoteaux and Tessier, 1971). All authors agree that they are the result of "lateritic" weathering (Capdecomme, 1952, 1953; Slansky et al., 1964).

The lower half of the working face of the Lamlam quarry (fig. 3), 25 meters deep and situated 12 km north of Thiès, shows (Flicoteaux et al., 1977) how sediments consisting of alternating apatites, montmorillonite-illite and chert, are changing to bedded, kaolinite and goethite-rich, aluminum phosphates. From bottom to top, the

strontium, commonly correlated with apatite, is isolated without bonding by any mineral phase. In aluminous phosphates overlying the series, strontium is, however, once again very abundant and present in aluminous phosphate minerals.

A comparison with the primary rock is not possible, because fresh phosphorites are lacking, but the relationship between the Taïba and Sidi Daoui deposits seems obvious. The apatite of Taïba is thought to be the result of more intense weathering of a primary material similar to that of non-weathered Sidi Daoui.

An Example of Intense Weathering: The Aluminous Phosphates of the "Plateau de Thies" (West Senegal)*

The alumino-calcic and aluminous phosphates of Thiès result from the transformation of clayey

*More details on the aluminum phosphate deposits of Senegal and their genesis will be given in the thesis of R. Flicoteaux at present in process of completion.

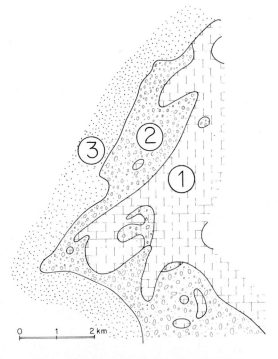

FIG. 2.—Schematic map of the Taïba deposit. 1. Limestone; 2. Phosphorite; 3. "Feral."

TABLE 4.—AVERAGE CHEMICAL COMPOSITION OF DIFFERENT PETROGRAPHIC GROUPS.

	1	2	3	4	5	6	7	8	9
	Average analysis of 85 samples	fluorapatite: 11 samples (calcite 2%; clays 1%)	facies without carbonate: 6 samples (calcite 1%; clays 6%)	facies with carbonate: 14 samples (15% clays)	Calculated values for a sample without carbonate, but 15% clays	limestone without phosphate: 2 samples	clay (<2 μm) fraction from facies without carbonate: 3 samples	clay (<2 μm) fraction from facies with carbonate: 14 samples	aluminum phosphate: 5 samples
SiO_2	15.59	2.17	13.65	12.90		1.36	55.74	59.88	22.07
Al_2O_3	2.85	0.57	1.41	3.24		0.41	18.25	17.63	24.93
MgO	0.46	0.06	0.14	0.71		0.59	2.26	2.77	0.05
CaO	42.32	53.23	45.14	43.82		54.09	3.03	1.55	7.92
Fe_2O_3	1.71	0.82	1.10	1.06		0.23	7.69	6.64	4.79
Mn_3O_4	0.05	0.03	0.04	0.08		0.02	0.06	0.04	0.02
TiO_2	0.15	0.02	0.20	0.17		0.00	1.06	0.91	0.98
Na_2O	0.11	0.04	0.05	0.19		0.02	0.11	0.04	0.74
K_2O	0.15	0.03	0.06	0.17		0.02	0.91	1.06	0.10
L.O.I.	7.05	2.57	2.72	16.11		41.93	7.89	8.37	12.97
P_2O_5	27.61	38.75	33.83	21.04		0.75	1.17	0.06	20.00
F	2.75	3.89	3.35	2.14		0.11	1.33	0.00	0.00
Sr	662	425	427	865	421	860	366	56	5615
Ba	59	47	36	63	44	10	131	71	980
V	432	224	294	839	412	81	1400	2871	381
Ni	153	84	60	246	97	25	450	631	19
Co	4	1	1	5	3	1	16	18	6
Cr	390	165	362	421	454	12	1094	2089	842
B	3	2	2	5	3	2	16	62	21
Zn	464	394	298	552	306	100	464	1218	259
Ga	2	1	1	2	3	1	21	20	24
Cu	84	45	38	162	48	125	147	140	79
Pb	1	2	1	2	2	2	15	2	44
Sn	2	1	2	2	1	2	2	2	4
Cd	62	45	49	55	44	15	2	0	67

Major elements are given in weight pervent, trace elements in ppm.

TABLE 5.—SOME CHARACTERISTICS OF THE APATITES OF TAÏBA COMPARED WITH SOME OTHER APATITES.

	Origin	$\dfrac{F}{P_2O_5}$	$\dfrac{CaO}{P_2O_5}$	%CO_2 Cal.	%CO_2 Meas.	a(Å)	c(Å)	References
	Fluorapatite from Durango	0.087	1.32	0.05		9.391	6.878	Young et al. (1969)
	Theoretical fluorapatite	0.089	1.32	<1.00				Altschuler et al., (1958)
TAÏBA	Facies without carbonate	0.097[1]	1.33[1]	1.82[1]	1.40[2]	9.353	6.888	
TAÏBA	Average	0.095[3]	1.35[4]	2.29[5]	1.20[6]			
TAÏBA	Facies with carbonate	0.092[7]	1.37[7]	4.02[7]		9.361	6.888	
	Francolite from Staffel	0.096	1.27	2.70		9.346	6.887	Brophy and Nash (1968)

Number of samples utilized: (1) 21; (2) 3; (3) 80; (4) 63; (5) 138; (6) 4; (7) 25.

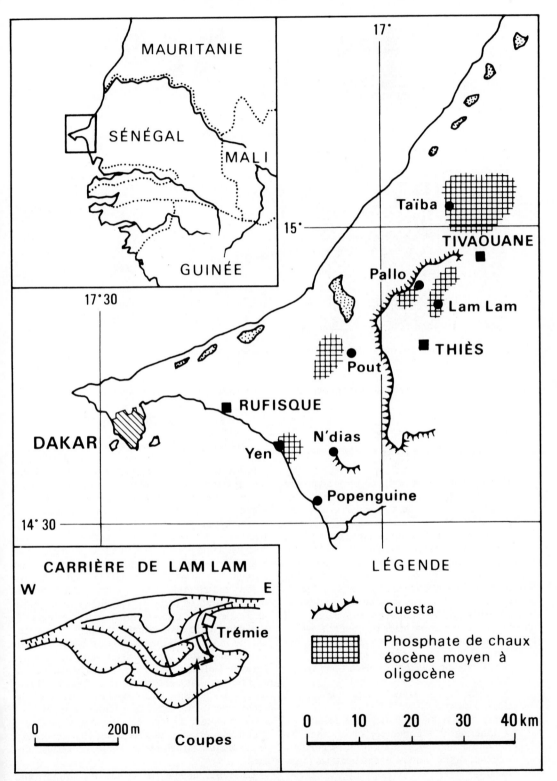

FIG. 3.—General location of Taïba and Thiès deposits.

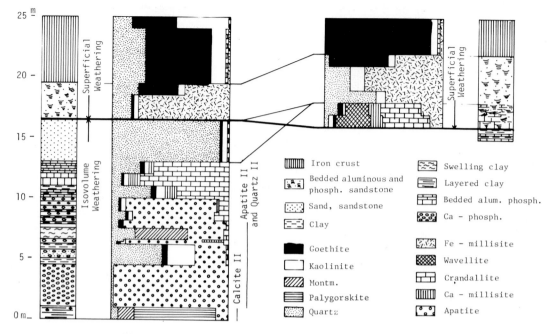

FIG. 4.—Unconformity between superficial weathering system and isovolume weathering system. Genesis of pseudo-breccias.

following evolutionary succession of phosphates appears:

$$\text{fluor-carbonate-apatite} \rightarrow \text{millisite Ca}$$
$$+ \text{ crandallite Sr} \rightarrow \text{crandallite Ca } (\rightarrow \text{wavellite}).$$

Calcium phosphate is replaced by a sequence of increasingly more aluminous phosphates. The first aluminum phosphate to appear is a calcic millisite, accompanied by strontium crandallite, which confirms that strontium is more mobile than calcium (Lucas et al., 1978). The evolution continues to the formation of calcium crandallite, more aluminous than millisite, and may locally lead to wavellite from which calcium is excluded. Some intermediate stages may be missing, especially when wavellite is directly associated with millisite. This evolution leads to minerals which are increasingly depleted in Na, K, Mg, Sr, Ba and also in P; it is accompnaied by:

— decarbonation of the fluor-carbonate-apatite;
— dissolution of the silica minerals: chert and detrital quartz;
— neoformation of kaolinite, first in situ by weathering of sedimentary clays, then by migration and precipitation in secondary cavities, in the form of zoned coatings (argilans);
— individualization of goethite formed by the iron removed from sedimentary clays; this goethite is either adsorbed on the kaolinites (argilo-ferrans) or concentrated in micronodules.

Throughout these mineralogical transformations the primary structures are maintained: stratification and microstructures are untouched. The reactions are isovolumetric, due to leaching by permanent ground water, continuously replenished by the rainfalls of a wet tropical climate.

The upper half of the working face shows the transition from a sandstone in which minerals are dissolved and zoned kaolinitic and goethitic coatings precipitated, to a sandstone with a zoned alumino-calcic phosphate cement, and finally to a ferruginous crust. The alumino-phosphatic cement is seen to form by epigenesis of kaolinite and goethite (argilo-ferrans) into ferruginous millisite (millisans), which can already be observed in some cavities within the bedded aluminum phosphates. At the same time, quartz decreases and cement increases. Residual quartz and ferruginous millisite are then epigenized into aluminous goethite. This evolution leads to increasingly ferric minerals, aluminum being partially retained. The primary structures are progressively effaced and replaced by secondary accumulation structures with marked vertical polarity.

Laterally, depending on the topography and the depth of weathering, variations of the petro-

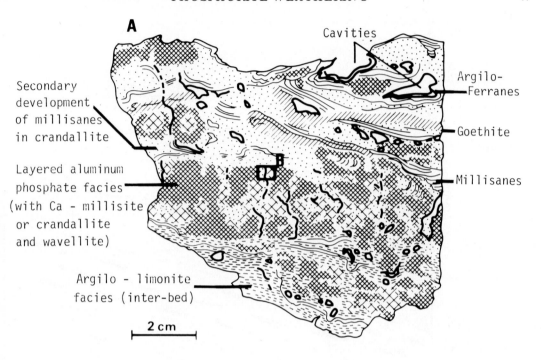

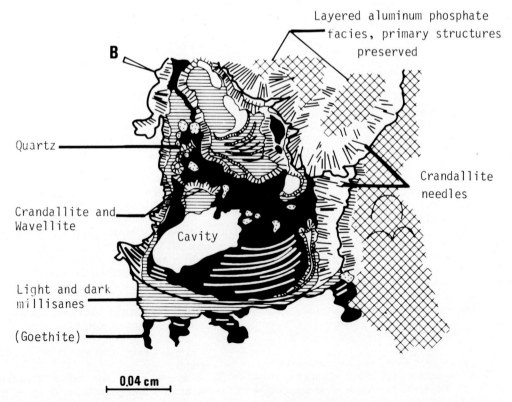

Fig. 5.—Macroscopic (A) and microscopic (B) aspects of transition from the bedded aluminum phosphates to pseudo-breccias with millisanes.

48   *LUCAS, FLICOTEAUX, NATHAN, PRÉVÔT AND SHAHAR*

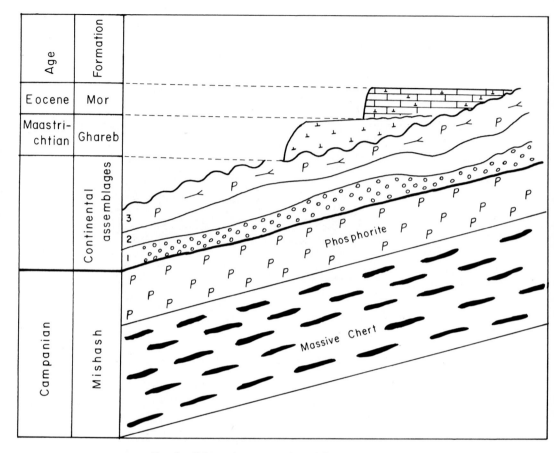

Fig. 6.—Schematic cross-section of the unconformities.

graphic facies can be observed (fig. 4). Thus stronger leaching induces more numerous dissolutions, leading to the destruction of the primary structures and to the transformation of the bedded aluminum phosphates into pseudo-breccias (fig. 5), the surface products of which are phosphatic "lateritoïds" (Besairie, in Arnaud, 1945; Flicoteaux and Tessier, 1971).

This upper half sequence is constantly characterized by:

— a lateral supply of P, Na, K, Ca, Sr;
— a dissolution of quartz and accumulation of cement (pedologic plasma);
— a formation of ferruginous millisite and aluminous goethite at the expense of kaolinite, following the succession

kaolinite → millisite Fe → goethite;

— a destruction of the primary structures.

Thus, the alumino-calcic and aluminous phosphates of Thiès are the result of superposition in time of two successive discordant weathering systems. The first, which needed a regional slope

replenishing the ground water, is an isovolume weathering by leaching. The second is a surficial weathering leading to iron crust formation, which implies an evolution toward a drier climate.

An Example of Weathering in an Aluminum-Poor Environment: Phosphate Mineral Assemblages in Senonian Unconformities in Southern Israel

One of the most striking features of the intra-Senonian and Senonian-Eocene unconformities in the northern and central Negev is the phosphate mineralogy which accompanies them. Three different phosphate assemblages occur at these unconformities:

(1) Phosphate nodules in layers, occasionally with a ferruginous matrix,
(2) "Lateritic" phosphates (Starinsky, 1964) i.e., iron oxides with apatite of secondary origin,
(3) A brown, green and yellow gypsiferous layer with iron phosphates, resulting from weathering.

Phosphate nodules (1) overlie the normal phosphorite (Mishash Formation of Campanian age) and are overlain by the "lateritic" phosphate (2), with the gypsiferous layer (3) on top (fig. 6). The sequence is often incomplete, and only one or two members may be present. The entire sequence is typically exposed at Har Orahot and at 'En Ofarim.

A pre-Eocene age for these sediments was recognized by several investigators (Bentor and Vroman, 1961; Starinsky, 1964). However, the occurrence of overlying sediments of proven Ghareb (Maastrichtian) age at Har Orahot and

elsewhere clearly shows their intra-Senonian genesis.

Some of the phosphate nodules (1) are composed of an apatite different from the carbonate-fluorapatite, usually found in the Negev phosphorites. The "normal" carbonate-fluorapatite has about 4 percent CO_2 in the lattice and a F/P_2O_5-ratio of about 0.12 (Nathan et al., 1979), whereas the apatite in these nodules has less than 1 percent CO_2 and a F/P_2O_5-ratio of about 0.10 (Analyses 1, 2 and 3, table 6).

The only possible way of achieving such a

TABLE 6.—CHEMICAL ANALYSES OF PHOSPHORITES FROM SOUTHERN ISRAEL

Sample No.	Ze 2[1]	H.H. 32[2]	E.N. 1[3]	E.O. 5[4]	E.O. 6[5]	E.O. 60[6]
CaO	51.4	51.6	53.3	39.1	23.8	19.9
P_2O_5	35.1	31.8	38.8	30.6	17.9	25.2
F	4.0	4.0	4.0	3.4	1.9	2.3
CO_2	4.7	6.3	0.9	1.2	0.4	1.1
SiO_2	0.2	3.7	—	—	—	—
Al_2O_3	0.2	0.9	—	—	—	—
Fe_2O_3	0.1*	1.1*	—	7.9	14.1	19.1
FeO	—	—	—	0.3	1.3	0.3
MgO	0.2	0.5	0.06	0.4	0.2	0.7
SO_3	2.1	1.3	1.5	6.4	20.4	9.6
Na_2O	0.9	0.6	0.4	1.9	0.3	0.7
Cl	0.3	0.01	0.05	1.4	0.05	0.05
K_2O	0.04	0.08	n.d.	0.2	0.1	0.02
O.M.	0.3	0.08	—	—	—	—
I.R. (HCl)	—	—	0.3	0.3	8.8	0.7
H_2O^+	—	—	1.9	—	—	—
Total	99.4	102.0	101.2			
F correction	−1.7	−1.7	−1.7			
Total	97.7	100.3	99.5			

— not determined
n.d. not detected
I.R. (HCl) Insoluble residue in H Cl
O. M. organic matter
* Total iron given as Fe_2O_3
[1] Ze2 "Normal" phosphorite from the Zefa field (Nathan et al., 1979)
[2] H.H. 32 "Normal" phosphorite from the Hazeva field (Nathan et al., 1979)
[3] E.N. 1 Nodular phosphorite, assemblage 1, Har Orahot (this work, analyst-I. Gal)
[4] E.O. 5 Gypsiferous iron phosphate, assemblage 3, 'En Ofarim (this work, analyst-I. Gal) Mineralogy: Francolite, phosphosiderite, strengite, gypsum, kidwellite?
[5] E.O. 6 Gypsiferous iron phosphate, assemblage 3, 'En Ofarim (this work, analyst-I. Gal) Mineralogy: Gypsum, phosphosiderite, kaolinite, pyrite, goethite, and dufrenite?
[6] E.O. 60 Gypsiferous iron phosphate, assemblage 3 'En Ofarim (this work, analysts I. Gal and N. Dalman) Mineralogy: Gypsum, francolite phosphosiderite, strengite, dufrenite, kidwellite?

decarbonation by a sedimentary process (low temperature) is by dissolution and reprecipitation, since a relatively high amount of energy is needed to expel CO_2 from the apatite lattice (Matthews and Nathan, 1977). It can also be seen that the decarbonation is accompanied by the partial loss of F.

The third phosphate type has the most interesting mineralogy. The following minerals were definitely identified:

gypsum	$CaSO_4 \cdot 2H_2O$
anhydrite	$CaSO_4$
francolite	$(Ca, Na)_5(PO_4, CO_3)_3(F, OH)$
fluorapatite	$Ca_5(PO_4)_3F$
pyrite	FeS_2
strengite	$Fe^{3+}PO_4 \cdot 2H_2O$
phospho-siderite	$Fe^{3+}PO_4 \cdot 2H_2O$
lipscombite	$Fe^{2+}Fe^{3+}(PO_4)_2(OH)_2$
fairfieldite	$Ca_2(Mn, Fe)(PO_4)_2 \cdot 2H_2O$
goethite	$FeO(OH)$
jarosite	$K\ Fe^{3+}(SO_4)_2(OH)_6$
alunite	$(K, Na)Al_3(OH)_6(SO_4)_2$
kaolinite	$Al_2Si_2O_5(OH)_4$
quartz	SiO_2

The following minerals are only tentatively identified:

kidwellite	$NaFe^{3+}(PO_4)_6(OH)_{10}(H_2O)_5$
dufrenite	$Fe^{3+}(PO_4)_3(OH)_5$
phospho-ferrite	$(Fe^{2+}, Mn)_3(PO_4)_3 \cdot 3H_2O$ probably oxidized
diadochite	$Fe_2^{3+}(PO_4)(SO_4)(OH) \cdot 5H_2O$

Many mineral phases are still unidentified, some of them are amorphous. Gypsum, francolite, strengite and phosphosiderite are the more abundant minerals.

The presence of authigenic anhydrite points to a highly saline environment. The most common phosphate minerals are strengite and phosphosiderite; this, added to the absence of vivianite, points to an oxidizing environment.

To conclude, the phosphate mineral assemblages, formed on land, point to the structural relief and different environments of deposition which probably existed during the deposition of the base (beginning) of the Ghareb Formation. They show an accentuation of the relief. The continental phosphate assemblages indicate the emergence of the structural highs, whereas the contemporaneous oil shale deposition in the basins show that the lows became deeper; on land, these assemblages indicate the transition from a lagoon (nodular phosphorite) to a tropical soil (laterite) and finally, to a very shallow pan, probably a coastal sabkha (anhydrite, gypsum, mainly ferric phosphates). It should be noted that soils, lagoons and sabkhas could develop simultaneously in different localities, in accordance with their local structural position and distance from the shore.

GENERAL DISCUSSIONS AND CONCLUSIONS

The deposits of Taïba and Sidi Daoui show similar characters, which make it seem that the primary deposits must have been alike, indeed probably identical. These similarities are common to other phosphorite deposits of the Cretaceous-Tertiary or younger periods. The studies of non-weathered marine apatites converge to the same mineral: carbonate-fluor-apatite with a high percentage of CO_2, up to 6 percent, and a higher than stoichiometric content of fluorine, up to 4 percent (Agulhas Bank: Parker and Siesser, 1972; Ortegal Cape: Lucas et al., 1978; Morocco: work in progress; Tunisia: Lucas et al., 1979a). This mineral is thus the more common and widespread one, and probably represents the species in equilibrium with the genetic environment of phosphorites (Lucas and Prévôt, 1975). It is this material which has undergone weathering, the most striking effect of which is loss of CO_2, as shown by the examples studied here, especially by the Sidi Daoui and Taiba deposits which are two weathering stages of very similar primary apatites. It is certain that the weathering processes depend on the mineral association, but anyhow one of its first results is a loss of CO_2 in the apatite. As long as carbonates are present in the rock, they protect the associated apatite, stopping the evolution from going further than the fluor-apatite stage. Thus, apatites with low CO_2 contents could indicate a hidden weathering; as a matter of fact it seems that fluor-apatite is never a primary mineral in this kind of sedimentation, but always a weathering product.

It is only after dissolution of the carbonates that apatite begins to disappear; the environment depleted in calcium becomes more acid, so that the calcium is removed from apatite which is dissolved.

When weathering becomes more intense, it attacks the other minerals from which additional cations such as aluminum and iron are leached. According to their availability, these elements combine with the phosphate. In a clayey environment, like Thiès, aluminum is the major available element, and a chain of alumino-calcic and aluminum phosphates develops. In an Al-poor environment, like that of the Negev phosphorites, iron is the available element, leading to the formation of different kinds of iron phosphates.

During these weathering processes, distribution and location of the trace elements change. Stron-

tium is a particularly interesting element, because it seems to be a good indicator of weathering. It is quickly leached from the apatitic lattice (Prévôt et al., 1977); but most of it stays in the rock, mainly in the clay minerals, before being incorporated into the new-formed phosphate minerals.

REFERENCES

ARNAUD, G., 1945, Les ressources minières de l'Afrique occidentale: Bull. Dir. Mines, Géol., A.O.F., 8, et Ann. Mines Charb., Paris, 100 p.

BENTOR, Y. K., AND VROMAN, A., 1961, The Geological Map of Israel, 1:100,000, Sheet 17: Nitsana: Geol. Surv. Israel, 3 sheets.

BRANCART, R., AND FLICOTEAUX, R., 1971, Ages des formations phosphatées de Lamlam et de Taïba (Sénégal occidental). Données micropaléontologiques, conséquences stratigraphiques et paléogéographiques: Bull. Soc. Géol. Fr., (7), v. 13, p. 399–408.

CAPDECOMME, L., 1952, Sur les phosphates alumineux de la région de Thiès (Sénégal): C. R. Ac. Sci. Paris, v. 235, p. 187–189.

————, 1953, Etude minéralogique des gîtes phosphatés de la région de Thiès (Sénégal): XIXè Congr. Intern. Géol., Alger, 1952, XI, II, p. 103–118.

EL MOUNTASSIR, M., 1977, La zone rubéfiée de Sidi Daoui; Altération météorique du phosphate de chaux des Ouled Abdoun (Maroc): Thèse 3ème cycle, Strasbourg, 126 p.

FLICOTEAUX, R., AND TESSIER, F., 1971, Précisions nouvelles sur la stratigraphie des formations du plateau de Thiès (Sénégal occidental) et sur leurs altérations. Conséquences paléogeographiques: C.R. Ac. Sci. Paris, v. 272, p. 364–366.

————, NAHON, D., AND PAQUET, H., 1977, Genèse des phosphates alumineux à partir des sédiments argilo-phosphatés du Tertiaire de Lamlam (Sénégal). Suite minéralogique. Permanences et changements de structures: Sci. Géol., Bull., v. 30, no. 3, p. 153–174.

GULBRANDSEN, R. A., 1970, Relation for carbon dioxide content of apatite of the Phosphoria Formation to regional facies: U.S. Geol. Surv., Prof. Pap. 700-B, p. B9–B13.

LUCAS, J., AND PRÉVÔT, L., 1975, Les marges continentales pièges géochimiques; l'exemple de la marge atlantique de l'Afrique à la limite Crétacé-Tertiaire. Bull. Soc. Géol. Fr., (7), XVII, v. 4, p. 496–501.

————, PRÉVÔT, L., AND LAMBOY, M., 1978, Les phosphorites de la marge nord de l'Espagne. Chimie, minéralogie, genèse: Océanol. Acta. v. 1, p. 107–118.

————, CHAABANI, F., AND PRÉVÔT, L., 1979a, Phosphorites et évaporites: deux formations de milieux sédimentaires voisins étudiées dans la coupe du Paléogène de Foum Selja (Metlaoui, Tunisie): Sci. Géol. Bull., v. 32, (in press).

————, MENOR, E., AND PRÉVÔT, L., 1979b, Le gisement de phosphate de chaux de Taïba (Sénégal). Un exemple d'enrichissement par altération: Sci. Géol. Bull., v. 32, (in press).

————, PRÉVÔT, L., AND EL MOUNTASSIR, M., 1979c, Les phosphorites rubéfiées de Sidi Daoui. Transformation météorique locale du gisement de phosphate des Ouled Abdoun (Maroc): Sci. Géol. Bull., v. 32, (in press).

MATTHEWS, A., AND NATHAN, Y., 1977, The decarbonation of carbonate-fluorapatite (francolite): Am. Min., v. 62, p. 565–573.

MENOR, E., 1975, La sédimentation phosphatée, Pétrographies, Minéralogie et Géochimie des gisements de Taïba (Sénégal) et d'Olinda (Brésil): Thèse Doct. Ing., Strasbourg, 153 p.

NATHAN, Y., SHILONI, Y., RODED, R., GAL, I., AND DEUTSCH, Y., 1979, The chemistry and geochemistry of the northern and central Negev phosphorites: Bull. Geol. Surv. Isr. (in press).

PARKER, R. J., AND SIESSER, W. G., 1972, Petrology and origin of some phosphorites from the South African continental margin: Jour. Sed. Pet. v. 42, p. 434–440.

PREVOT, L., LUCAS, J., NATHAN, Y., AND SHILONI, Y., 1977, Répartition des éléments traces dans les phosphorites marines: Second Symposium on Origin and Distribution of Elements, UNESCO, Paris, 1977. Intern. Assoc. Geochim. Cosmochim. (in press).

SLANSKY, M., LALLEMAND, A., AND MILLOT, G., 1964, La sédimentation et l'altération latéritiques des formations de Taïba: Bull. Serv. Carte Géol. Als. Lorr., v. 17, p. 321–324.

SEPM SPECIAL PUBLICATION No. 29, P. 53–60, NOVEMBER 1980

POST-DEPOSITIONAL ALTERATION OF THE CARBONATE-FLUORAPATITE PHASE OF MOROCCAN PHOSPHATES

J. M. McARTHUR
Dept. Geology
University College
Gower Street
London WC1E 6BT, Great Britain

ABSTRACT

Post-depositional weathering and interaction with ground water removes Na, Sr, CO_3 and SO_4 from the structure of carbonate-fluorapatite. The stability of carbonate-fluorapatite increases as the content of these substituents decreases. Highly substituted carbonate-fluorapatite (Na_2O 1.5%, CO_2 6%) is therefore more susceptible to weathering than poorly substituted apatite (Na 0.5%, CO_2 1.5%). Cerium/REE ratios are altered by weathering and submarine reworking; strontium may be enriched by the latter process. Uranium and yttrium respond erratically to sub-aqueous reworking and weathering.

INTRODUCTION

The content of Na, Sr, CO_3, SO_4, U, Y and REE's within the carbonate-fluorapatite phase of sedimentary phosphates vary markedly between deposits and to a lesser degree within deposits. The variability of Na, Sr, CO_3 and SO_4 concentrations has been interpreted on a broad scale as reflecting the effects of weathering in its widest sense (McArthur 1978a). Such broad syntheses, however, suffer the drawback of a poorly defined comparative framework; chemical comparisons between deposits separated by thousands of kilometers and hundreds of millions of years are obviously less satisfactory than detailed comparisons within a single deposit, within which differential uplift, erosion and post-depositional alteration may have occurred.

This paper presents a detailed study of the effects of weathering on the chemistry of carbonate-fluorapatite. A chemical comparison is presented of three types of Moroccan phosphate which have been subjected to different degrees of post-depositional alteration. The samples formed contemporaneously in similar environments. A tight comparative framework is therefore present which allows a close examination of the chemical effects of post-depositional alteration.

Occurrence and Geology of Moroccan Phosphate

The geology and distribution of both the onshore and offshore Moroccan phosphates have been discussed by Choubert and Faure-Muret (1962), Nutter (1969), Summerhayes (1970) and McArthur (1974, 1978a, 1978b), among others. Only a brief summary is given here.

Phosphorite of Eocene age crops out on the Moroccan continental margin in a band extending from just north of Cap Blanc to just south of Cap Sim (fig. 1). The phosphorite examined in this study was recovered mainly from areas off Cap Sim and Cap Blanc.

Off Cap Sim, deposition of Eocene phosphatic limestones was followed by uplift associated with the Atlas orogeny. The phosphates were eroded and re-deposited as pebbles, cobbles and boulders within Miocene phosphatic glauconitic conglomerates (Summerhayes, 1970). These samples contain no pyrite, have very low contents of organic carbon and appreciable contents of goethite, although they are not the result of lateritic weathering (McArthur, 1978a, b).

Some show well-developed weathering margins. They are rounded and occur offshore of the High Atlas, an area tectonically unstable in the past. It is evident from these observations that these samples have been exposed to weathering. The presence of weathering margins, however, suggests that the degree of weathering was not severe.

Off Cap Blanc, Eocene pelletal and non-pelletal phosphorites occur. The pelletal phosphorite is conglomeratic as well as pelletal, consisting of coarse sand to pebble sized phosphatized limestone, matrix supported in unevenly bedded phosphatized limestone. It formed by disaggregation and reworking of the phosphatized lime-mud which now forms the matrix, a process which did not affect the non-pelletal phosphatized limestones (Summerhayes, 1970; McArthur, 1974, 1978b).

Both types have poorly developed weathering margins and contain organic matter and pyrite (McArthur, 1978a, b). These factors, plus the fact that the samples occur in a tectonically stable area off the Moroccan Meseta (Nutter, 1969)

TABLE 4.—DETRITAL COLLOPHANE CONTENTS OF MOROCCAN NON-PELLETAL PHOSPHATIZED LIMESTONES

Sample No.	Uranium concentration (ppm)	*No. of detrital collophane grains	Degree of phosphatization
135	507	200	well phosphatized
1022(2)	483	100	very well phosphatized
959	369	80	not well phosphatized
988(a)	328	120	well phosphatized
1038	259	100	not well phosphatized
136	206	140	well phosphatized
Remaining samples	<150	<20	many grains possibly being phosphatized bone fragments

*counted over equal areas to 50× magnification and adjusted for size variations.

teration—Weathering in an onshore environment may be complicated by repeated secondary enrichment and leaching by fluctuating levels of ground water and possibly by sub-aerial exposure.

Despite such possible complications all elements except yttrium have been depleted in the apatite structure. Carbonate has decreased more than sulphate. The large increase in Y with a corresponding decrease in Ce suggest that weathering may alter the rare earth fractionation pattern in apatite. The constancy of uranium is surprising in view of its known mobility in apatite (Altschuler et al., 1958; Sakanoue et al., 1968). Also surprising is its apparent constancy in process B.

Post-Depositional Alteration in Other Phosphates

Weathering of carbonate-fluorapatite in Moroccan phosphates removes major structural substituents. Trace substituents show more erratic behavior during weathering but also decrease, with odd exceptions.

Extremes of weathering have not affected the Moroccan samples, however. What happens when weathering reaches a very advanced state? In table 5 (adapted from Cook, 1972) substituent contents are shown in five phosphorites which have been affected to different degrees by lateritic weathering. The data have been recalculated to 36.4 percent P_2O_5 to remove the effects of diluents. Samples 4 and 5 contain too little apatite to ensure that apatite dominates the bulk chemistry. In samples 1 to 3, where it does so, Na, CO_2 and F show little variation; uranium increases slightly although the increase is within analytical error, while strontium decreases slightly.

The substituent contents of the Queensland apatite—which are much below the contents of Moroccan apatite—appear relatively unaffected by extremes of lateritic weathering. The Queensland and Moroccan phosphorites appear, therefore, to behave in directly opposing ways during weathering. This apparent discrepancy is easily resolved, however.

The structural framework of highly substituted apatites suffers greater stress than does that of a sparsely substituted apatite. Highly substituted apatite is therefore more reactive than poorly

TABLE 5.—ELEMENT RATIOS OF LATERIZED PHOSPHORITES
(Modified from Cook, 1972)

	INCREASING LATERIZATION				
	1	2	3	4	5
Original Analyses					
P_2O_5	36.4	30.6	21.2	9.40	2.40
Fe_2O_3	0.98	14.3	35.1	51.0	47.9
Analyses recalculated to a constant P_2O_5 of 36.4%					
Na_2O%	0.42	0.42	0.38	0.61	0.60
CO_2%	1.30	1.43	1.38	1.16	3.79
F%	3.30	2.74	3.45	3.30	3.03
Sr(ppm)	300	178	172	1550	9100
U(ppm)	45	48	52	135	152
Errors	Sr ± 50 ppm				
	U ± 5 ppm				

TABLE 6.—ELEMENT RATIOS IN PELLETAL AND NON-PELLETAL QUEENSLAND PHOSPHATES (DATA FROM COOK, 1972)

		Pelletal Phosphate (Subaqueous)	Non-Pelletal Phosphate (Intertidal/Subaerial)
Ratios to P_2O_5 of Substituents	Na_2O	1.5	0.28
	CO_3	6.4	3.8
	Sr	10	3.4
	Y	17	2.1
	U	2.2	2.0
	La	6.8	0.4

substituted structures (Lehr et al., 1967; McArthur, unpublished results) and therefore liable to rapid alteration by weathering. The more weathering proceeds the more stable apatite becomes and the more prolonged and severe becomes the weathering required to alter it. The carbonate-apatite composition shown in table 5 is clearly at the stable end of the weathering sequence.

The observation that Sr is a more mobile phase than is Na in carbonate-fluorapatite (McArthur, 1978a) is confirmed by the greater mobility of Sr relative to Na in these apatites. Further confirmation that weathering can reduce the substituent contents of carbonate-fluorapatite is shown by table 6 which lists element/P_2O_5 ratios for pelletal and nonpelletal phosphorites from Queensland. The former originated in a subaqueous setting, the latter in an intertidal/subaerial setting (Cook, 1972). The substituent contents of the latter are the lower reflecting the effects of subaerial weathering. Both types have substituent contents well below those found in Moroccan samples, however. If the original composition of the Queensland apatite was similar to the Moroccan apatite, as seems likely (McArthur, 1978a), then the existing differences within the Queensland deposits represent the vestiges of bigger differences in the past.

CONCLUSIONS AND SUMMARY

(1) Weathering removes Na, Sr, CO_3 and SO_4 from the structure of carbonate-fluorapatite. Removal is easiest in highly substituted apatites ($Na_2O \sim 1.5\%$, $CO_2 \sim 6\%$) and difficult in poorly substituted apatites ($Na_2O \sim 0.5\%$, $CO_2 \sim 1.5\%$) requiring very severe conditions in the case of the latter.

(2) Trace elements such as U and REE are generally removed during weathering. Secondary enrichment and element retention are common, however resulting in complex effects which make interpretation of trace substituent data very difficult.

(3) Reworking of carbonate-fluorapatite within a sub-aqueous environment does not alter the major substituent (Na, CO_3 and SO_4) concentrations in the highly substituted Moroccan offshore phosphate, possibly because further substitution would de-stabilize the structure. Strontium is more mobile and may be enriched during sub-aqueous reworking.

(4) The Na, Sr, CO_3 and SO_4 contents of carbonate-fluorapatite may be used as a crude 'weathering index' for phosphates. Unweathered Moroccan carbonate-fluorapatite contains about 1.6 percent Na_2O, 2.6 percent SO_4, 8.3 percent CO_3 and 0.23 percent Sr (on a pure apatite basis, $\sim 30\%$ P_2O_5). Concentrations are lower in weathered samples. The high limiting concentrations may be characteristic of the original composition of apatite in other deposits (McArthur, 1978b).

(5) Cerium/Y ratios are altered by reworking and weathering. As Y is a good indicator of trivalent rare earth behavior the value of Ce/REE ratios as genetic indicators seems doubtful.

REFERENCES

AGER, D. V., 1974, The Western High Atlas of Morocco and their significance in the history of the North Atlantic: Proc. Geol. Ass. v. 85, p. 23–42.
ALTSCHULER, Z. S., CLARKE, R. S., AND YOUNG, E. J., 1958, Geochemistry of uranium in apatite and phosphorite: U.S. Geol. Survey Prof. Paper 314D, 90 p.
———, 1978, Trace elements as discriminants of origin in marine phosphorites: Abstracts, 10th Int. Cong. Sedimentol., Phosphate Symposium, Jerusalem, July 1978.
BERNER, R. A., 1971, Principles of Chemical Sedimentology, McGraw Hill.
CHOUBERT, G., AND FAURE-MURET, A., 1962, Evolution du Domaine Atlasique Marocain depuis les Temps Paléozoiques, in "Livre de Paul Fallot" Tome 1., Mem. Soc. Géol. France, p. 447–527.
COOK, P. J., 1972, Petrology and geochemistry of the phosphate deposits of northwest Queensland, Australia: Econ. Geol. v. 67, p. 1193–1213.

GULBRANDSEN, R. A., 1970, Relation of CO_2-content of apatite of the Phosphoria Formation to regional facies: U.S. Geol. Surv. Prof. Pap. 700-B, p. B9–B13.

HØGDAHL, O. T., MELSOM, S., AND BOWEN, V. T., 1968, Neutron activation analysis of lanthanide elements in seawater: Adv. Chem. Series, v. 73, p. 308–325.

LEHR, J. R., McCLELLAN, G. M., SMITH, J. P., AND FRAZIER, A. W., 1967, Characterization of apatite in commercial phosphate rock: Colloque International sur les Phosphates Minéraux Solides. Toulouse, 16–20 May, 1967.

LONGINELLI, A., AND NUTTI, S., 1968, Oxygen isotopic composition of phosphorites from marine formations: Earth Planet. Sci. Lett., v. 5, p. 13–16.

McARTHUR, J. M., 1974, The geochemistry of phosphorite from the continental margin off Morocco: Unpub. Ph.D. Thesis, Imperial College, London University.

———, 1978a, Systematic variations in the contents of Na, Sr, CO_3 and SO_4 in marine carbonate-fluorapatite and their relation to weathering: Chem. Geol., v. 21, p. 89–112.

———, 1978b, Element partitioning in ferruginous and pyritic phosphorite from the continental margin off Morocco: Mineral. Mag., v. 42, p. 221–228.

McKENZIE, F. T., 1975, Sediment cycling and the evolution of sea water, in Chemical Oceanography (2nd ed). J. P. Riley and G. Skirrow (eds). Academic Press.

NUTTER, A. H., 1969, The origin and distribution of phosphate in marine sediments from the Moroccan and Portuguese continental margins: Unpub. D.I.C. Thesis, Imperial College, London.

PRICE, N. B., AND CALVERT, S. E., 1978, The geochemistry of phosphorites from the Namibian Shelf: Chem. Geol., v. 23, p. 151–170.

SAKANOUE, M., YONEDA, S., ONISHI, K., KOYAMA, K., KOMURA, K., AND NAKANISHI, T., 1968, Alpha-radioactive nuclides of uranium, protactinium and thorium in uranium deposits: Geochem. Journal., v. 2, p. 71–86.

SUMMERHAYES, C. P., 1970, Phosphate deposits on the northwestern African continental shelf and slope: Unpub. Ph.D. Thesis, Imperial College, London.

SEPM Special Publication No. 29, p. 61–71, November 1980

U-SERIES, OCEANOGRAPHIC AND SEDIMENTARY EVIDENCE IN SUPPORT OF RECENT FORMATION OF PHOSPHATE NODULES OFF PERU

W. C. BURNETT
Department of Oceanography
The Florida State University
Tallahassee, Florida 32306

AND

H. H. VEEH
School of Earth Sciences
Flinders University of South Australia
Bedford Park, S. A. 5042
Australia

AND

A. SOUTAR
Scripps Institution of Oceanography
La Jolla, California 92037

ABSTRACT

All available evidence which relates to the question of Recent formation of indurated phosphate deposits on the sea floor off the coasts of Peru and Chile is reviewed. Uranium-series results, oceanographic parameters, and sedimentary associations are all shown to be consistent with a Recent age for those nodules with uranium isotopic compositions in equilibrium with seawater. New data are presented concerning uranium distribution at different levels within two individual phosphate nodules. Uranium isotopic compositions are constant throughout the thickness of both samples analyzed. Furthermore, variations in the absolute concentration of uranium at different levels within the nodules display a sympathetic association to the relative amounts of apatite present in the same layers. This argues against secondary addition of uranium and supports our hypothesis of Holocene formation of phosphate nodules which contain no significant ^{230}Th and have ^{234}U$/^{238}$U activity ratios close to that of modern seawater.

INTRODUCTION

When geologists first noted the apparent correlation between areas of oceanic upwelling and occurrence of marine phosphorite, it seemed logical that this represented a cause-effect association. As a result, most models of phosphorite genesis assumed that upwelling was a key element in their formation (Kazakov, 1937: Brongersma-Sanders, 1957; McKelvey, 1967). In view of this observed association, it was somewhat surprising when Kolodny (1969) discovered that all the phosphorite samples (most of which were from areas of present-day upwelling) which he attempted to date by uranium-series disequilibrium were beyond the limit of the method (approx. 200 $\times$ 10^3 years). Kolodny suggested that if Recent phosphorites do exist at all, perhaps they would be found in warm waters such as off the west coasts of Central America or Africa, areas from which he did not have samples. His prediction was confirmed within a few years by radiometric dating of nodules from off the coasts of Peru

and South-West Africa (Baturin et al., 1972; Veeh et al., 1973; Veeh et al., 1974, Burnett and Veeh, 1977).

In a recent paper, McArthur (1978) has challenged the view that the indurated nodules found off the coasts of Peru and Chile are geologically youthful. Because these deposits apparently are low in Na and S relative to other sea-floor phosphorites, McArthur believes these deposits may have been subaerially weathered, losing U as well as Na and S, and were then resubmerged. According to this interpretation, U would then have been added to the phosphate nodules by secondary addition, effectively invalidating the uranium-series ages. In response to McArthur's remarks, we will review evidence reported earlier which is germane to this question and present some new data which bear on the argument of post-depositional addition of uranium.

Our discussion in this paper will be restricted to the question of whether or not *indurated* phosphorite nodules on the sea-floor off Peru and Chile are forming at the present time. There is

61

now substantial documentation for small amounts of unconsolidated and other types of phosphatic material being deposited in today's oceans. Goldberg and Parker (1960), for example, have reported the occurrence of phosphatized wood dredged from 410 m in the Gulf of Tehuantepec. Carbonate-fluorapatite was reported by D'Anglejan (1968) as forming incipiently within modern sediments by replacement of skeletal carbonate in a core sample of foraminiferal ooze from 700 m depth off Baja California. Manheim *et al.* (1975) have shown that the shells of some Recent benthic foraminifera are being phosphatized on the sea floor off Peru. The direct observation by scanning electron microscopy of micron-sized authigenic crystals of apatite sampled from Recent sediments off Peru was reported by Burnett (1977). One other unequivocal case of modern formation of unconsolidated phosphorite concerns the biogenic formation reported by Doyle *et al.* (1978). These

authors showed that at least two species of pelecypods in stressed environments develop phosphatic kidney stones. The stones, which bear a strong resemblance to some phosphatic sands, may later be excreted by these pelecypods although this has not as yet been confirmed.

Since the hypothesis of Recent formation of indurated phosphorites off Peru and Chile has been seriously questioned (McArthur, 1978) and since this concept is central to our understanding of the genesis of marine phosphorites, a review of all the evidence relevant to the time of formation of these deposits is appropriate. This paper will focus on three different lines of evidence which pertain to this question: (a) Uranium-series data; (b) Oceanographic setting of the Peru-Chile deposits; and (c) Sedimentary associations.

Uranium-Series Results

Our objective in considering the uranium-series

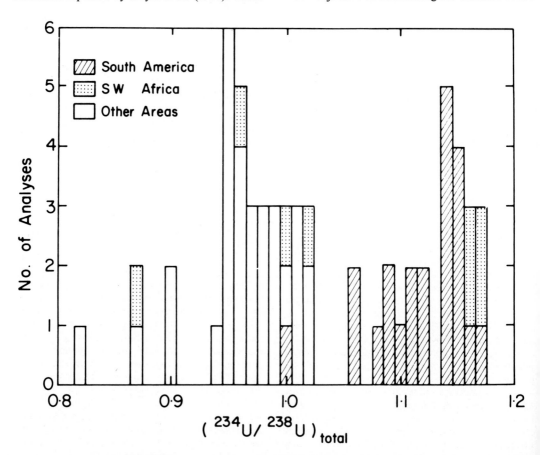

FIG. 1.—Histogram of $^{234}U/^{238}U$ activity ratios of the total uranium for sea-floor phosphorites analyzed thus far. Samples designated "other areas" refer to nodules from the California Borderland, Chatham Rise, Agulhas Bank and Blake Plateau reported in Kolodny and Kaplan (1970). Uranium-series data for phosphate samples from off Southwest Africa are from Veeh *et al.* (1974). The South American results are from Burnett and Veeh (1977) and Baturin *et al.* (1972).

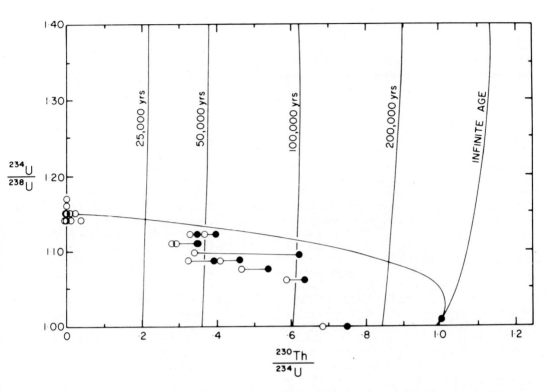

Fig. 2.—$^{230}Th/^{234}U$ versus $^{234}U/^{238}U$ for sea-floor phosphate nodules from Peru-Chile. Open circles represent $^{230}Th/^{234}U$ activity ratios corrected for common thorium (initial ^{230}Th present when nodule formed) while closed circles are uncorrected. The horizontal curve shows the theoretical development with time of the isotope ratios for a phosphorite starting with a $^{230}Th/^{234}U$ activity ratio of zero and a $^{234}U/^{238}U$ ratio of 1.14 as exists in present day sea water. Since this curve is valid only for a closed system, it is not surprising that the data points fall consistently below the line due to constant loss of ^{234}U. The vertical curves show the apparent ages for any point. Burnett and Veeh (1977).

results on sea-floor phosphorites will be to show that these data can be used to differentiate geologically young (less than a few thousand years old) from older deposits. It is not our intention to argue here in support of absolute ages of sea-floor phosphorites as deduced by uranium-series methods. The various assumptions and rationale towards that end were presented in Burnett and Veeh (1977).

Since the uranium in phosphorites is apparently derived from seawater, we would expect that the uranium isotopic composition in a recently formed phosphorite would inherit the uranium-series disequilibrium present in today's ocean water. The histogram (fig. 1) of $^{234}U/^{238}U$ activity ratios in sea-floor phosphorites analyzed thus far shows that virtually all the phosphate nodules from off Peru and Chile have excess amounts of ^{234}U, while those from most other areas are either in equilibrium ($^{234}U/^{238}U \simeq 1$) or slightly deficient in ^{234}U. Phosphorites from South-West Africa display variable isotopic results, some having seawater

values and others being at equilibrium. Phosphorites from off Peru and Chile which display $^{234}U/^{238}U$ activity ratios equivalent to the accepted seawater value of 1.14 ± 0.03 (Ku *et al.*, 1977) also have low $^{230}Th/^{234}U$ activity ratios (Burnett and Veeh, 1977). There are at least two ways to interpret these uranium-series results: (a) The phosphate nodules are less than a few thousand years old, i.e., the excess ^{234}U has not had sufficient time to decay away and the ^{230}Th has not had enough time to grow into the system; or (b) The nodules formed without any initial uranium, or any initial uranium that may have been present as well as ^{230}Th produced by decay of this uranium were somehow lost and uranium from modern seawater entered the nodules very recently. Although the second situation remains a possibility, our arguments will show that the hypothesis of Recent formation is more consistent with the data at hand.

If secondary addition of uranium to sea-floor phosphorites was actually a significant process, it is hard to explain why deposits from other areas such as the Chatham Rise, the California Border-land, Blake Plateau, Pourtales Terrace and else-where do not display excess ^{234}U activities (Ko-lodny and Kaplan, 1970; Burnett and Gomberg, 1977). As a matter of fact, marine apatite may actually lose some ^{234}U to seawater because of oxidation following radioactive decay (Kolodny and Kaplan, 1970). It appears therefore, that any "openness" in the seawater-uranium-apatite sys-tem involves a loss of ^{234}U from the apatite to seawater. Any error this may cause in the urani-um-series interpretation, therefore, would make the sample appear *older* (more towards equilibri-um) than is actually the case. Thus, we cannot expect spuriously low ages in phosphate nodules to result from migration of ^{234}U. The effect of ^{234}U "leakage" is shown in fig. 2 by the data points (from Burnett and Veeh, 1977) which, except for the least radiogenic samples, fall con-sistently below the curve ideally describing the locus of ^{234}U/^{238}U and ^{230}Th/^{234}U as a function of time. The implied loss of ^{234}U from the system appears to increase with sample age, suggesting that leakage of ^{234}U is a continuous process.

Although biogenic phosphate materials such as shark's teeth and fish bones are known to pick up uranium (as well as other components) from the environment, we do not feel that this type of process represents a contradiction to our hypothesis concerning inorganic phosphate de-posits. The hydroxyapatite of biological materials is apparently unstable under marine conditions and quickly undergoes diagenetic changes after deposition until it is chemically and structurally similar to the carbonate-fluorapatites found in sea-floor phosphorite deposits (Tooms et al., 1969). Carbonate-fluorapatite or francolite as it has been called by McConnell (1958), on the other hand, is apparently fairly stable under marine conditions. Ratios of major components within the francolite lattice, such as F/P_2O_5 for example, are constant both within and between many sea-floor deposits.

During some of our earlier uranium-series stud-ies on sea-floor phosphorites from Peru-Chile, two samples (KK-71-161 and A-183) were ana-lyzed both on exterior and interior sections (Veeh et al., 1973; Burnett and Veeh, 1977). Both sam-ples showed higher U concentrations on the ex-terior than the interior portions of the nodules. McArthur (1978) has used these results as evi-dence supporting secondary addition of uranium to the nodules. To test this hypothesis, we ana-lyzed a more complete set of samples from KK-71-161 and a set of four contiguous layers from one of our apparently modern samples, PD-15-17 (there was not sufficient material remaining from A-183). The samples were analyzed for U and ^{234}U/^{238}U activity ratios by essentially the same methods as reported in Veeh et al. (1973) and Burnett and Veeh (1977). The amounts of apatite present in each sub-sample was also determined by an X-ray technique similar to that reported in Burnett (1977). The results (fig. 3), clearly illustrate that the distribution of uranium in these phosphorite nodules is simply a function of the amount of apatite present, being variable in KK-71-161 while relatively constant in PD-15-17. The most significant point, however, is the fact that ^{234}U/^{238}U activity ratios throughout the thickness of both nodules remain constant within analytical error. This, of course, argues against post-deposi-tional addition of uranium since uranium from modern seawater would have a higher activity ratio than older uranium contained within the interior of the nodule. Not only do these uranium-series data suggest Recent formation of phos-phorite but the lack of any gradient within the ^{234}U/^{238}U activity ratios implies that the nodule must have grown fast relative to the half-life of ^{234}U (about 250,000 years). We would expect a decline in the amount of excess ^{234}U within the interior of the nodule assuming that the inner portion is the oldest part of the sample. Evident-ly, the amount of time required to form these nodules was less than the resolution of the ^{234}U/^{238}U method, i.e. on the order of a few thousand years.

Another point about our uranium data which is consistent with a Recent origin for these nodules is the substantial quantity of U(IV) contained within the Peru-Chile phosphorites. The South American deposits contain uranium which is 40 to 70 percent tetravalent (Burnett and Veeh, 1977). Since U(IV) is probably lattice-bound in marine apatite (Altschuler et al., 1958), it would seem likely that the uranium was incorporated during formation of the apatite rather than at some later period. The quantities of U(IV) present also argue against subaerial exposure and weathering of these deposits as McArthur (1978) has suggested. It has already been demonstrated that subaerial weath-ering alters U(IV) to U(VI) in marine phosphorite

Fig. 3.—Uranium concentration as a function of depth in two phosphate nodules from off Peru. The relative amounts of apatite as determined by X-ray diffraction are shown for comparison. ^{234}U/^{238}U activity ratios are shown next to the uranium data points. a) KK-71-161: 5° 0.9'S, 81° 25.0'W; 280 m depth; 48 ± 5 × 10^3 yr. old (Burnett and Veeh, 1977). b) PD-15-17: 15° 17.8'S, 75° 23.5'W; 370 m depth; ≤ 3 × 10^3 yr. old (Burnett and Veeh, 1977).

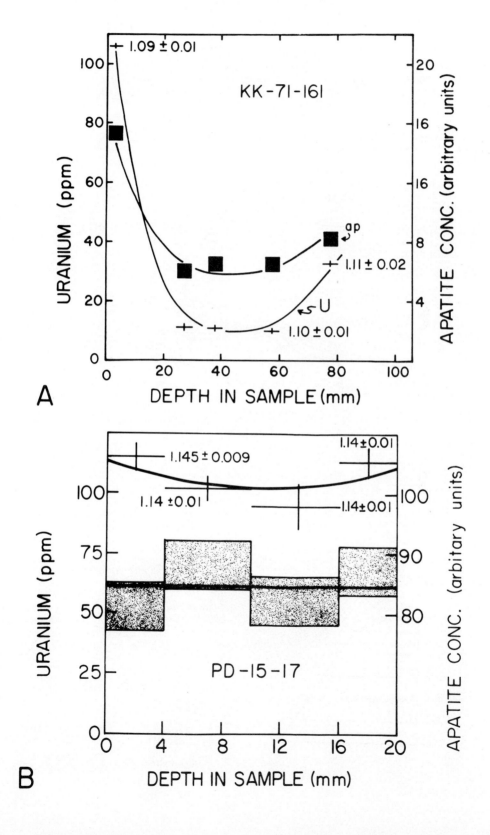

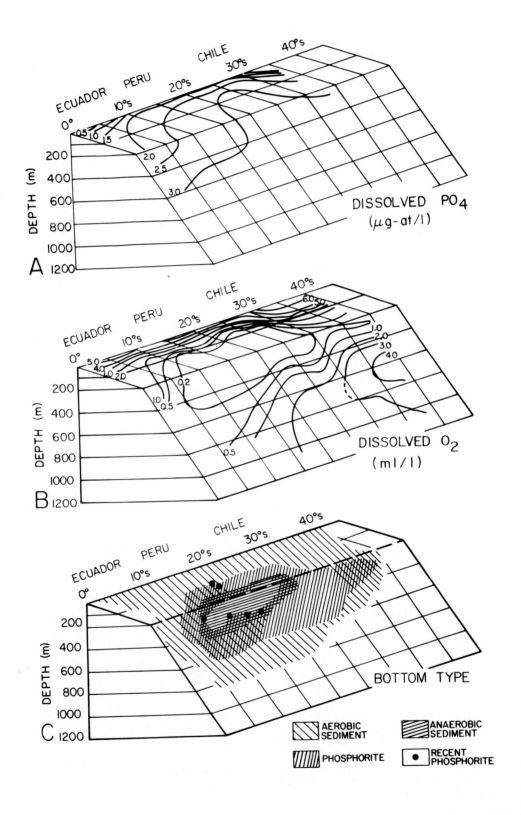

(Altschuler *et al.*, 1958). This fact was used in our interpretation of subaerial exposure of phosphorites which occur on the Pourtales Terrace in the Straits of Florida (Burnett and Gomberg, 1977).

The fractionation of uranium isotopes between oxidation states has also been shown to be minimal in the samples interpreted as being Recent from off Peru-Chile. Since the fraction of ^{234}U which is converted to the higher oxidation state is a function of radioactive decay, and thus of time, it follows that samples which are very youthful will display the least difference in the isotope composition of uranium (IV) as opposed to U(VI). This is exactly what we discovered in our earlier investigations of the Peru-Chile phosphorites (Burnett and Veeh, 1977). We find it most difficult, therefore, to explain these data in terms of ancient formation and secondary addition of uranium from sea water at some later time.

Oceanographic Setting

In a previous paper (Burnett, 1977) it was suggested that the most likely environment for precipitation of apatite in the marine environment is within pore waters of anoxic sediments such as those found off Peru. The chemistry of pore waters is known to be influenced by the environmental conditions under which the sediments are deposited. Sholkovitz (1973) showed, for example, that the phosphate content of pore waters in the Santa Barbara Basin is highest where the dissolved oxygen in the bottom waters is lowest. This is probably a result of increased preservation of organic phosphorus due to incomplete combustion in the overlying oxygen-deficient waters. Since we would expect apatite precipitation to be most likely in those areas with the highest phosphate concentrations it follows that the sites of most recent phosphorite formation would be in areas currently most depleted in oxygen.

The distributions of dissolved phosphate and dissolved oxygen in bottom waters, as well as likely bottom sediment type on the continental margin off the west coast of South America, are shown as schematic block diagrams of the western South American Margin (fig. 4). These maps are based on data from over 50 stations from various expeditions run by Scripps Institution of Oceanography. Also shown are the locations of phosphorite samples with Holocene ages based on our uranium series measurements. It is apparent that the modern phosphorites formed where dissolved oxygen is lowest and dissolved phosphate is high. Although not conclusive, the apparent relationship between the distribution of the phosphorite nodules with Holocene uranium-series ages and relevant oceanographic parameters would seem to be more than fortuitous. We suggest that the relationship is real and lends support to our hypothesis of Recent formation of these nodules.

Sedimentary Associations

When the Peru-Chile phosphorite nodules are examined visually, it is immediately apparent that the external characteristics are not typical for phosphorite nodules described from other locations. Dietz *et al.* (1942), for example, described the California Borderland deposits as follows: "In general, the nodules are hard and dense and have a smooth glazed surface and a fresh appearance." In contrast to this description, the most recently-formed nodules from off Peru have surfaces which are dull to earthy in appearance although some of the older nodules, off Chile, have an appearance somewhat like that described for the California samples. A few examples of the Peru-Chile nodules and, for comparison, samples from the Pourtales Terrance are illustrated in fig. 5. It is our opinion that the "glazed" surfaces so often observed on sea-floor nodules are the result of mechanical abrasion caused during periods of increased wave or current action on the sea floor. It seems plausible, therefore, that older samples which may have experienced periods of reworking on the ocean floor would exhibit a glazed or polished appearance while younger nodules which have been sampled in place may display a more textured surface such as encountered in the deposits off Peru. This is not meant to imply that any phosphate nodule with a "dull" surface is modern. It does seem, on the other hand, that all the nodules described from the sea-floor with "glazed" surfaces are definitely not of Recent origin.

Another very striking piece of evidence which

FIG. 4.—Block diagrams showing distribution of dissolved phosphate and dissolved oxygen in bottom waters, as well as bottom type off the west coast of South America. These data collected during the South Tow (May, 1972) and Krill (August, 1974) Expeditions of the Scripps Institution of Oceanography. a) Dissolved phosphate ($\mu g - at/l$) in bottom waters off South America. Recent phosphorites occur only in areas where bottom water phosphate is between 2.5 and 3.0 $\mu g = at/l$. b) Dissolved oxygen (ml/l) in bottom waters off South America. Phosphorites with the youngest uranium-series ages only occur where dissolved oxygen is extremely low. c) Map of likely bottom sediment type on the sea floor off South America. Bottom sediments divided into diatomaceous laminated anaerobic sediment, aerobic sediment and phosphorite. Areas of overlap between these divisions are also shown. Occurrences of Recent phosphorite according to our uranium-series measurements (Burnett and Veeh, 1977) are shown by solid dots.

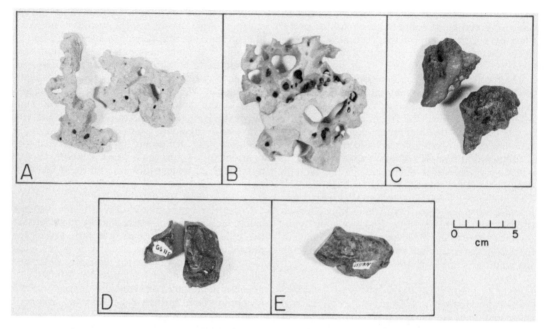

FIG. 5.—Photograph of modern phosphate nodules from off Peru (A & B) in contrast to an older nodule from off Chile (C) and samples from the Pourtales Terrace (D & E) of probable Miocene Age. See Burnett and Gomberg (1977) for further information on the Pourtales samples and Burnett and Veeh (1977) for the Peru-Chile deposits. A) PD-12-05: 12° 5.5′S, 77° 46.6′W; 345 m; uranium-series age: $\leq 2 \times 10^3$ yr. B) PD-15-17: 15° 17.8′S, 75° 23.5′W; 370 m; uranium-series age: $\leq 3 \times 10^3$ yr. C) PD-21-25: 21° 25.0′S, 70° 22.0′W; 100 m; uranium-series age: $> 200 \times 10^3$ yr. D) GS-11P: 24° 14.1′N, 81° 17.0′W; 380 m; uranium-series age: $> 200 \times 10^3$ yr. E) GS-41NN: 24° 28.4′N, 80° 35.3′W; 285 m; uranium-series age: $> 200 \times 10^3$ yr.

not only supports our interpretation of the uranium-series data, but has important implications concerning apatite-seawater equilibrium, is the presence of solution features within the phosphate nodules. These features were discovered during examination of freshly-fractured surfaces of these nodules by a scanning electron microscope (SEM). The solution features are apparent in only a few of the nodules examined. Indeed, what is really significant is the fact that they were observed only in nodules with uranium-series ages in excess of a few tens of thousands of years. None of the "modern" nodules (according to our radiometric determinations) examined by SEM showed any evidence of dissolution of the phosphatic material.

The dramatic change in crystal morphology of the constituent apatite is clearly illustrated in fig. 6 by a succession of SEM photos from nodules of increasing uranium-series age. The apatite crystals shown in the first two photos are from a nodule (PD-12-05) with a uranium-series age of less than 2000 years (all uranium-series ages from Burnett and Veeh, 1977). The euhedral crystals are easily seen to be prismatic with hexagonal basal faces. Many of the micron-sized crystals are doubly terminated. The next photo

shows a nodule (PD-19-30) dated at about 37,000 years. The cluster of apatite crystals shown reveals very little crystal morphology apparently because of the effects of solution. The "rosette" feature seen in the next photo is from a nodule (PD-19-37), which at 48,000 years, is slightly older. The surfaces of the apatite crystals are very obviously pitted, a feature which we interpret as due to solution. Another view of the same nodule in the following photograph shows an entire sequence of apatite crystals with pitted surfaces. For purposes of comparison, the last photo in fig. 6 is of a fractured surface of a nodule from off California. The smooth quartz crystal in the foreground contrasts with the pitted and weathered mass of apatitic material behind it. It is quite apparent that some time after formation, the apatite in these nodules began to dissolve. Actually, this is not altogether too surprising in view of the uranium isotopic data which show a progressive loss of ^{234}U from marine apatite with increasing age. Perhaps this loss of ^{234}U is related to partial dissolution of the apatite crystals as seen in these SEM photos.

For the purpose of our present argument, we wish to emphasize the point that these SEM observations match exactly what we may have

Fig. 6.—Scanning electron micrographs of freshly fractured surfaces of phosphate nodules from off Peru-Chile showing development of solution features with age in these deposits. One sample (F) from off California shown for comparison. A) PD-12-05: $< 2 \times 10^3$ yr. B) PD-12-05: $< 2 \times 10^3$ yr. C) PD-19-30: $37 \pm 5 \times 10^3$ yr. D) PD-19-37: $48 \pm 3 \times 10^3$ yr. E) PD-19-37: $48 \pm 3 \times 10^3$ yr. F) 11876: $> 200 \times 10^3$ yr.

predicted based on our interpretation of the uranium-series results. It would seem almost incomprehensible that this relation could exist if our uranium-series data had no meaning. Certainly, if solution is a continuous process, then older samples would show the most pronounced effects. Our hypothesis of Recent formation for samples such as PD-12-05 is, therefore, consistent with and supported by the SEM observations noted above.

SUMMARY AND CONCLUSION

The weight of evidence presented here strongly suggests that the indurated phosphate nodules found off Peru and Chile with uranium isotopic compositions in equilibrium with seawater are of Holocene age. Uranium-series disequilibrium studies support this view in light of the following arguments: (a) The low activites of ^{230}Th in the "modern" deposits can only be explained by formation within the last few thousand years; (b) The depth distribution of uranium within individual nodules does not, as McArthur (1978) suggests, imply secondary addition of uranium to the nodules, but is simply a function of variations in the amount of apatite present; and (c) The Peru-Chile deposits contain substantial quantities of U(IV), thus implying that weathering has not significantly affected the substitution chemistry of these deposits.

In addition to the uranium data, areas of high dissolved phosphate and lowest dissolved oxygen in the bottom waters off Peru-Chile have been shown to match those areas where Holocene (according to the uranium-series data) deposits are found. The dull, earthy appearance and surface texture of the South American samples also seem to be in agreement with a younger age.

Finally, the appearance of solution features as seen by the SEM in samples with relatively high uranium-series ages and their virtual absence in samples dated as being Recent gives further credibility to our interpretation of present-day formation of phosphate nodules on the sea-floor off Peru and Chile.

Acknowledgements

The authors wish to express their gratitude to Scripps Institution of Oceanography for making the phosphorite samples available for study. The critical reviews of Dr. Kenneth Wolgemuth and an anonymous referee contributed markedly to the quality of this final version. One of us (WCB) also wishes to express his appreciation to Y. K. Bentor who made arrangements which made it possible to present this paper orally at the Tenth International Congress on Sedimentology (Jerusalem, Israel, 1978).

REFERENCES

ALTSCHULER, Z. S., CLARKE, R. S., AND YOUNG, E. J., 1958, Geochemistry of uranium in apatite and phosphorite: U.S. Geological Survey Prof. Paper 314 D., p. 45–87.
BATURIN, G. M., MERKULOVA, K. I., AND CHALOV, P. I., 1972, Radiometric evidence for Recent formation of phosphatic nodules in marine shelf sediments: Mar. Geol., v. 13, p. M37–M41.
BRONGERSMA-SANDERS, M., 1957, Mass mortality in the sea: In Hegpeth, J. W., editor, *Treatise on Marine Ecology and Paleocology*, v. 1, Geol. Soc. Amer. Mem. 67, p. 941–1010.
BURNETT, W. C., 1977, Geochemistry and origin of phosphorite deposits from off Peru and Chile: Geol. Soc. America Bull., v. 88, p. 813–823.
———, AND GOMBERG, D. M., 1977, Uranium oxidation and probable subaerial weathering of phosphatized limestone from the Pourtales Terrace: Sedimentology, v. 24, p. 291–302.
———, AND VEEH, H. H., 1977, Uranium-series disequilibrium studies in phosphorite nodules from the west coast of South America: Geochim. Cosmochim. Acta, v. 41, p. 755–764.
DIETZ, R. S., EMERY, K. O., AND SHEPARD, F. P., 1942, Phosphorite deposits on the sea floor off Southern California: Geol. Soc. America Bull., v. 53, p. 815–848.
D'ANGLEJAN, B. F., 1968, Phosphate diagenesis of carbonate sediments as a mode of *in situ* formation of marine phosphorites: Observations in a core from the Eastern pacific: Canadian Jour. Earth. Sci., v. 5, p. 81–87.
DOYLE, L. J., BLAKE, N. J., WOO, C. C., AND YEVICH, P., 1978, Recent biogenic phosphorite: Concretions in Mollusk kidneys: Science, v. 199, p. 1431–1433.
GOLDBERG, E. D., AND PARKER, R. H., 1960, Phosphatized wood from the Pacific sea floor: Geol. Soc. America Bull., v. 71, p. 631–632.
KAZAKOV, A. V., 1937, The phosphorite facies and the genesis of phosphorites, *in* Geological investigations of agricultural ores, U.S.S.R. Trans. Sci. Inst. Fertilizers and Insectofungicides, no. 142, p. 93–113.
KOLODNY, Y., 1969, Are marine phosphorites forming today?: Nature, v. 224, p. 1017–1019.
———, AND KAPLAN, I. R., 1970, Uranium isotopes in sea floor phosphorites: Geochim. Cosmochim. Acta, v. 34, p. 3–24.
KU, T.-L., KNAUSS, K. G., AND MATHIEU, G. G., 1977, Uranium in open ocean: concentration and isotopic composition: Deep-Sea Res., v. 24, p. 1005–1017.
MANHEIM, F., ROWE, G. T., AND JIPA, D., 1975, Marine phosphorite formation off Peru: Jour. Sed. Petrology, v. 45, p. 243–251.

McArthur, J. M., 1978, Systematic variations in the contents of Na, Sr, CO_3 and SO_4 in marine carbonate-fluorapatite and their relation to weathering: Chemical Geology, v. 21, p. 89–112.

McConnell, D., 1958, The apatite-like mineral of sediments: Econ. Geology, v. 53, p. 110–111.

McKelvey, V. E., 1967, Phosphate deposits: U.S. Geol. Survey Bull. 1252-D, p. D1–D21.

Sholkovitz, E., 1973, Interstitial water chemistry of the Santa Barbara Basin sediments: Geochim. Cosmochim. Acta. v. 37, p. 2043–2073.

Tooms, J. S., Summerhayes, C. P., and Cronan, D. S., 1969, Geochemistry of marine phosphate and manganese deposits: Oceanog. Marine Biol. Ann. Rev., v. 7, p. 49–100.

Veeh, H. H., Burnett, W. C., and Soutar, A., 1973, Contemporary phosphorite on the continental margin of Peru: Science, v. 181, p. 845–847.

———, Calvert, S. E., and Price, N. B., 1974, Accumulation of uranium in sediments and phosphorites on the South West African shelf: Marine Chemistry, v. 2, p. 189–202.

SULFUR ISOTOPES IN PHOSPHORITES

Y. NATHAN and H. NIELSEN

Geological Survey of Israel and Geochemisches Institut der Universität, Göttingen

ABSTRACT

The study of sulfur isotopes of the sulfate within the carbonate-fluorapatite lattice and of some gypsum, associated with phosphorites in two important phosphorite provinces, the Late Cretaceous-Eocene Mediterranean belt and the Permian Phosphoria Formation, shows that the origin of the sulfate within the carbonate-fluorapatite is marine, the $\delta^{34}S$ for these samples usually being equal to or higher than the corresponding seawater values. The unusually high values obtained for many samples suggest that at least these phosphorites were formed in an early diagenetic reducing environment during bacterial sulfate reduction. The low $\delta^{34}S$ values of the gypsum associated with the phosphorites show that at least part of the gypsum originates from oxidized biogenic sulfide (pyrite), thus supporting the former hypothesis.

INTRODUCTION

Sulfur occurs in phosphorites in four different forms: 1) as part of the organic matter 2) as sulfides (mainly pyrite) 3) as sulfates (mainly gypsum) and 4) as sulfate (SO_4^{-2}) within the apatite structure.

The presence of sulfate (SO_4^{-2}) in the apatite lattice as an isomorphous substitution for phosphate (PO_4^{-3}) has been suggested by many researchers and is today generally accepted (Gulbrandsen, 1969; McConnell, 1973). Its significance, on the other hand, is still controversial. According to Smirnov et al. (1962) and Gulbrandsen (1969), the sulfate content of apatite in phosphorites is an indicator of paleosalinity (reflecting the environment of deposition). Reviewing this opinion, Smirnov (1966), concludes from experimental work, that the degree of replacement of PO_4^{-3} by SO_4^{-2} depends on the sulfate content of the aqueous phase in equilibrium with the phosphate during its formation.

McArthur (1978), on the other hand, suggests that all marine carbonate-fluorapatites have the same sulfate content when formed and that the variations found are due to later weathering. Schneider (1968) investigated the sulfur content in bones and teeth of recent and fossil organisms. He found no systematic differences between the sulfur concentrations of diagenetic phosphates from freshwater and marine environments of deposition.

It is well established that the isotopic composition of sulfur in sedimentary environments can give valuable information about the environmental parameters (facies) during sediment formation and especially about the participation of microorganisms in diagenetic processes of the "biological sulfur cycle." Sulfur isotope determinations were, therefore, considered a promising way to unravel the origin of the different sulfur species in phosphorite deposits, and to reach a better under-

standing of the genesis of the phosphorites themselves. A similar approach has recently been used by Bliskovskiy et al. (1978).

Samples and Methods

The Phosphoria samples are Permian in age; the geology of the deposit has extensively been studied (McKelvey et al., 1959), and the chemical composition of the phosphorite has been described by Gulbrandsen (1966). The samples used in this work have been taken from the original samples which were analyzed by Gulbrandsen (1966), and bear the same numbers.

The Israeli samples are all from the Mishash Formation in the Negev and are Campanian; the deposits and their chemistry have recently been described by Nathan et al., (1979). The Moroccan samples are Ypresian and come from the Nzalet deposit. The geology of the Moroccan deposits has extensively been studied (Boujo, 1976), and their chemistry is now being studied by Prévôt (1978). The Tunisian samples are from Gafsa and are Eocene. These deposits and their chemistry have been described by Sassi (1974).

All samples were ground to pass through a 200 mesh sieve and were thoroughly washed with distilled water to remove soluble sulfates. In some cases, the soluble sulfates were then precipitated as barium sulfate. The washed phosphorite (in most cases) was dissolved in acid and the sulfate subsequently precipitated as barium sulfate. The results (table 1) refer to sulfur from the sulfate within the apatite lattice and sulfur from the soluble sulfate disseminated in the same sample. Gypsum was the only sulfate mineral identified in the analyzed samples. Sulfur in the organic matter and sulfides (if any) remained in the insoluble residue. The sulfur isotopic analyses were carried out at the stable isotope laboratory of the Geochemisches Institut, Göttingen. Sample

TABLE 1.—SULFUR ISOTOPIC COMPOSITION IN APATITES AND SULFATES OF PHOSPHORITES

No.	Locality	Age	SO_3 content in apatite %	$\delta^{34}S$‰ in apatite	$\delta^{34}S$‰ in sulfate
18	Idaho, USA*	Permian	1.46	+18.1	
23	Montana, USA	Permian	2.37	+15.0	
27	Idaho, USA	Permian	0.94	+17.5	
42	Idaho, USA	Permian	2.49	+17.4	
44	Idaho, USA	Permian	1.77	+19.8	
55	Wyoming, USA	Permian	1.90	+19.5	
57	Utah, USA	Permian	2.66	+14.2	
58	Utah, USA	Permian	1.19	+19.7	
YS 1515	Hor Hahar, Israel	Campanian	n. det.	+22.1	
YS 1516	Hor Hahar, Israel	Campanian	n. det.	+29.4	
YS 1517	Hor Hahar, Israel	Campanian	n. det.	+18.5	
Or 1	Oron, Israel	Campanian	0.90	+22.9	
Or 13	Oron, Israel	Campanian	0.88	+22.0	−8.3
Ze 5	Zefa, Israel	Campanian	1.95	+ 9.0	−4.7
HH 40	Hazeva, Israel	Campanian	0.78	+23.5	
LP 37223	Nzalet, Morocco	Ypresian	2.35	+20.7	
LP 37231	Nzalet, Morocco	Ypresian	2.27	+20.2	
SD 11	Gafsa, Tunisia	Eocene	4.09	+19.8	
SD 45	Gafsa, Tunisia	Eocene	3.16	+21.8	
SD 55	Gafsa, Tunisia	Eocene	3.83	+19.6	

*A full description of the Phosphoria Formation samples (18–58) is given in Gulbrandsen (1966); there is a slight difference between the SO_3 results in this table and those given by Gulbrandsen (ours are lower). This may be due to the washings; they are given, so as to have all the results obtained by the same method.

preparation was performed in the conventional manner (reduction of sulfate to H_2S, precipitation as CdS, oxidation to SO_2 by V_2O_5). The isotope data are given in $\delta^{34}S$ notation, i.e. per mil deviation of the abundance ratio $^{34}S/^{32}S$ of the measured sample from a standard, represented by troilite sulfur of the Cañon Diablo meteorite.

Results and Discussion

The chemical and isotope results are given in table 1. Figure 1 (after Nielsen, 1978) compiles nearly all the published reliable $\delta^{34}S$ values of evaporite sulfates of different geologic ages. These data have been applied to evaluate the "age curve of oceanic sulfate."

A comparison of the results listed in table 1 with the age curve displayed in figure 1, shows, that, with one single exception (sample Ze 5), all the investigated apatites have $\delta^{34}S$ values equal to, or above the coeval sea-water value, while the associated sulfates (gypsum) are distinctly depleted in ^{34}S with respect to both. As an example, the value for the Permian ocean is assumed to be +11‰, but all the examined samples (eight from the Phosphoria Formation) range above +14‰ with an unweighted mean of +17.6 ± 2.1‰. In figure 2 the $\delta^{34}S$ values of the Phosphoria samples are plotted as function of their sulfate contents. The importance of this relationship is discussed below.

A similar correlation may exist for the Campanian samples. With the exception of the weathered sample Ze 5, all $\delta^{34}S$ values of apatite sulfate are close to or above the assumed seawater value for the Campanian ocean. The five Eocene samples from Tunisia and Morocco have $\delta^{34}S$ values which are about equal to the Eocene ocean value, but it should be pointed out that these are samples which were chosen because of their very high sulfate content, and that the one Tunisian sample (S D 45) which has a slightly higher $\delta^{34}S$ also has a slightly lower sulfate content than the two other Tunisian samples.

The $\delta^{34}S$ values found by Bliskovskiy et al. (table 1, p. 145, 1978) for Permian and Late Cretaceous to Eocene samples, are in the main similar to ours. Table 2, which is based on their results, shows that the two Permian samples examined have both high $\delta^{34}S$ values = 19.1 and 23‰ and, while three Late Cretaceous samples give values lower than corresponding sea-water, these are strongly weathered samples and are therefore not relevant to this discussion; (we shall refer to them together with our Ze 5 result). The five other Late Cretaceous samples show values equal to or higher than the ocean value. Finally, the two Eocene samples have $\delta^{34}S$ values of 25.2 and 37‰, again extremely high.

The above data agree well with the conclusion that the primary source of the sulfur in apatites from phosphorites is sea-water. This was also the conclusion of Bliskovskiy et al., (1978). The influence and contribution of sea-water in phosphorites is also clearly seen in their trace element composition (Tooms et al., 1969) and is particularly marked in their rare earths composition (Altschuler et al., 1967). The significantly high ^{34}S content, found in many of the investigated samples, however, defines the environment of phosphorite deposition as a (partly) "closed system" with extensive bacterial sulfate reduction.

Reduction of dissolved sulfate is a specific "respiration" mechanism, applied by microorganisms living in anaerobic environments (such as *Desulphovibrio desulfuricans*). The hydrogen sulfide, resulting from this biological reaction, is expelled from the cell and is frequently trapped as FeS_2, pyrite. Due to a strong S isotope fractionation involved in the reduction step, these biogenic pyrites are isotopically "light" with respect to the source sulfate, the δ difference ranging from 10 to 60‰. If only a limited reservoir of sulfate is accessible to bacterial reduction, the preferential extraction of the light isotope yields a systematic increase in $δ^{34}$S of the remaining sulfate. In so far as the fractionation factor

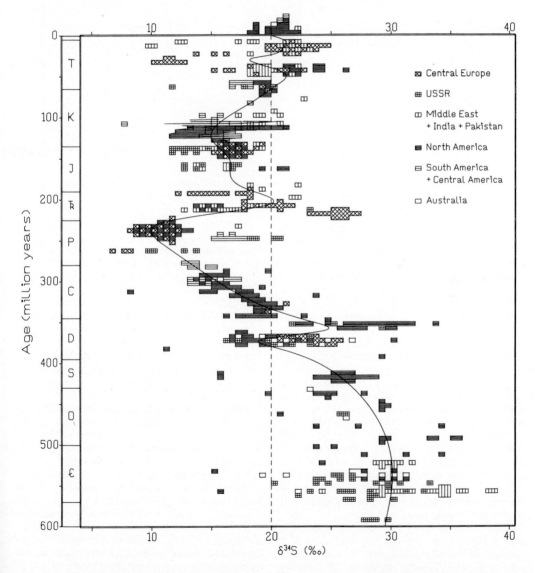

Fig. 1.—$δ^{34}$S distribution in marine evaporites and the $δ^{34}$S age curve of oceanic sulfate during the Phanerozoic (slightly modified, after Nielsen, 1978, fig. 16-B-13).

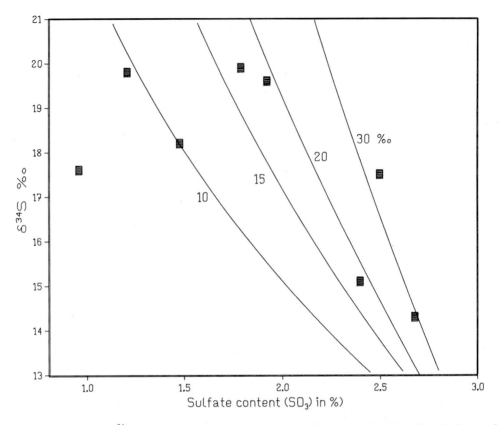

Fig. 2.—Correlation of $\delta^{34}S$ with sulfate content (expressed as SO_3) in the Permian Phosphoria samples. Curves give theoretically expected $\delta^{34}S$ increase with sulfate consumption by bacterial H_2S production in a "closed system" reservoir of dissolved sulfate. Indices 10, 15, 20 and 30 give the net ^{34}S depletion of the extracted sulfides, corresponding to the slopes of the individual curves (see text).

involved in the reduction step remains constant with time, for a closed system the increase in $\delta^{34}S$ with sulfate consumption can be calculated exactly with the "Rayleigh distillation equation."

In a freshly deposited sediment only the uppermost millimeters or centimeters remain in a steady exchange of pore solutions with the overlying water column, but at deeper levels the trapped water forms a more or less "closed system." Any bacterial activity at depth, therefore, will result in a substantial loss of sulfate from the interstitial water and in a systematic $\delta^{34}S$ increase in the remaining sulfate. This has been verified in many investigations on modern sediments, and in most cases the observed $\delta^{34}S$ values agree well with the theoretical prediction.

With this relationship in mind, an attempt is made in figure 2 to correlate the individual $\delta^{34}S$ values of the Phosphoria samples with their sulfate contents via the Rayleigh equation. The curves shown are computed for different model assumptions, all of which apply a starting $\delta^{34}S$ value

of +11‰ for unaffected Permian sea-water and a starting sulfate concentration in the pore water corresponding to 3% SO_3 in the apatite structure. The curves then give the theoretically expected δ increase with sulfate consumption, if the net fractionation at each instant gives a depletion of 10, 15, 20, and 30‰ in $\delta^{34}S$ of the freshly formed sulfide (for background information see Nielsen, 1978). Such model calculations obviously cannot explain quantitatively the data obtained from each individual sample, but they show at least that the trend of $\delta^{34}S$ variation with sulfate content is best explained with phosphorite deposition in a "quasi closed system" environment with extensive bacterial sulfate reduction—i.e. during diagenesis in a sediment rich in organic matter.

This association, however, between phosphorite and organic matter is apparently not accidental and seems to have an important bearing on the genetic interpretation of many (if not all) phosphorite accumulations of economic importance. In a reducing fjord, Nissenbaum et al.

(1972) observed a marked enrichment of phosphate in the interstitial water, accompanied by a systematic increase in $\delta^{34}S$ up to +39‰. Gaudette and Lyons (1978), from their own data, come to the conclusion, that "phosphate is removed from the pore water during diagenetic transformation of the organic matter (i.e. during microbial sulfate reduction) and is incorporated in fluorapatite." Furthermore, the association phosphorites—organic matter is well established for many natural occurrences and sulfides and/or sulfates (gypsum) are common accessory minerals of phosphorite deposits. The low values of $\delta^{34}S$ (from +5.0 to −20.2‰, tables 1 and 2; even a value of −36.1‰ was found by Bliskovskiy et al., 1978) for all examined sulfates associated with phosphorites show clearly that they are, at least in part, the result of oxidation of sulfides (pyrite), implying that sulfides are usually formed during phosphorite deposition. All this confirms the hypothesis that phosphorites were formed in an early diagenetic reducing environment.

The diagenetic mobilization of phosphorus and the formation of apatite concentrations from interstitial waters is the model proposed by Bushinskii (1966) and favored by Kolodny (1978) in a recent review of the genesis of phosphorites. This is also the opinion of Price and Calvert (1978) based on a geochemical study of phosphorites from the Namibian shelf. They conclude: "the origin of the phosphorites is believed to be the result of the diagenetic precipitation of phosphorus within sediments . . .." Finally, the fact that no clear correlation could be found in phosphorites between petrographic types and chemical composition (Gulbrandsen, 1966; Nathan et al., 1979) also points to an early diagenetic environment for the genesis of phosphorite. The low values of $\delta^{34}S$ and the sulfur content of the weathered samples are easily explained. The weathering mechanism is dissolution and re-

precipitation, because SO_4^{-2}, like CO_3^{-2}, cannot be expelled at low temperatures from the structure in the solid state. Since the weathering solutions carry secondary sulfate originating predominantly from the oxidation of biogenic sulfide, the process will cause a systematic lowering of the $\delta^{34}S$ value of the phosphorite. Furthermore, the sulfate content of the weathered samples reflects the sulfate concentration in the solutions. If the latter is lower than in the interstitial water, from which the phosphorites were deposited, the sulfate content of the weathered samples will also be lower than that of the fresh samples. Weathering solutions with abnormally high sulfate contents, on the other hand, will yield higher sulfate contents in the weathered phosphorite samples than in the unweathered marine ones.

More work is needed and is now in progress on two points: 1) Cambrian phosphorites—Cambrian is also a period rich in phosphorites. Bliskovskiy et al. (1978) do not show $\delta^{34}S$ enrichment for these phosphorites; but since they analyzed only three samples, more data are needed to decide whether Cambrian phosphorites are different in this respect, reflecting a different genesis. 2) The relationship between SO_4^{-2} content and $\delta^{34}S$. Samples with high and low sulfate concentrations from the same basin are now being prepared for isotope analyses.

ACKNOWLEDGEMENTS

We thank Dr. R. A. Gulbrandsen of the U.S. Geological Survey for his generous gift of the valuable suite of samples from the Phosphoria Formation and for his encouragement and interest in this work. We thank Miss L. Prévôt of the Centre de Sédimentologie of Strasbourg for the Moroccan samples. Heimo Nielsen thanks Mr. Fredj Chaabani for the Tunisian samples. Mrs. Gal of the Geological Survey of Israel and Mrs. Noltmeyer of the Geochemisches Institut der

TABLE 2.—SULFUR ISOTOPIC COMPOSITION IN APATITE AND SULFATES OF PHOSPHORITES
(taken from Table 1, p. 149, Bliskovskiy et al., 1978)

No.	Locality	Age	SO_3 content of apatite %	$\delta^{34}S$‰ in apatite	in sulfate
7	Seleuk, USSR	Early Permian	3.50	+19.1	
8	Rocky Mts., USA	Early Permian	n. det.	+23.3	
11	Dakhla, Egypt	Late Cretaceous	1.85	+6.8	
12	El Mahamid, Egypt	Late Cretaceous	1.30	+11.0	
13	Chilisay, USSR	Late Cretaceous	1.97	+14.0	−20.2
14	Safaga, Egypt	Late Cretaceous	0.96	+18.7	
15	Vostochnoye, Syria	Late Cretaceous	0.84	+20.8	
16	Mardin, Turkey	Late Cretaceous	n. det.	+21.4	
17	Abu-Tartur, Egypt	Late Cretaceous	1.88	+22.0	+4.6
18	Guru-Fat'minsk, USSR	Eocene	3.8	+25.2	
19	Guliob, USSR	Eocene	n. det.	+37.2	

greatly improved our knowledge of diagenetic and authigenic processes involved in the formation of marine apatites.

Because a great variety of morphological and genetic forms of phosphorite are known to exist on the western margin of southern Africa, this region can be expected to play a decisive role in the elucidation of current problems associated with phosphorite genesis. The nature and distribution of diagenetic phosphatic material on the southern African continental margin has been described by Parker and Siesser (1972), Parker (1975) and Birch (1979), whereas the authigenic varieties are discussed by Tankard (1974a,b), Birch (1977a, in press a) and Bremner (1978). These contributions are reviewed, but the main objective of the present work is to compare the two genetic phosphate types and to construct a model to account for their penecontemporaneous formation. This model is applied to other phosphogenic provinces.

NOMENCLATURE

Phosphorites are sedimentary rocks containing more than 50 percent apatite minerals, i.e. >18 percent P_2O_5 (Bushinsky, 1969); however two problems of nomenclature are manifest in the present work. Because no genetic classification exists for phosphorites, the name 'Authigenic' has been given in the following discussion to phosphatic materials which have formed by precipitation, interstitial growth or pelletal accretion, whereas 'Diagenetic' refers to rocks that have originated by replacement of a calcareous precursor. The 18 percent P_2O_5 content restriction is impractical as it acts to divide the latter suite of rocks. Bulk and especially microanalyses of phosphate-rich rocks, particularly conglomeratic varieties, vary from 12 to 24 percent P_2O_5 for a single hand specimen. Geologists (Parker and Siesser, 1972; Summerhayes, 1973; Parker, 1975; Birch, 1979a,b) working on the South African phosphorite occurrences have preferred to choose a phosphate level which differentiates normally from anomalously phosphatic material, rather than adhering to an arbitrary P_2O_5 content of 18 percent. Local basement rocks contain less than 1 percent P_2O_5 and a clear hiatus in the

P_2O_5 content of limestones occurs at 5 percent. The latter figure has therefore been accepted by South African research workers as the minimum phosphate value for this suite of rocks.

DESCRIPTION OF PHOSPHATIC MATERIALS

Phosphatic material formed diagenetically occurs most commonly as rocks, but fragments are found in the sand-size fraction, whereas authigenic phosphates are most abundant in pelletal form. The phosphatic varieties described below are:

DIAGENETIC PHOSPHATES

1. Arenaceous:
    (a) Foraminiferal lime packstones (AI)
    (b) Glauconite/quartz packstones (AII)
    (c) Goethite-rich lime packstones (AIII)
2. Conglomeratic:
    (a) Glauconitic packstones with enclosed foraminiferal pebbles (CI)
    (b) Goethite-rich limestones containing abundant macrofossils and bone (CII)

AUTHIGENIC PHOSPHATES

1. Pellets:
    (a) Oolitic (PI)
    (b) Nucleated (PII)
    (c) Structureless (PIII)
2. Quartzitic packstone (Q)
3. Layered (L)

Diagenetic Phosphate-rich Rocks

Diagenetic phosphate-rich rocks comprise two conglomeratic and three arenaceous varieties (Parker, 1971; Birch, 1979b):

Type AI is a quartzitic microfossiliferous limestone in various stages of phosphatization (fig. 1). Planktonic foraminifera usually dominate, but benthic varieties, bryozoans, coraline algae, echinoderm plates and spines can be important locally. Inshore samples may have a rich, but poorly sorted, terrigenous fraction including rock fragments, feldspar, jasper and chalcedony (fig. 1). Cement is a mixture of apatite and micrite and/or rarely glauconite. Type AII contains minor quartz and glauconite with subordinate amounts

FIG. 1.—Photographs and photomicrographs of diagenetically formed phosphate-rich rocks. (A, B)—Arenaceous phosphate-rich foraminiferal limestone (AI type) exhibiting phosphatization zone on upper and lower margins. Planktonic foraminifera, quartz, calcareous debris and micrite/francolite cement make up the rock. (C, D.)—A near-shore, arenaceous phosphate-rich rock (AI type) comprising quartz, chalcedony, glauconite, rock fragments and francolite cement. (E–H)—Conglomeratic phosphate-rich rock with abundant glauconite (CI type). Foraminiferal pebbles containing poorly sorted quartz, and glauconite-filled foraminifera set in a matrix of glauconite and minor quartz. Note the zones of phosphatization are concordant with the edges of enclosed pebbles (G) and the distinct layering (E). (I, J)—Conglomeratic phosphate-rich rock (CII type) comprising microfossiliferous pebbles set in a goethite-rich matrix.

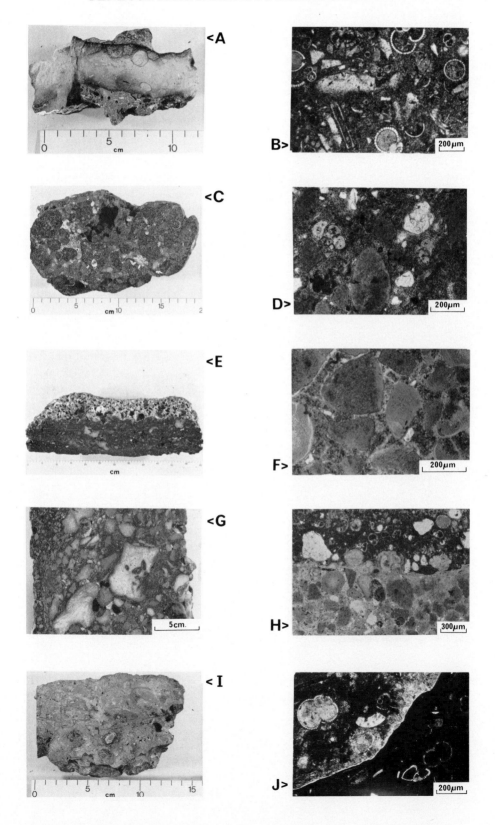

of planktonic and benthonic foraminifera. These rocks are characterized by a goethite/apatite cement (fig. 1). Abundant glauconite and minor quartz and planktonic foraminifera make up Type AIII (fig. 1). An intimate mixture of delicate foraminiferal tests, large angular quartz grains and rounded glauconite is an indication of the complex origin of these rocks. An apatitic cement can include glauconitic and micritic phases.

Rocks assigned to the conglomeratic class CI have a matrix similar to the AIII subgroup and the enclosed pebbles resemble either AI or AIII phosphatic types (fig. 1). Class CII is distinguished by a conglomeratic texture produced by the presence of enclosed macrofossils, microfossiliferous pebbles, large bone fragments, and coraline algae (fig. 1). The matrix contains minor glauconite, quartz and foraminifera. Enclosed pebbles contain no glauconite or quartz and <10 percent foraminifera. The cement is typically goethite.

The constituents of these rock types form part of a continuous series, ranging from nearshore samples containing quartz and rock fragments, through mid-shelf glauconite-rich varieties to deep-water microfossiliferous types. The rocks are commonly referred to as nodules. This is a misnomer as they are usually tabloid or lenticular, varying from 5 to 50 cm in thickness (fig. 2). Rounded examples, indicative of extensive reworking, are common.

Authigenic Phosphate-rich Rocks and Pellets

Authigenically formed phosphatic material occurs most frequently as resinous, dark brown and reddish-brown ovoid or spherical pellets, predominantly in the fine and medium sand-size fraction (1.5 to 3.0φ). The pellets are very well to well rounded and very well sorted (Tankard, 1974a; Birch, 1977a; Bremner, 1978). Some pellets exhibit a smooth, even surface under the electron microscope, whereas other pellets have an irregular fresh surface composed of micron-size aggregates (fig. 3). Prismatic crystals 0.5 to 4μm long with hexagonal base sections found on the surface of some pellets may indicate secondary mineralization (Birch, in press a). A large proportion

of pellets (Type PI) contain nuclei of quartz, feldspar of biogenic debris and also a well-developed oolitic internal structure (fig. 3). Concentric layers (Type PII) of apatite are separated from one another by a dark coating of organic matter. These features are indicative of accretionary growth. A considerable portion of the grains exhibit a structureless or heterogeneous interior (Type PIII) and are probably reworked fragments of a larger phosphatic rock.

Only two examples of authigenically formed phosphate-rich rock (Type Q) have been dredged from the continental shelf off southern Africa (Rogers, 1977; Birch, in press a). One sample is flattened with a 'honey-comb' appearance derived from numerous large pits (fig. 2). It has a smooth surface, but exhibits no internal zonation or structure. The rock has a grain-supported texture and comprises >50 percent well-sorted angular quartz with minor finely dispersed organic matter. The second sample is a small fragment of phosphatic rock recovered from near Lüderitz (Rogers, 1977; Bremner, 1978) which contains 20 percent phosphate pellets set in an apatitic cement.

Several morphological varieties of authigenically-derived phosphatic rock occur in the Varswater Quarry on the coastal terrace at Saldanha Bay (Tankard, 1974a) (fig. 4). Discontinous and irregular phosphate-rich beds (Type Q) comprise 30–80 percent fine to medium sand-size quartz, minor phosphatized bone, shell and heavy minerals set in a light brown apatite cement. The rock has been described (Tankard, 1974a) as a "medium to fine grained collophane packstone." A distinctly mottled appearance is indicative of preferential phosphate mineralization in the interstices of the fabric (fig. 2). Rounded phosphatic cobbles and pebbles are found on the upper surface of the basal bed and deep hollows in the rock have been made by boring organisms. A rock (Type L) composed of fine layers (20 to 50 mm) of pure phosphate from Saldanha Bay could only have formed by precipitation of apatite directly from the water column (fig. 2) (Birch, in press a). Other examples (fig. 2) of pure authigenic phosphate formed by direct precipitation (Bremner, 1978)

FIG. 2.—Photographs and photomicrographs of diagenetic and authigenic phosphate-rich rocks. (A–D)—Morphology of rocks formed by replacement of micrite in bottom sediment. Dense, knobby protuberances on upper surface (B) of conglomeratic rock (A). Large, but thin, flat phosphatic rocks (D) suggest that replacement was restricted to the upper sediment surface (<0.5 m). Primary structures on sea floor preserved by (?) rapid phosphatization (C). (E–J)—Authigenic phosphate-rich rocks. (E)—Phosphatic mudstone exhibiting desiccation cracks suggesting exposure of upper surface. (Photograph by kind permission of Dr. J. M. Bremner). (F)—Quartzitic packstone from Saldanha showing preferential mineralization by interstitial precipitation of apatite. (G)—Thin, varve-like layers of (H) mainly francolite with minor quartz, replaced skeletal debris and phosphate pellets (nucleated). The fabric of this rock suggests a process of apatite precipitation directly from overlying sea-water. (I, J)—Authigenic packstone from continental margin off Cape Town showing large pits. The rock is composed of well-sorted, angular quartz set in an organic-rich francolite cement (J).

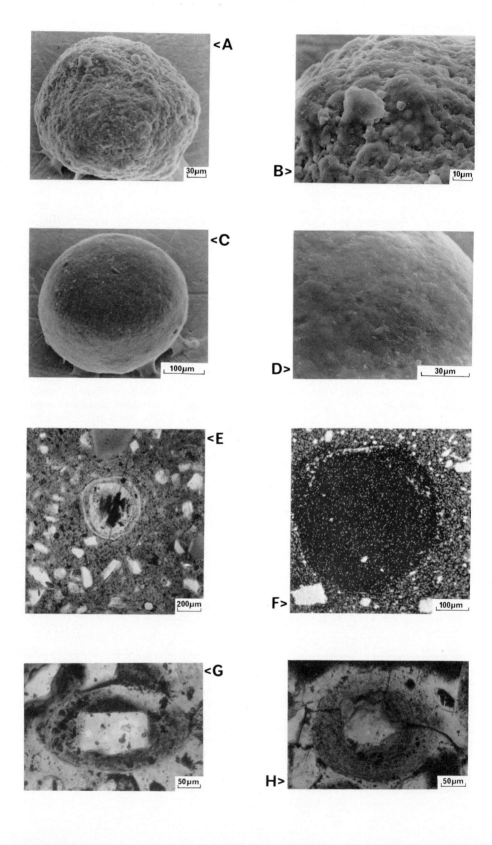

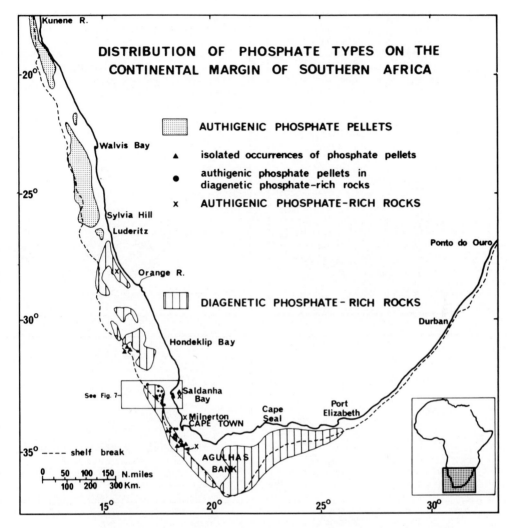

FIG. 4.—Distribution of phosphate types on the continental margin of southern Africa.

from off the South-west African coast have an upper surface completely covered by mud cracks, indicative of exposure and dehydration.

DISTRIBUTION OF PHOSPHATIC PELLETS AND ROCKS

A clear regional separation exists in the distribution of phosphate types on the western and southern margins of southern Africa. Phosphatic materials formed diagenetically occur predominantly south of Lüderitz, whereas authigenic varieties are located mainly in the north.

Distribution of Diagenetic Phosphate-rich Rocks.—No diagenetic phosphate-rich rocks have been recovered from the continental margin north of Sylvia Hill (fig. 4) (Rogers, 1977; Bremner,

FIG. 3.—Photographs and photomicrographs of authigenically formed phosphate pellets. (A–D)—Phosphate pellets from continental margin of South Africa showing varied microsurface characteristics. Primary surface (A, B) composed of micron-sized aggregates and smooth weathered surface (C, D) of reworked material. (E, F)—Authigenically formed phosphate pellet with glauconitized edge and containing abundant organic matter is enclosed in the quartz-rich matrix of a phosphatic rock which originated diagenetically through replacement of micrite in bottom sediment. X-ray image of Si (F) emphasizes the compositional divergence between the two genetic types of phosphatic material. (G, H)—Phosphate pellets with concentric layering and nuclei of quartz and calcite.

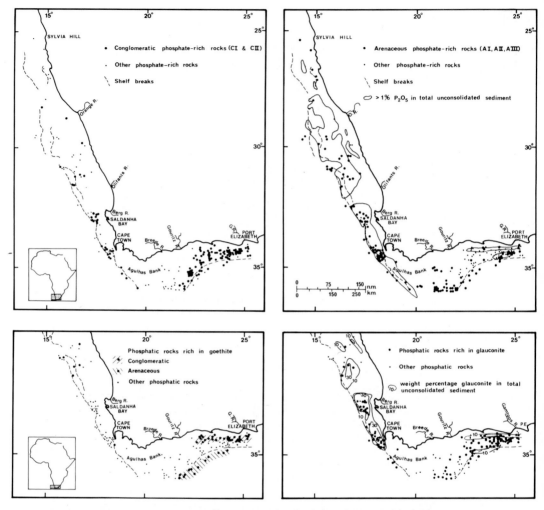

FIG. 5.—Distribution of diagenetically derived phosphatic rock types.

1978), and only three samples are located east of Port Elizabeth. Many tens of tons of phosphatic rock were dredged from 252 localities from the entire width of the margin (50 m to >1000 m).

Phosphate-rich rocks formed diagenetically are exposed over large areas of the Agulhas Bank, off Cape Town and west of Saldanha and Hondeklip Bays (fig. 4) (Birch, 1979b). This distribution partly reflects an increased dredging effort in these localities, but the pattern is also partly controlled by the degree of sedimentation. The Agulhas Bank and east coast is kept reasonably free of sediment by the Agulhas Current and therefore, the eastern limit of phosphatic rocks at Port Elizabeth is probably real, whereas the decrease in recovery density north of Saldanha Bay is more likely to be due to increased sediment cover. The abundance of phosphatic rock frag-

ments in the overlying sediment (fig. 5) supports this contention. Extensive dredging, controlled by detailed seismic and side scan sonar work, has established that the outcrops of diagenetic phosphate-rich rocks exist as a near-continuous 'pavement' or capping at least 0.5 m thick over large areas in the three above-mentioned localities (du Plessis and Birch, 1977).

Distribution of Goethite-rich Phosphatic Rocks.—The majority of phosphatic rocks (Types AII and CIII) rich in goethite occur on the eastern Agulhas Bank and north of the Berg River off the west coast (fig. 5). There is evidence (Birch, 1975) to suggest that the occurrence of goethite in phosphatic rocks is related to the input of iron from large perennial rivers draining onto the Agulhas Bank (Gamtoos, Gouritz and Breede Rivers) and onto the western margin (Berg and

Olifants Rivers). The reason for two parallel concentrations of goethite-rich sediment (fig. 5) is unclear, but the distribution may be related to the position of shorelines and fluvial input during regressive periods.

Distribution of Conglomeratic and Arenaceous Phosphate-rich Rocks.—Conglomeratic rocks (Types CI and CII), usually rich in glauconite, make up the majority of the phosphatic material recovered from the southern margin. These rocks occur almost to the exclusion of other types on the eastern Agulhas Bank, but are commonly associated with arenaceous varieties off Cape Town and Saldanha Bay (fig. 5). Arenaceous rocks (AI, AII and AIII) predominate on the west coast north of Saldanha Bay, probably because they are located in deep (>200–300 m) water.

Conglomeratic and arenaceous goethite-rich phosphorites (Types AII and CII) are well differentiated regionally on the Agulhas Bank. The former type is concentrated on the inner shelf where reworking was most intense during regressive/transgressive cycles, whereas the latter

group is restricted to the slope at depths beyond the influence of eustatic events. Only arenaceous rocks are found on the tip of Agulhas Bank in relatively shallow depths. This would suggest that this region was affected by only one episode of phosphatization.

Distribution of Phosphatic Rocks Rich in Glauconite.—The distribution of glauconite in unconsolidated sediment and the occurrence of glauconite-rich phosphatic rocks (Types AII and CI) coincide closely on the shelf off Cape Town and Saldanha Bay, but are unrelated on the inner shelves of the Agulhas Bank and between Orange River and Hondeklip Bay (fig. 5). This divergence is due to the glauconite from these regions being genetically different. Glauconite from the latter two deposits originate diagenetically from terrigenous sediment rich in illitic minerals, whereas glauconite from the southern part of the Agulhas Bank and off Cape Town and Saldanha formed by replacement of apatite pellets (Birch, 1979a).

Distribution of Authigenic Rocks and Pellets.— Phosphate pellets occur on the middle shelf south

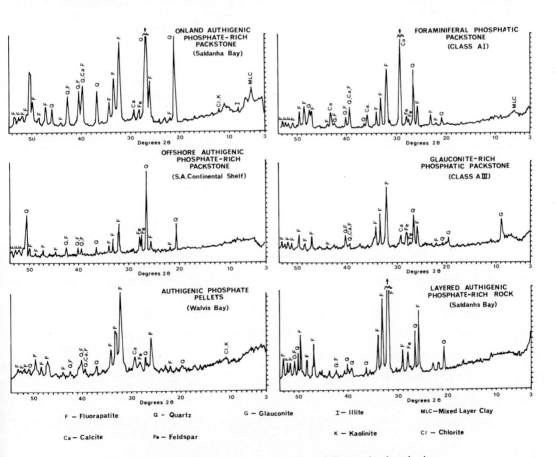

F — Fluorapatite   Q - Quartz   G — Glauconite   I — Illite   MLC—Mixed Layer Clay

Ca— Calcite   Fe — Feldspar   K — Kaolinite   Cl — Chlorite

Fig. 6.—X-ray diffractograms of authigenic and diagenetic phosphorites.

of the Kunene River and between Walvis Bay and Lüderitz (Bremner, 1975, 1978; Rogers, 1977). Small, isolated occurrences of pelletal material are located off Hondeklip Bay and west of Cape Town, but phosphate pellets are absent from surficial sediments east of this point (fig. 4) (Birch, 1975).

Authigenic phosphate-rich rock and pellets have until recently been mined at Saldanha Bay. Minor, irregular pelletal deposits are located over wide areas of the coastal terrace between Hondeklip Bay and Cape Town (Tankard, 1975), whereas phosphatic rock has been found only sporadically in cuttings and boreholes between Hondeklip Bay and Milnerton (Carrington and Kensley, 1969; Tankard, 1975; Rogers, pers. comm.). Phosphatic rock formed authigenically has been dredged from the continental margin north of Lüderitz and south of Cape Town (fig. 4) (Birch, 1975; Rogers, 1977).

MINERALOGY

X-ray diffraction studies were undertaken to identify the dominant minerals comprising the phosphatic material and to determine the nature of the mineral phase and CO_2 content of the apatite. In addition to the major constituents (apatite, calcite, glauconite, quartzite) diagenetic and authigenic phosphorites contain feldspar, illite, chlorite/kaolinite and mixed-layer clays as indicated on most of the diffractograms of these materials (fig. 6).

The Mineralogy of the Apatite Phase

All the phosphatic materials described in the present work exhibit well-defined lines at d-spacings reported by Rooney and Kerr (1967) for the mineral francolite, a fluorine-rich (>1% F) carbonate-apatite.

Using the peak-pair method described by Gulbrandsen (1970), the average CO_2 content of the apatite in phosphate pellets from the South-west African shelf has been determined as 3.6 percent (Bremner, 1978), which is similar to the CO_2 content of pellets off South Africa (3.8% CO_2, Birch, 1975). Authigenically derived phosphatic rock from Saldanha Bay and the South African shelf contains an average of 2.6 percent and 1.8 percent CO_2 respectively. These values are markedly different from the CO_2 content of the apatite phase in phosphatic rocks of the replacement type which has been determined by both Parker (1971) and Birch (1975) to be 5.5 percent (range 4.8 to 6.1).

It would appear from these figures that the highest CO_2 values are associated with phosphorites formed by replacement of calcareous sediment, whereas low CO_2 values are related to authigenic varieties which originate in carbonate-poor sediments. However, high CO_2 values reported for other authigenic material from South-west Africa by Rogers (1977) (5.5%) and Baturin (1969) (6.3%) render any relationship between the CO_2 content of phosphorite and genesis or depositional environment extremely doubtful.

Gulbrandsen (1970) suggested that the CO_2 content of Phosphoria phosphorites of North America increases with water temperature at the time of deposition. However, the CO_2 content of concretionary phosphorites from South-west Africa encompass a wide range of values, ie. 1.17 percent (Baturin, 1969) and 3.6 percent (Bremner, 1978) to 6.3 percent (Baturin, 1969), whereas the values for Miocene pelletal material vary between 2.6 percent for Saldanha Bay (Birch, 1975) and 5.5 percent for South-west Africa (Rogers, 1977). Thus, phosphatic materials formed in similar environments and of the same age have a widely varying CO_2 content. Leaching during weathering has been shown (McArthur, 1978) to reduce the CO_2 content of apatites; this or some replacement variable may be more important in determining the CO_2 concentration of apatites than the temperature during deposition.

GEOCHEMISTRY

Whole rock analyses of phosphatic materials were made by X-ray fluorescence spectrometry by Parker (1975) and Birch (1979b), whereas the distribution of individual mineral phases was

TABLE 1.—THE AVERAGE CO_2 CONTENT OF THE APATITE PHASE IN AUTHIGENIC AND DIAGENETIC PHOSPHATE-RICH MATERIAL

	Authigenic Phosphate-Rich Material				Diagenetic Phosphate-Rich Material	
	Pellets		Rocks		Rock	
	South West Africa (Bremner, 1978)	South Africa	Saldanha Bay	South African continental shelf	South African west coast	Agulhas Bank (Parker, 1971)
%CO_2	3.6	3.8	2.6	1.8	5.5	5.5

TABLE 2.—X-RAY FLUORESCENCE ANALYSIS OF AUTHIGENIC AND DIAGENETIC PHOSPHATE-RICH MATERIALS

| | Diagenetic Phosphate Rock | Authigenic material from Saldanha Bay | | Authigenic material from South West Africa Bremner, 1978 |
		rock	pellets	
No. of analysis	36	2	1	4
SiO_2	18.34	50.12	4.15	4.97
Al_2O_3	1.79 (2.19)	1.25 (2.51)	1.73 (1.80)	1.12 (1.18)
Fe_2O_3[a]	7.12 (8.72)[b]	0.57 (1.14)[a]	1.77 (1.85)[b]	2.56 (2.89)[b]
MgO	1.33 (1.63)	0.20 (0.40)	0.28 (0.29)	0.83 (0.93)
CaO	38.12 (46.68)	24.49 (49.10)	46.97 (48.99)	46.93 (52.56)
Na_2O	0.80 (0.98)	0.18 (0.36)	0.68 (0.71)	0.50 (0.56)
K_2O	1.25 (1.53)	0.28 (0.56)	0.26 (0.27)	0.38 (0.40)
P_2O_5	16.87 (20.66)	17.45 (34.98)	33.16 (34.59)	28.04 (31.4)
S	0.40 (0.49)	1.82 (3.65)	0.17 (0.18)	2.31 (2.59)
F	2.25 (2.76)	1.80 (3.61)	3.44 (3.59)	3.2 (3.58)
CO_2	11.30 (13.83)	ND	3.81 (3.97)	3.6 (4.03)
C_{org}	0.43 (0.53)	1.28 (2.57)	ND	2.7 (3.02)
F/P_2O_5	0.13	0.10	0.10	0.11
CaO/P_2O_5	2.26	1.40	1.42	1.67

(a) Total Fe as Fe_2O_3 (b) Total Fe as FeO   ND Not determined
Figures in brackets are values expressed on a quartz-free basis.

traced by electron microprobe (Birch, in press b).

Bulk Geochemistry of Authigenic and Diagenetic Material

The bulk geochemistry of authigenic phosphate pellets from Saldanha Bay and South-west Africa are similar, except for a very much higher FeO, S and MgO content in the latter material (table 2). The abundant Fe and S indicate either an increased pyrite content and a more reducing environment off South-west Africa as compared to Saldanha Bay or that weathering and leaching of the latter onland deposit (cf. McArthur, 1978) has taken place. The reason for the higher Mg constituent is unclear.

In comparing the bulk chemical values for the authigenic pellets and rock from Saldanha, cognizance should be made of the 50 percent SiO_2 content of the latter material. Pellets contain more Na_2O and Fe_2O_3 than the rocks, whereas the latter are richer in Al_2O_3, MgO, K_2O and S. Depleted S in the pellets could be due to more severe weathering and leaching in the unconsolidated sediments and the higher concentration of lithopile elements (Al, Mg, K) in the rocks is due to the presence of terrigenous minerals (feldspars and clay minerals) in the sediment prior to lithification. The marginally higher Fe content of the pellets may be residual after oxidation of FeS.

A clear divergence exists in the whole rock chemistry of authigenic and diagenetic material (table 2). Abundant calcareous debris and glauconite result in higher Fe_2O_3, MgO, K_2O and CaO/P_2O_5 values for the latter rock type, whereas higher P_2O_5 and C_{org} and generally enhanced S values typify the reducing environment under which the authigenic material originated. F/P_2O_5 values for all samples are remarkably consistent.

Electron Microprobe Investigations

Electron microprobe analyses indicate that the chemical composition (taking into account the varying quartz abundance) of the authigenic phosphate pellets and rock from Saldanha Bay, from the western margin of South Africa, and from South-west Africa are very similar (table 3). The pellets from South-west Africa have the highest Fe and S (pyrite) content of the three regions, again emphasizing a more organic-rich paleo-environment of formation or indicating that oxidation has taken place during aerial weathering in the former two cases. The composition of the authigenic phosphate-rich rock from the South African shelf is distinctly different from the other authigenic material. It is distinguished by high Al, K and Na which is possibly due to a higher soda- and potash-feldspar content.

Higher Fe and S values of electron microprobe analyses of authigenic material and a slightly higher CaO/P_2O_5 ratio in rocks of the replacement type demonstrate the genetic divergence of these two material types.

TABLE 3.—MICROPROBE ANALYSIS OF AUTHIGENIC AND DIAGENETIC PHOSPHATE-RICH MATERIALS

	Matrix of diagenetic rock	Authigenic Rock		Authigenic Pellets		
		South African Shelf	Saldanha Bay	South African Shelf	Saldanha Bay	South West Africa (Bremner, 1978)
No. of analysis	26	3	5	20	7	31
SiO_2	5.42	12.06	2.46	5.11	3.38	2.70
Al_2O_3	1.72 (1.82)	3.93 (4.47)	1.27 (1.30)	1.40 (1.48)	1.39 (1.44)	1.11 (1.14)
$FeO^{(a)}$	1.09 (1.15)[b]	2.67 (3.04)	1.50 (1.54)	3.15 (3.32)	2.74 (2.84)	4.95 (5.09)
MgO	0.78 (0.82)	1.16 (1.32)	0.35 (0.36)	1.08 (1.14)	0.57 (0.59)	0.90 (0.92)
CaO	48.02 (50.77)	42.63 (48.48)	49.37 (50.62)	45.48 (47.93)	48.18 (49.87)	45.18 (46.43)
Na_2O	1.36 (1.44)	1.41 (1.60)	0.30 (0.31)	0.88 (0.93)	0.49 (0.51)	1.09 (1.12)
K_2O	0.40 (0.42)	0.91 (1.03)	0.32 (0.33)	0.51 (0.54)	0.35 (0.36)	0.34 (0.35)
P_2O_5	26.73 (28.26)	26.69 (30.35)	35.10 (35.99)	32.18 (23.91)	34.18 (35.38)	28.62 (29.41)
S	0.75 (0.79)	1.52 (1.73)	1.62 (1.66)	1.67 (1.76)	1.58 (1.64)	4.27 (4.39)
CaO/P_2O_5	1.80	1.60	1.41	1.41	1.41	1.58

(a) Total Fe as FeO   (b) Total Fe as Fe_2O_3
Figures in brackets are values expressed on a quartz-free basis

Element Distribution within Phosphatic Rocks and Pellets

Pelletal material is either internally structureless of exhibits well-defined concentric layering. Oolitic structures are defined by concentric rings of pyrite which are concordant with the pellet rim. Such layering never extends to the central-most part of the pellet. Increased K and Si at the rim of some pellets is evidence of incipient glauconitization. X-ray scans of Fe, S, Al and Si indicate that quartz, clay minerals and pyrite are randomly disseminated through some pellets which lack internal structure. The difference in the element distribution patterns of authigenic and diagenetic material is well illustrated by X-ray scans of phosphorite pellets which have been incorporated into the matrix of replaced phosphorites (fig. 3 E and F).

Qualitative studies using X-ray imagery indicate that the matrix of phosphatic rocks formed by replacement processes comprises a heterogeneous mixture of silt-sized quartz, micrite and finely divided glauconite (up to 5% K_2O). The microenvironment provided by foraminiferal tests is frequently a site for preferred authigenic mineral formation (Bjerkli and Östmo-Saeter, 1973). A study of foraminiferal tests (Birch, in press b) in the matrix of diagenetic material has supplied interesting new data on the formation of glauconite and apatite minerals. Foraminiferal tests are frequently filled by various mixtures of glauconite, apatite and quartz. The filling may be a homogeneous mixture of minerals or the composition may change regularly from chamber to chamber. The mineral particles could have entered the tests either as fragments or colloids of calcite and clay which subsequently altered to apatite and glauconite respectively or they may have been introduced as the latter mineral phases. However, the low K_2O content (<6% K_2O on a carbonate-free basis) of the infillings suggests that the material was still in the process of alteration at the time of burial.

In some areas foraminiferal tests are filled with highly ferruginous phosphatic mixtures (Fe_2O_3 ~30%; P_2O_5 ~16%). The majority of the Fe is not associated with K_2O (ie. non-glauconitic) or S (not pyritic), but occurs as a ferric hydroxophosphate. The fact that phosphate becomes bonded to Fe ions only under oxic, low pH conditions (Manheim et al., 1975) has environmental implications for rocks originating by replacement.

AGE OF PHOSPHATIZATION

Early attempts (Siesser, 1972; Dingle, 1971, 1973) at dating phosphate mineralization was made by association with other rock types. Dingle (1975) postulated two main phases of phosphatization for the diagenetic material on the Agulhas Bank, namely Early Eocene and late Miocene/early Pliocene.

Siesser (1978) refined these age estimates using planktonic foraminifera and calcareous nannoplankton in diagenetic phosphorites from 33 stations off the south and east coasts of southern Africa. Mineralization probably started during the Middle Miocene and continued into Pliocene times, but appears to have ceased prior to the Quaternary. Uranium isotope investigations (Kolodny and Kaplan, 1970) and electron microscope evidence (Baturin and Dubinshuk, 1974) indicate no recent phosphate diagenesis.

The age postulated by Bremner (1978) for the authigenic pelletal deposits off South-west Africa based on correlation with firmly dated, equivalent lithofacies to the south is Middle to Late Miocene. Concretionary phosphorite in the diatomaceous muds has been dated (Veeh, *et al.*, 1974) radiometrically from modern to 74,105 years, whereas Baturin *et al.* (1972) obtained ages of approximately 24×10^3 years for the friable material. Small quantities of concretionary phosphorite is believed (Bremner, 1978) to be forming in this environment at the present day.

Several lines of evidence have led Tankard (1975) to suggest a Miocene age for the onland phosphorite-bearing Saldanha Formation. Diagnostic fossils are a well-rounded Miocene shark tooth, an early Miocene penguin and a Miocene assemblage of molluscan fauna. Mineralization occurred during a 55 meter transgression.

A MODEL FOR THE PENECONTEMPORANEOUS FORMATION OF MARINE APATITES BY AUTHIGENIC AND DIAGENETIC MECHANISMS

A model is proposed in this work to explain the various phosphate types occurring on the western margin of southern Africa in terms of penecontemporaneous formation by both authigenic and replacement mechanisms.

The paleo-environment under which phosphatization occurred on the open shelf (fig. 7) has been reconstructed from studies of Tertiary sediments (Dingle, 1971, 1973, 1975) and phosphatic rocks (Birch, 1975). The regional distribution of phosphates indicates an association with upwelling of cold, nutrient-rich South Atlantic Central Water (Clowes, 1950) and related high biological activity. Diffuse, subsurface upwelling in the zone of divergence between the oceanic South East Trade Wind Drift and the Benguela Current System results in an increased nutrient content and

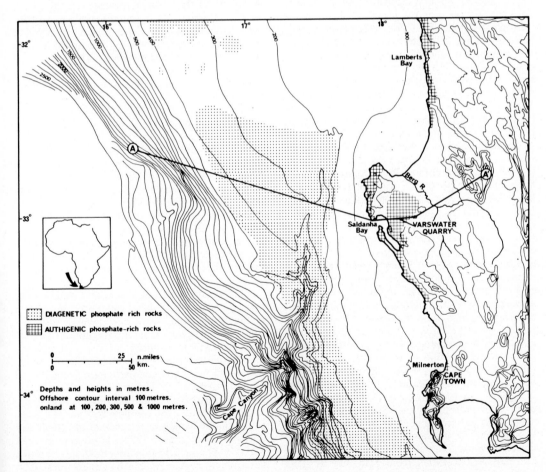

FIG. 7.—Regions of diagenetic and authigenic phosphate formation on the western margin of southern Africa (see fig. 9 for schematic representation of section A-A').

enhanced biological productivity over the outer shelf and slope (Bang, 1971, 1973; Hart and Curry, 1960).

The prime genetic process involved in the formation of phosphatic rock on the Agulhas Bank and off the west coast of South Africa is considered to be the replacement of calcium carbonate by calcium phosphate (Parker and Siesser, 1972; Parker, 1975; Birch, 1979b). This process has been documented by careful surface-to-center analyses of phosphatized limestones both by bulk chemical (Parker, 1971) and micro-chemical (Birch, 1975) methods. It has been determined (Ames, 1959) that a concentration of only 1μg at. P/1 (0.1 ppm PO_4^{-3}) in saline solution will be sufficient to initiate the replacement process and the total concentration of orthophosphates in most sea water is 0.7μg at. P/1 (0.07 ppm PO_4^{-3}) (Brewer, 1975). It would therefore not require a radical change in the phosphate content of sea-water for mineralization to be implemented, if other physico-chemical conditions were suitable. Low pH and oxic conditions are suggested by the presence of iron oxide (goethite) cement and ferric hydroxo-phosphate infillings of foraminifera, whereas reducing microenvironments are indicated by pyrite in foraminiferal tests. These conditions are similar to those reported for phosphorites from other parts of the world (Summerhayes, 1970; Parker, 1971). The source of the phosphate is generally considered to be the phosphorus liberated by decaying protoplasm of marine organisms. Some episodes of phosphatization on the Agulhas Bank can be related to periods of prolific biogenic productivity (eg. phosphatized foraminiferal limestones), but no evidence is available for contemporaneous biogenic activity in other phosphatic rocks (eg. in the glauconite-rich conglomeratic and arenaceous types. See fig. 1). In the latter case, mineralization was by replacement of minor quantities of completely degraded (micron-size), organically-poor (<0.5% C_{org}; Birch, 1975) calcareous debris (micrite). Phosphatized foraminiferal pebbles exhibiting concordant phosphatized margins also indicate that mineralization was after or contemporaneous with reworking and unrelated to high biogenic activity. Sufficient phosphorus may have been liberated by biogenic decay to cause phosphatization of foraminiferal sediment relatively rich (up to 2% C_{org}) in organic matter, but the phosphorus required to replace micrite in the latter two cases was derived from a source other than protoplasm (cf. Siesser, 1978). The average phosphate content of upwelled water is 2μg at. P/1 (~0.2 ppm) (Spencer, 1975) and upwelled water on the slope and shelf around southern Africa varies from 1 to 3μg at. P/1 (~0.1 to 0.3 ppm) (Hart and Curry, 1960; Mostert, 1966; Calvert and Price, 1971; De Decker, 1970a,b;

Drs. M. J. Orren and G. Eagle, pers. comm., 1978), ie. up to three times the minimum PO_4^{-3} concentration required to initiate diagenetic phosphatization. As the replacement process is temperature dependent (Ames, 1959), it is possible that the absence of modern-day mineralization (Baturin and Dubinshuk, 1974) is due to the low temperatures (~9.0 C) associated with nutrient-rich bottom water (De Decker, 1970a). The Agulhas Bank is wide (~110 km) and very flat (~0.026°) and therefore extensive parts of it would have been covered by shallow and even pooled water during Tertiary sea level lows. It is suggested that during these periods phosphorus-rich upwelled water (Shannon, 1966) was moved onto the Bank by the prevailing onshore wind and sufficiently heated by solar radiation for phosphate diagenesis to be initiated. With a retreating sea, successively deeper zones of the Agulhas Bank became suitable for mineralization. This would account for the frequent association of phosphatic rock with regressive/transgressive cycles (Pasho, 1972; Summerhayes, 1970). Phosphatization of the upper layers (~0.5 m) of the bottom sediment produced a near-continuous 'pavement' of phosphatic rock. The finely dispersed glauconite component of phosphatic rocks resulted from an enrichment of Fe in the sediment by biogenous input (Martin and Knauer, 1973) and glauconitization of the clay particles in the bottom sediment (Birch, in press b).

The conglomeratic textures originated when the phosphatized bottom sediment was reworked during a succeeding transgression. Renewed carbonate deposition and a further period of phosphatization occurred when the zones of deposition moved back across the shelf. The disaggregated phosphatic pebbles then became incorporated into the second generation rocks. The two regressive cycles required for the formation of conglomeratic phosphate-rich rocks is compatible with stratigraphic data obtained from the rock record (Siesser and Dingle, in press).

In proposing authigenic apatite formation by interstitial growth, pelletal accretion and direct precipitation from sea-water several physico-chemical constraints must be overcome.

The conditions required for the precipitation of apatite from sea-water are similar to those that would favor calcium carbonate precipitation (Gulbrandsen, 1969). The presence of Mg^{2+} ions also inhibits the precipitation process, probably because the Mg^{2+} ions compete for the Ca^{2+} sites in the apatite structure (Bachra et al., 1965 and Martens and Harriss, 1970). However, Brooks et al. (1968) and Berner et al. (1970) have shown that calcium carbonate can be supersaturated in pore waters without precipitating due to the inhibiting effect of organic matter. Moreover, Burnett

(1977) and Atlas (1975) show that the Ca/Mg ratio could be increased above the threshold for apatite precipitation by certain diagenetic reactions or combination of reactions in pore waters, eg. Mg^{2+} replacing Fe^{3+} in clays, dolomitization or formation of Mg-rich silicates.

Extensive open-pit mining and detailed paleontological work (Hendey, 1974, 1976, 1978; Dingle *et al.*, in press) has provided accurate paleo-environmental control for the authigenic phosphorite deposits of the Saldanha Bay area. The phosphates were derived from within the confines of a shallow, restricted estuary during a 55 meter transgression (Tankard, 1974a). Decay of vast quantities of organic matter and an enrichment in P is indicated by the presence of abundant organic matter in the phosphorite pellets (Tankard, 1974a). Upwelling, high productivity and periodic mass mortality of phytoplankton occur in this region at the present-day (Clowes, 1954; Shannon, 1966; De Decker, 1970a,b; Bang, 1973; Birch, 1977b) and, although not as intense, this environment is similar to the upwelled inshore waters off South-west Africa where modern-day concretionary apatite is forming within diatomaceous muds (Baturin, 1969, 1971, 1972; Bremner, 1978; Price and Calvert, 1978). It is estimated (Tankard and Rogers, in press) that the paleo-environment of the Saldanha Region during the southerly shift of climatic zones in the Miocene (Tankard, 1974a,

1975) resembled that of present-day South-west Africa.

It is envisaged (Birch, in press a) that the authigenic phosphorites of Saldanha were derived within a sheltered estuary adjacent to a region of intense, wind-generated upwelling and high biological productivity. Phytoplankton would decay, releasing vast quantities of P to the seawater. The offshore wind generating the upwelling would also act to move the surface waters of the estuary seawards and thus P-rich upwelled water would be drawn into the estuary enhancing its already high phosphorus level. Increased solar heating during low tide in summer may be sufficient to increase water temperature in the shallow intertidal areas of the estuary above the solubility limit of apatite at a time when upwelling and P-generation was also at a maximum. Generally higher sea-water temperatures (Arrhenius, 1963) during the Miocene and possibly the action of micro-organisms, especially algae and some enzymes (Charles, 1953; McConnell, 1965) facilitated optimum conditions for the genesis of apatite.

The grain-supported fabric of the phosphatic packestones of Saldanha indicates that apatite precipitated or grew interstitially (fig. 8), whereas rocks composed of fine (5–30 cm), varve-like layers of virtually pure phosphate (fig. 2a) imply a cyclic precipitation of apatite directly from the water column. Differences in morphology, inter-

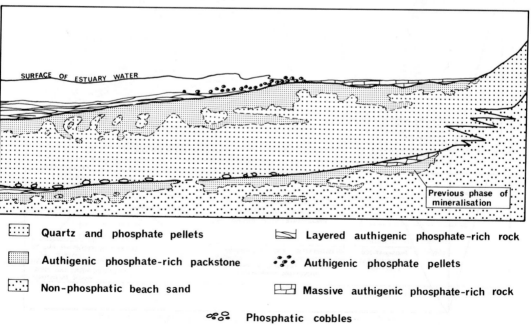

SURFACE OF ESTUARY WATER

Previous phase of mineralisation

Quartz and phosphate pellets

Authigenic phosphate-rich packstone

Non-phosphatic beach sand

Layered authigenic phosphate-rich rock

Authigenic phosphate pellets

Massive authigenic phosphate-rich rock

Phosphatic cobbles

FIG. 8.—The mode of formation envisaged for the massive and layered phosphatic rocks as well as for the phosphate pellets and phosphate-rich packstones from Saldanha Bay.

Peninsula (fig. 10). Nutrient-rich water is drawn shorewards over the shelf during periods (April to June) of prolonged upwelling and the associated high biological productivity contributes large volumes of organic detritus to the sea floor.

Black ovoidal, structureless pellets (125–250μm) and biogenous phosphatic particles contain diatom fragments, quartz, feldspar and pyrite with minor clay minerals including glauconite. The particles are subrounded to rounded and well sorted and are most abundant (15–20% apatite by weight) in the sands of the middle bay and in adjacent lagoons.

Abundant 'nodular' phosphate pebbles occur on the flat-topped offshore banks at 100–200 m depth. These deposits have formed by the phosphatization of foraminiferal limestone of Miocene age and of some dolomite.

The phosphogenic province of Baja California is strikingly similar to that off the west coast of southern Africa. Phosphatization of foraminiferal limestone with accompanying glauconite deposits on the outer shelf and phosphate pellets in the nearshore and in lagoons bordering the coast is a distribution pattern exactly analogous to the African occurrence.

Moroccan Phosphogenic Province.—The description of Moroccan phosphorites given below is taken from Tooms and Summerhayes (1968); Summerhayes (1970); Summerhayes et al. (1973); and McArthur (1978).

Three main phosphatic rock types occur on the Moroccan continental shelf, ie. glauconite-rich conglomerates, pellets and phosphatized limestones. The conglomerates comprise phosphatized limestone pebbles in a matrix of partially phosphatized lime mud containing glauconite, quartz, foraminifera and argillaceous material. Pelletal phosphorites are made up of sand-sized apatite pellets enclosed in a partially phosphatized lime mud. The pellets are generally structureless, but regionally up to 20 percent can be oolitic or exhibit concentric layering. The center is commonly rich in organic matter and nuclei are of quartz, calcite, dolomite rhombohedra and foraminifera.

Mineralization of foraminiferal limestones and conglomerates took place by replacement of calcareous material in regions remote from detrital sources at moderate and shallow depths respectively. Abundant iron oxide indicates oxidizing conditions, whereas pyritic foraminiferal infillings suggest reducing conditions in microenvironments. Although many of the pellets are considered to have formed by replacement, Summerhayes notes that growth rims around grains and oolitic structures must represent a mechanism of primary authigenic accretion.

The onshore Moroccan phosphorites are mainly well-sorted pelletal ooliths with nuclei of quartz and calcite (Salvan, 1952, 1957; Visse, 1948, 1953 in Summerhayes, 1970). The non-phosphatic components are quartz (with the same size distribution as the pellets), foraminifera, radiolaria, diatoms and vertebrate remains. Glauconite is absent.

Summerhayes postulates a lagoonal environment for the unconsolidated pelletal phosphorite deposits and an open shelf origin for the glauconitic and foraminiferal phosphorite rocks. The nature and distribution of the Moroccan deposits are therefore closely parallel to that on the western margin of southern Africa.

It is clear that similarities exist in the nature, genesis, and environment of formation for the phosphorite deposits of Baja Peninsula, Morocco and the south-western margin of Africa. These examples are not isolated occurrences. A voluminous literature exists in which pelletal phosphorite is associated with a shallow, restricted lagoonal environment and also with reworking and high energy regimes, eg. Florida (Riggs and Freas, 1965; Freas and Riggs, 1968; Trueman, 1971); the west and east coasts of North America (Galliher, 1931; Hoots, 1931; Dickert, 1966; Pevear, 1966; Pevear and Pilkey, 1966; Gibson, 1967; Rooney and Kerr, 1967), as well as from other onland deposits (Visse, 1948; Cayeux, 1941; Steinitz, 1976). Similarly, the relationship between calcareous (zooplankton), open shelf sediments and replacement type phosphorites (conglomeratic and arenaceous) is also widespread, eg. off Spain and Portugal (Nutter, 1969; Lucas and Prévôt, 1975; Lucas et al. 1978) and New Zealand (Pasho, 1976; Cullen, 1978).

SYNTHESIS

Authigenic phosphorite and phosphate-rich materials form in shallow, restricted lagoonal or estuarine environments, in low latitudes (<40°) adjacent to a hot and arid hinterland. Intense, wind-induced upwelling of nutrient-rich water results in the generation of vast quantities of siliceous phytoplankton which, on decay, greatly enrich the bottom water in phosphates. Apatite is precipitated directly from the water column to form layered or massive phosphorites, or apatite may grow or precipitate within interstices in the sediment to form phosphatic packstones. Phosphate pellets probably form by accretion at the water/sediment interface if suitable nuclei are available or granular material may be produced by fragmentation of newly formed phosphatic packstone during periodic storms. The authigenic process is greatly facilitated by solar heating in the shallow lagoonal environment, by reduced terrigenous supply and possibly by the activity of microorganisms.

Phosphorites and phosphate-rich sediments formed diagenetically are located on open shelves and offshore topographic highs (banks, ridges, seamounts) which are dominated by carbonate sedimentation. The deposition of calcareous zooplankton is related to diffuse, divergent upwelling of water rich in nutrients. Lime mud mantling the sea floor is phosphatized and all the components of the bottom sediment are lithified into a thin, near-continuous capping of phosphate-rich rock. Diagenetic phosphorites are commonly associated with eustatic/tectonic instability of continental margins (Summerhayes, 1970; Pasho, 1972; Parker, 1975; Cullen, 1978; Birch, 1979b) and with unconformities in the rock record. Since the phosphate content of upwelled water is frequently above that required for initiation of diagenetic phosphatization, other factors must be critical to the formation of these rocks. The replacement process is temperature dependent and therefore increased solar radiation in the shoaling waters of transgressive and regressive seas may have facilitated mineralization on wide, flat-lying shelves where diagenetic phosphorites predominate. These conditions, combined with generally warmer seas of the mid-Tertiary (Tooms *et al.*, 1969), may account for the apparent increase in phosphate mineralization during this period (Summerhayes, 1970).

A mixing of authigenic and diagenetic forms of phosphorite may occur during transgressive/regressive cycles due to superimposition of environmental regimes.

ACKNOWLEDGEMENTS

The writer is indebted to the Director of the Geological Survey of South Africa, Dr. W. L. van Wyk, for permission to use and publish data contained in the present work. Diagrams were prepared by Ms. S. Sayers and Ms. S. Smith; Mr. C. Basson undertook the photography; and the typing was done by Mrs. G. Krummeck. This assistance is sincerely appreciated. Dr. J. M. Bremner kindly read an early draft of the manuscript and made useful comments and suggestions.

REFERENCES

ALTSCHULER, Z. A., CLARKE, R. S., AND YOUNG, E. J., 1958, Geochemistry of uranium in apatite and phosphorite: U.S. Geol. Surv. Prof. Paper 314-D, p. 45–90.

AMES, L. L., 1959, The genesis of carbonate apatites: Econ. Geology, v. 54, p. 829–841.

ARRHENIUS, G. O., 1963, Pelagic sediments, *in* M. N. Hill (ed.), The Sea, v. 3, Interscience Publishers, N.Y., p. 655–727.

ATLAS, E. L., 1975, Phosphate equilibria in seawater and interstitial waters: Unpubl. Ph.D. thesis, Oregon State Univ., 154 p.

BACHRA, B. N., TRAUTZ, O. R., AND SIMON, S. L., 1965, Precipitation of calcium carbonates-III; the effect of magnesium and fluoride ions on the spontaneous precipitation of calcium carbonate and phosphates: Arch. Oral. Biol., v. 10, p. 731–738.

BANG, N. D., 1971, The Southern Benguela Current region in February, 1966. Part II. Bathythermography and air-sea interactions: Deep-sea Res., v. 18, p. 209–224.

———, 1973, Characteristics of an intense ocean frontal system in the upwelled regime west of Cape Town: Tellus, v. 25, no. 3, p. 256–265.

BATURIN, G. N., 1969, Authigenic phosphate concentrations in Recent sediments of the Southwest African shelf: Dokl. Earth Sci. Sect. English Transl., v. 189, p. 227–230.

———, 1971, Formation of phosphate sediments and water dynamics: Oceanology, v. 11, p. 372–376.

———, 1972, Phosphorus in interstitial waters of sediments of the southeastern Atlantic: Oceanology, v. 12, no. 6, p. 849–855.

———, Merkulova, K. I., and Chalov, P. I., 1972, Radiometric evidence for recent formation of phosphatic nodules in marine shelf sediments: Marine Geol., v. 13, no. 3, p. M37–M41.

———, AND DUBINSHUK, V. T., 1974, Microstructures of Agulhas Bank phosphorites: Marine Geol., v. 16, p. M63–M70.

BERNER, R. A., SCOTT, M. R., AND THOMLINSON, C., 1970, Carbonate alkalinity in the pore waters of anoxic marine sediments: Limnol. Oceanog., v. 15, p. 544–549.

BIRCH, G. F., 1975, Sediments on the continental margin off the west coast of South Africa: Unpubl. Ph.D. thesis, Univ. Cape Town, 210 p.

———, 1977a, Phosphorites from the Saldanha Bay region of South Africa: Roy. Soc. S. Afr., v. 42, p. 223–240.

———, 1977b, Surficial sediments on the continental margin off the west coast of South Africa: Marine Geol., v. 23, p. 305–337.

———, 1979a, The nature and origin of mixed glauconite/apatite pellets from the continental margin off South Africa: Marine Geol., v. 29, p. 313–334.

———, 1979b, Phosphatic rocks on the western margin of South Africa: Jour. Sed. Pet., v. 49, p. 93–110.

———, in press a, Phosphorite pellets and rock from the western continental margin and adjacent coastal terrace of South Africa: Marine Geol.

———, in press b, The association of glauconite and apatite minerals in phosphatic rocks from the South African continental margin: Trans. Geol. Soc. S. Afr.

BJERKLI, K., AND ÖSTMO-SAETER, J. S., 1973, Formation of glauconie in foraminiferal shells on the continental shelf off Norway: Marine Geol., v. 14, p. 169–178.

BREMNER, J. M., 1975, Faecal pellets, glauconite, phosphorite and bedrock from the Kunene-Walvis continental margin: GSO/UCT Mar. Geol. Prog. Tech. Rept., Geol. Dept. Univ. of Cape Town, v. 7, p. 59–68.

————, 1978, Sediments on the continental margin off South West Africa between Sylvia Hill and the Kunene River: Unpubl. Ph.D. thesis, Univ. Cape Town, 310 p.

BREWER, R. G., 1975, Minor elements in sea water, in Chemical Oceanography (ed.) Riley, J. P. AND G. Skirrow, 2nd edition, v. 1, p. 415–491, Academic Press, London, 606 p.

BROOKS, R. R., PRESLEY, B. J., AND KAPOLAN, I. R., 1968, Trace elements in the interstitial waters of marine sediments: Geochim. Cosmochim. Acta, v. 32, p. 397–414.

BURNETT, W. C., 1977, Geochemistry and origin of phosphorite deposits from off Peru and Chile: Geol. Soc. Amer. Bull., v. 88, p. 813–823.

BUSHINSKY, G. I., 1969, Old phosphorites of Asia and their genesis: Israel Progr. Sci. Trans., Jerusalem, 266 p.

CALVERT, S. E., AND PRICE, N. B., 1971, Upwelling and nutrient regeneration in the Benguela Current, October, 1968: Deep-Sea Res., v. 18, p. 505–523.

CARRINGTON, A. J., AND KENSLEY, B. F., 1969, Pleistocene molluscs from the Namaqualand coast: Ann. S. Afr. Mus., v. 52, no. 9, p. 189–223.

CAYEUX, L., 1934, The phosphatic nodules of the Agulhas Bank: Ann. S. Afr. Mus., v. 31, p. 105–136.

————, 1941, Etudes des Gites Minéraux de la France; Les phosphates de chaux sédimentaires de France (métropolitaine et d'outremer): no. 2, Serv. Carte Géol. de France (Paris).

CHARLES, G., 1953, Sur l'origine des gisements de phosphates de chaux sédimentaires: 10th Int. Geol. Congr., v. 11, p. 163–184.

CLOWES, A. J., 1954, The South African pilchard (Sardinops ocellata); the temperature, salinity and inorganic phosphate content of the surface layer near St. Helena Bay, 1950–1952: Invest. Rept. Div. Fish. S. Afr., v. 16, p. 1–47.

————, 1950, An introduction to the hydrology of South African waters: Invest. Rept. Fish. Mar. Biol. Surv. Div. Un. S. Afr., v. 12, 42 p.

COLLET, L. W., 1905, Les concrétions phosphatées de l'Agulhas-Bank: Proc. Roy. Soc. Edin., v. 25, p. 862–893.

CULLEN, D. J., 1978, The distribution of submarine phosphorite deposits on the central Chatham Rise, east of New Zealand: N. Z. Oceanographic Institute Oceanogr. Fld. Rept., v. 12, 29 p.

D'ANGLEJAN, B. R., 1965, The marine deposit of Baja California, Mexico: Present environment and Recent history: Unpubl. Ph.D. thesis, Univ. California, San Diego, 196 p.

————, 1967, Origin of marine phosphorites off Baja California, Mexico: Marine Geol., v. 5, p. 15–44.

DE DECKER, A. H. B., 1970a, Notes on the oxygen-depleted sub-surface current off the west coast of South Africa: Invest. Rept. Div. Fish. S. Afr., v. 84, p. 1–24.

————, 1970b, An oxygen-depleted sub-surface current off the west coast of South Africa: Invest. Rept. Sea Fish, Div. S. Afr., v. 84, p. 1–24.

DICKERT, P. F., 1966, Tertiary phosphatic facies of the coast range, in Bailey, (ed.), Geology of northern California: California Div. Mines and Geology Bull., v. 190, p. 289–304.

DIETZ, R. S., EMERY, K. O., AND SHEPARD, F. P., 1942, Phosphorite deposits on the sea floor off southern California: Bull. Geol. Soc. Amer., v. 53, p. 815–848.

DINGLE, R. V., 1971, Tertiary sedimentary history of the continental shelf off southern Cape Province, South Africa: Trans. Geol. Soc. S. Afr., v. 74, p. 173–186.

————, 1973, Post-Palaeozoic stratigraphy of the eastern Agulhas Bank, South African continental margin: Marine Geol., v. 15, p. 1–23.

————, 1975, Agulhas Bank phosphorites: a review of 100 years of investigation: Trans. Geol. Soc. S. Afr., v. 77, p. 261–264.

————, LORD, A. R., AND HENDEY, Q. B., in press, New sections in the Varswater Formation (Neogene) of Langebaan Road, South-western Cape: Trans. Geol. Soc. S. Afr.

DU PLESSIS, A., AND BIRCH, G. F., 1977, The nature of the sea floor south of Cape Seal in a block bound by the longitudes 23°15′E and 23°35′E and latitudes 34°10′S and 34°25′S: GSO/UCT Mar. Geol. Prog. Bull., no. 9, p. 75–85, Geol. Dept. Univ. of Cape Town.

FREAS, D. H., AND RIGGS, S. R., 1968, Environments of phosphorite deposition in the Central Florida phosphate district, in Brown, L. F. (ed.), Proc. 4th Forum Geology of Industrial Minerals, Bureau of Econ. Geol. Univ. Texas, Austin, p. 117–128.

GALLIHER, E. W., 1931, Collophane from Miocene brown shales of California: Am. Assoc. Petroleum Geologists Bull., v. 15, p. 257–269.

GIBSON, T. G., 1967, Stratigraphic palaeoenvironments of the phosphate Miocene strata of North Carolina: Bull. Geol. Soc. Am., v. 78, no. 5, p. 631–650.

GULBRANDSEN, R. A., 1969, Physical and chemical factors in the formation of marine apatite: Econ. Geol., v. 64, no. 4, p. 365–382.

————, 1970, Relation of carbon dioxide content of apatite of Phosphoria Formation to regional facies: U.S. Geol. Surv. Prof. Paper 700-B, p. B9–B13.

HART, T. J., AND CURRY, R. I., 1960, The Benguela Current: Discovery Rept., v. 31, p. 123–298.

HENDEY, Q. B., 1974, The Late Cenozoic Carnivora of the south-western Cape Province: Annals S. Afr. Museum, v. 63, p. 1–369.

————, 1976, The Pliocene fossil occurrences in 'E' Quarry, Langebaanweg, South Africa: Annals S. Afr. Museum, v. 69, p. 215–247.

————, 1978, The age of the fossils from Baard's Quarry, Langebaanweg, South Africa: Annals S. Afr. Museum, v. 75, p. 1–24.

Hoots, H. W., 1931, Geology of the eastern part of the Santa Monica Mountains, Los Angeles County, California: U.S. Geol. Survey Prof. Paper 165-C, p. 83–134.

Kazakov, A. V., 1937, The phosphorite facies and the genesis of phosphorites, *in* Geological investigations of agricultural ores USSR, Leningrad Scientific Instit. Fertilizers and Insecto-Fungicides Trans., v. 142, p. 95–115.

Kolodny, Y., and Kaplan, I. R., 1970, Uranium isotopes in sea-floor phosphorites: Geochim. Cosmochim. Acta, v. 34, p. 3–24.

Lucas, J., and Prevot, L., 1975, Les marges continentales pièges géochimiques; l'example de la marge atlantique de l'Afrique à la limite Crétacé-Tertiaire: B.S.G.F., 7, no. 4, p. 496–501.

————, ————, and Lamboy, M., 1978, Les phosphorites de la marge nord de l'Espagne, Chimie, minéralogie, genèse: Oceanologica Acta, v. 1, no. 1, p. 55–72.

Manheim, P., Rowe, G. T., and Jipa, D., 1975, Marine phosphorite formation off Peru: Jour. Sed. Pet., v. 45, no. 1, p. 243–252.

Martens, C. S., and Harriss, R. C., 1970, Inhibition of apatite precipitation in the marine environment by magnesium ions: Geochim. Cosmochim. Acta, v. 34, p. 621–625.

Martin, J. H., and Knauer, G. A., 1973, The elemental composition of plankton: Geochim. Cosmochim. Acta, v. 37, p. 1639–1653.

McArthur, J. M., 1978, Systematic variations in the contents of Na, Sr, CO_3 and SO_4 in marine carbonate-fluorapatite and their relation to weathering: Chem. Geol., v. 21, p. 89–112.

McConnell, D., 1965, Precipitation of phosphates in sea water: Econ. Geol., v. 60, p. 1059–1062.

McKelvey, V. E., Swanson, R. W., and Sheldon, R. P., 1953, The Permian phosphorite deposits of western United States: 19th Internat. Geol. Cong., Algiers, 1952, Comptes Rendus., sec. II, pt. 11, p. 45–64.

Mostert, S. A., 1966, Distribution of inorganic phosphate and dissolved oxygen in the south west Indian Ocean: Invest. Rept. Div. Sea Fish. S. Afr., v. 54, p. 1–24.

Murray, J., and Renard, A. F., 1891, Deep-sea Deposits: Rept. Sci. Res. HMS Challenger 1873–1876. HMSO, London, 525 p.

————, and Philippi, E., 1908, Die Grundproben der deutschen Tiefsee Expedition 1898–1899 auf dem Dampfer "Valdivia": Wiss. Ergeb. Dtsch. Tiefsee-Exped., v. 10, Jena, p. 181–187.

Nutter, A. H., 1969, The origin and distribution of phosphate in marine sediments from the Moroccan and Portuguese continental margins: Unpubl. D.I.C. thesis, Univ. London, 158 p.

Parker, R. J., 1971, The petrography and major element geochemistry of phosphorite nodule deposits on the Agulhas Bank, South Africa: SANCOR Mar. Geol. Prog. Bull. no. 2, Dept. Geol. Univ. Cape Town, 92 p.

————, 1975, The petrology and origin of some glauconitic and glauco-conglomeratic phosphorites from the South African continental margin: Jour. Sed. Pet., v. 45, no. 1, p. 230–242.

————, and Siesser, W. G., 1972, Petrology and origin of some phosphorites from the South African continental margin: Jour. Sed. Pet., v. 42, p. 434–440.

Pasho, D. W., 1972, Character and origin of marine phosphorites: Geol. Dept. Univ. of Southern California, Geol. Publication, v. 72-S, p. 1–88.

————, 1976, Distribution and morphology of Chatham Rise phosphorites: N.Z. Oceanographic Institute. Memoir, v. 77, 28 p.

Pevear, D. R., 1966, The estuarine formation of United States Atlantic coastal plain phosphorite: Econ. Geology, v. 61, p. 251–256.

————, and Pilkey, O. H., 1966, Phosphorite in Georgia continental shelf sediments: Bull. Geol. Soc. Am., v. 77, p. 849–858.

Price, N. B., and Calvert, S. E., 1978, The geochemistry of phosphorites from the Namibian shelf: Chem. Geol., v. 23, no. 2, p. 151–171.

Riggs, S. R., and Freas, D. H., 1965, Stratigraphy and sedimentation of phosphorites in the Central Florida Phosphorite District: Am. Inst. Min. Metall. Petrol. Engrs., Preprint no. 65H84, p. 1–17.

Rogers, J., 1977, Sedimentation on the continental margin off the Orange River and the Namib Desert: Unpubl. Ph.D. thesis, Geol. Dept. Univ. Cape Town, 220 p.

Rooney, T. P., and Kerr, P. F., 1967, Mineralogic nature and origin of phosphorite, Beaufort County, North Carolina: Geol. Soc. Amer. Bull., v. 78, p. 731–748.

Salvan, H. M., 1952, Phosphates, *in* Géologie des Gites Minéraux Marocains, 19th Internat. Geol. Congr., Algiers, Monogr. Regionales Sér. 3, Maroc. no. 1.

————, 1957, Les rapports entre facteurs tectoniques et la sédimentation phosphatée dans les gisements Marocains: Compt. Rend. 20th Internat. Geol. Congr. Mexico, 1956, sect. 5, p. 347–354.

Shackleton, N. J., and Kennett, J. P., 1975, Palaeotemperature history of the Cenozoic and the initiation of Antarctic glaciation: oxygen and carbonate isotope analysis in DSDP sites 277, 279 and 281: Init. Rep. Deep Sea Drill. Proj., v. XXIX, p. 743–755.

Shannon, L. V., 1966, Hydrology of the south and west coasts of South Africa: Invest. Rept. Div. Sea Fish. S. Afr., v. 58, p. 1–62.

SIESSER, W. G., 1972, Limestone lithofacies from the South African continental margin: Sediment. Geol., v. 8, p. 83–112.

———, 1978, Age of phosphorites on the South African continental margin: Marine Geol., v. 26, p. M17–M28.

———, AND DINGLE, R. V., in press, Tertiary sea-level movements around southern Africa: A.A.P.G.

SIMPSON, D. R., 1964, The nature of the alkali carbonate apatites: Amer. Min. v. 49, p. 363–376.

SPENCER, C. P., 1975, The micronutrient elements, *in* Chemical Oceanography, 2nd ed., v. 2 (ed.) Riley, J. P. and Skirrow, G., p. 245–300.

STEINITZ, G., 1976, Palaeography of the Menuha and Mishash Formations in the eastern Ramon area: Isr. Jour. Earth Sci., v. 25, p. 70–75.

SUMMERHAYES, C. P., 1967, Marine environments of economic mineral deposition around New Zealand: A review: N.Z. J. Mar. Freshwater Res., v. 1, p. 267–282.

———, 1970, Phosphate deposits on the Northwest African continental shelf and slope: Unpubl. Ph.D. thesis, Univ. of London, 282 p.

———, 1972, Aspects of the mineralogy and geochemistry of Agulhas Bank sediments. Parts I and II: SANCOR Mar. Geol. Prog. Tech. Rept., Geol. Dept. Univ. of Cape Town, v. 4, p. 83–95.

———, 1973, Distribution, origin and economic potential of phosphatic sediments from the Agulhas Bank, South Africa: Trans. Geol. Soc. S. Afr., v. 76, p. 271–277.

———, BIRCH, G. F., ROGERS, J., AND DINGLE, R. V., 1973, Phosphate in the sediments off Southwestern Africa: Nature, v. 243, p. 509–511.

TANKARD, A. J. T., 1974a, Petrology of the phosphorite and aluminum phosphate rock of the Langebaanweg-Saldanha area, south-western Cape Province: Anns. S. Afr. Mus., v. 65, no. 8, p. 217–249.

———, 1974b, Chemical composition of the phosphorites from the Langebaanweg-Saldanha area, Cape Province: Trans. Geol. Soc. S. Afr., v. 77, p. 185–190.

———, 1975, The marine Neogene Saldanha Formation: Trans. Geol. S. Afr., v. 78, p. 257–264.

———, AND ROGERS, J., in press, Progressive late Cenozoic desiccation on the west coast of southern Africa: Jour. Biogeogr.

TOOMS, J. S., AND SUMMERHAYES, C. P., 1968, Phosphatic rocks from the north west African continental shelf: Nature, v. 218, p. 1241–1242.

———, ———, AND CRONAN, P. S., 1969, Geochemistry of marine phosphate and manganese deposits, *in* Oceanogr. Mar. Biol. Rev., (ed.) H. H. Barnes, v. 7, p. 49–100.

TRUEMAN, N. A., 1971, A petrological study of some sedimentary phosphorite deposits: Bull. Austral. Miner. Dev. Labs., v. 11, p. 1–65.

VEEH, H. H., CALVERT, S. E., AND PRICE, N. B., 1974, Accumulation of uranium in sediments and phosphorites on the South West African shelf: Marine Chemistry, v. 2, p. 189–202.

VISSE, L., 1948, Contribution à l'étude pétrographique des phosphates Moracains: Bull. Soc. Géol., France, Ser. 5, v. 18, p. 675–684.

———, 1953, Les faciès phosphatés: Rev. Inst. France Petr. Ann. Combust. Liqu., v. 7, p. 87–99.

SEPM Special Publication No. 29, p. 101–116, November 1980

PHOSPHORUS CONCENTRATIONS IN THE UNCONSOLIDATED SEDIMENTS OF THE TROPICAL ATLANTIC SHELF OF AFRICA SOUTH OF THE EQUATOR—OCEANOGRAPHIC COMMENTS

PIERRE GIRESSE
Département de Géologie, Université Marien N'Gouabi
P.O. Box 69, Brazzaville, R. P. Congo
present address: CRSM, Université de Perpignan, Avenue de Villeneuve, 66025 Perpignan, France

ABSTRACT

Upwelling which supplies nutrients and sediments from plankton has frequently been evoked in fossil phosphatogenesis. Upwelling is intense off the southern coast of Angola and off Namibia but declines toward the equator.

Fixation of phosphate is more important near the margin of the shelf than either nearer the coast or farther out; this fixation is particularly intense off Namibia.

The phytogenic or zoogenic nature of the organic matter seems irrelevant to phosphatogenesis in the alluvial oozes of the Congo. Oxidation of organic matter produces CO_2 which increases the solubility of phosphorus; thus too rapid sedimentation is unfavorable to phosphatogenesis; this situation obtains in the deltaic deposits.

Paleoclimatic and paleoceanographic variations in this area during the late Quaternary point to the role of temperature as an additional factor.

Within the fecal pellets of the Congo, P_2O_5 and organic carbon are eliminated as glauconitization progresses. If oxidation is very rapid, iron in the form of goethite and also phosphorus can be concentrated simultaneously, and this also occurs in some pellets and in certain sulfidic lagoonal silts. On the Namibian shelf, the pellets and all porous supports can evolve with equal ease towards phosphatogenesis (very advanced, in this case) as towards glauconitization.

In phosphatogenesis, two contradictory processes are, therefore, at work: strong concentrations of organic matter is a favorable, high rates of sedimentation an unfavorable factor. In basins of the open ocean, very rich in organic matter, the path of phosphatogenesis is the more likely one, wherever a scarcity of iron inhibits glauconitization.

INTRODUCTION

The Atlantic shelf of Africa south of the equator was, during the Holocene transgression, and still is, the site of various initial stages of phosphatogenesis. Several of the physico-chemical parameters controlling these processes can, sometimes very precisely, be determined by an analysis of the present aqueous environment as well as of the sediments now being formed and lithified. A study of this kind is helpful in the verification of hypotheses formulated to explain fossil sediments.

Only a short time ago, the only example of recent phosphatogenesis reported in the literature, concerned the Pacific shelf of America at the latitude of the Gulf of Tehuantepec (Kolodny, 1969).

The Atlantic shelves of South Africa, Southwest Africa (Namibia) and Angola present oceanic conditions nearly as favorable for phosphatogenesis as those of the west coast of the American continent. Emelyanov and Senin (1969) observed near the mouth of the Kunene River, at a water depth of 100 to 500 m, P_2O_5 contents in sediments of 0.22–4.25 percent (average 1.85%) in contrast to an average value of 0.34 percent for the remainder of the same depth sediments of the Atlantic African shelf. Later, it was shown (Emelyanov, 1973; Baturin and Dubintchuk, 1973 and Baturin, 1974) that one particular facies, the diatom ooze, is the most phosphorous (up to 27.88% P_2O_5) and that its deposition is contemporaneous with the Holocene transgression.

Toward the equator, the P-content clearly decreases, but our knowledge of the environmental sedimentary conditions is more precise here, permitting additional observations of processes taking place at present.

The Waters

The most common phosphate ion in sea water is HPO_4^{-2} (Ivanoff, 1972).

Deep waters (fig. 1)—The highest concentrations of phosphorus (2 to 3 mg at/m^3) in the Atlantic Ocean waters at depths between 1000 and 2000 m occur in the southern part near the Antarctic. During the southern winters, these 1000–2000 m deep waters spread northward along the west-African coast and constitute a rich reservoir (one of the richest in all the oceans) for the continental margin of Africa (Goldberg, 1960).

According to the general maps of the average

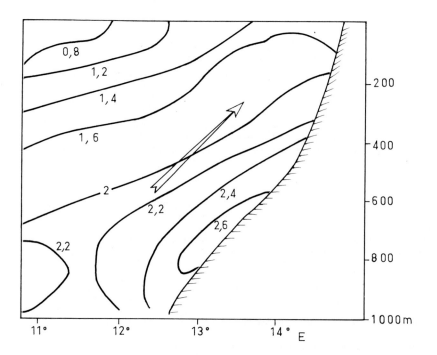

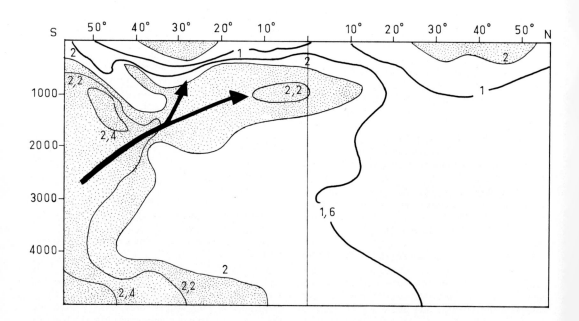

FIG. 1.—Top: P-content (mg atm/m³) off 24° S (Walvis); after E. D. Goldberg (1960). Bottom: Average P-distribution (mg atm/m³) in the Atlantic Ocean, N and S of equator; after E. D. Goldberg (1960); note higher P-contents S of equator.

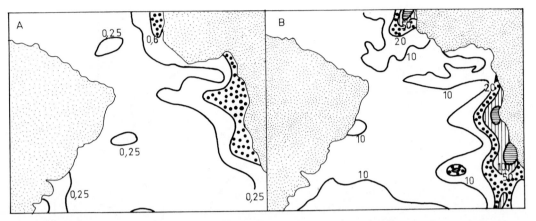

FIG. 2.—Content of dissolved phosphate and plankton density in the surface water of the S. Atlantic off the African coast (after A. Guilcher, 1965). A: Phosphate content (mg P_2O_5/m^3; B: Plankton density (1000 ind/l).

P—isopleths of Goldberg (1960), P-contents of 2.2 mg at/m^3 are found northward up to latitude 10° N between 500 and 1000 m, but on the surface of the southern hemisphere (except during occasional but very intense periods of upwelling) they exceed 2 mg at/m^3 only between 21° and 38°S. Thus, for the latitude of the Congo, the important consequences during Pleistocene glaciations of the spread of Antarctic intermediate and bottom waters to medium latitudes should be considered, as well as the oceanic dynamics thus generated.

Ascending Currents (fig. 2)—The ascending currents (upwelling) represent a classical mechanism by which intermediate waters highly concentrated in nutrient salts and particularly in phosphates are transported onto the shelves. It is generally agreed that these currents represent, directly and indirectly, one of the major sources of phosphorus for shelf and slope deposits.

It should, however, be pointed out that the synthesis of phosphate in the laboratory requires phosphate concentrations much higher than even those in these favorable waters. The natural concentrations of P_2O_5 in sea-water should, therefore, be considered in relation to the conditions of the environment or micro-environment which they create in the interstitial waters and in the sediments rather than by the degree of chemical saturation which they represent. If the concentration of P_2O_5 brought about by upwelling is insufficient to modify the environment, the area concerned is not more favorable than any other: a case in point is the area south of the Canary Islands, where P_2O_5-concentrations in the sediment even decrease in the area of maximum upwelling (Tooms et al., 1970).

Off the southwest African coast, upwelling brings water onto the shelf from a depth of 300–500 m in the south and of 150–200 m in the north (Simpson, 1970). Where upwelling reaches the zone of photosynthesis, a real biological explosion takes place (2–3 g/m^3 of plankton, i.e., about ten times the content of normal ocean water) (Senin, 1970).

The Shelf Waters (fig. 3)—The waters richest in phosphorus on the exterior margin of the shelf (between 150 and 215 m) correspond to areas where upwelling persists over a large part of the year. In the Atlantic Ocean off Africa south of the equator this frequency is related to large general movements of oceanic circulation for which Dufour and Stretta (1973) have proposed, for the months of November–December, the following picture described from north to south:

— **The South-Equatorial Current** is bordered to the north by the zone of north-equatorial convergence; here, between 1°N and 5°S the thermocline rises to 30 m attesting to an upwelling caused by a divergence of circulation directions. On both sides of this divergence, the primary productivity, as measured by the rate of carbon fixation, attains 0.6 g C/m^2/day and leads, among other manifestations, to a remarkable increase in the density of pelagic foraminifera: 4 ind/m^3.

— **The Tradewind Drift** between 5° and 8°S permits a drift of the coastal waters of Angola and the Congo toward the northwest, while simultaneously the deep waters rise onto the shelf where productivity is also equal to 0.6 C/m^2/day. This upwelling was observed off the Congo during the cold season by Berrit and Donguy (1959). The maps of Hentschel and Wattenberg (1930) show, at a depth of 50 m, a tongue of high phosphate contents which appears first along the coasts of

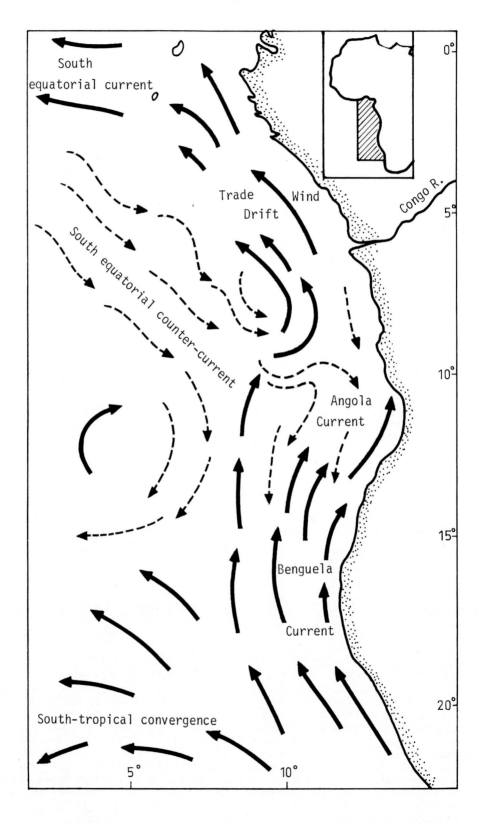

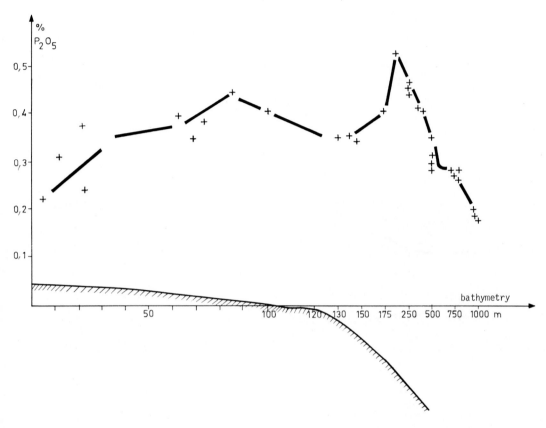

Fɪɢ. 4.—Distribution of P_2O_5 in sediments as function of water depth off the Congo coast.

Angola and the Congo, and extends westward until it merges with the rich waters of the equatorial divergence.

— The zone of **the Equatorial Countercurrent**, highly variable with the seasons, of which the Angola Current is the continuation; this zone between 8° and 12°S is the poorest with a productivity of less than 0.3 C/m²/day.

— The zone of **the Benguela Current** down to 16°S and then the subtropical convergence show higher productivities. Measurements are incomplete, but as far as known, values are constantly above 0.615 g C/m²/day. Seasonal concentrations of 2.5 g C/m²/day have periodically been measured at Benguela itself (Wooster and Reid, 1960).

During the southern winter, an important shift toward the north occurs (sometimes by 10° latitude) and the cold currents pushing northward may reach or pass the mouth of the Congo River.

North of Pointe-Noire, the average annual values are of the order of 0.5 g C/m²/day, i.e. equal to those of Abidjan (Dandonneau, 1973); but the proximity of the Congo estuary and the resultant higher turbidity of the waters are unfavorable for photosynthesis which should be more intense farther offshore. In the vicinity of the Congo estuary, where several of our measurements were made, the continental waters, like those of other tropical rivers, are relatively poor in nutrients (Dandonneau, 1973). Silica and organic matter, however, are plentiful and should favor a diatom bloom. The phosphates thus extracted by photosynthesis are rapidly returned to the ocean either by simple excretion or by bacterial action on the organic compounds of the organic matter which are quickly mineralized. As will be shown later in connection with phosphatogenesis, the phosphorus bound in and then liberated from organic matter is much more significant than the

Fɪɢ. 3.—Generalized circulation pattern during southern summer in the S. Atlantic off the African coast; after Moroshkin et al., 1970 and Dufour and Stretta, 1973.

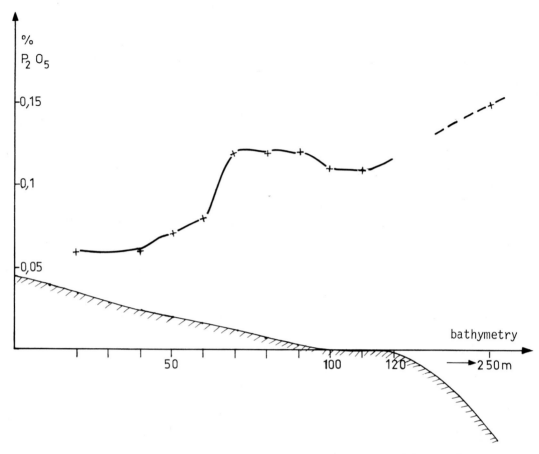

Fɪɢ. 5.—Distribution of P_2O_5 in sediments as function of water depth off the Ivory Coast.

mainly inorganic phosphorus directly extracted from the water.

The Sediments

Bathymetric Factors—Whatever the frequency of ascending currents in a given coastal section or the concentration of phosphorus of the deep water reservoir, a P_2O_5-content increasing from the coast to off-shore and then decreasing farther out from a depth of 800–1000 m can generally be observed in unconsolidated surface oozes.

Off the Congo (fig. 4): A study of the physico-chemical characteristics of the biotope of the bathyal crab *Geryon quinquedens*, which we have carried out, has given precise information completing the data collected in the littoral section: P_2O_5-contents relative to total sediment on the shelf remain within the usual boundaries and do not exceed 0.3 to 0.4 percent; the highest concentration (>0.5%) are found at a depth of 250–500 m; toward 750 m they clearly decrease to values of less than 0.2 percent at about 1000 m, a depth

where, whatever the water composition, the dead biomass is largely oxidized before reaching the bottom. In this connection, Bromley (1967) has noted that phosphate and phosphorus is already being regenerated from the descending organic matter and non-negligible P_2O_5-concentrations can be expected only above 1000 m. On the Congo talus, the crab *Geryon* disappears from the benthos at 850 m, but other, non-nutritional, ecological factors may intervene here.

It should be noted that we were unable to recognize, in the core samples taken on the slope, an increase of P_2O_5 with burial depth, considered characteristic by some authors (Fairbridge, 1967).

Off the Ivory Coast (fig. 5): The measurements made by Martin (1973) on the shelf off the Ivory Coast reveal low P_2O_5-contents, but a rather regular increase from a depth of 20 m (0.06%) to 250 m (0.15%).

Off Gabon (fig. 6): The oozes, exposed to the open ocean along the Ogooué delta are influenced by upwelling during the dry season and richer in phosphorus (0.1 to 0.25% P_2O_5) than those sheltered in the fluvio-marine bays behind the large sandy island of Mandji (<0.1%). These low values agree well with our other observations (Giresse, 1969).

The areas of alluvial sedimentation of the large rivers, like Niger, Congo or Ogooué, show no bathymetric gradient: continental sedimentation exceeds oceanic one. The same is true for other tropical shelves, like those of the Orinoco or of Sarawak (Porrenga, 1967).

Off Angola (fig. 7) and *South-west Africa*: Along the west-African margin, the role of upwelling in the development of the biomass and thus in the deposition of organic matter and combined phosphorus is evident, wherever the frequency of these dynamics increases. Thus, off Luanda (Angola) P_2O_5-contents of the oozes at a depth of about 40 m are on the average five times higher than at the same depth along the shelf off Ivory Coast. They attain 1.2 percent, a value placing them already into the initial stages of phosphatogenesis (Emelyanov, 1973).

This feature is exceptionally well developed off South-west Africa. The deposits richest in P_2O_5 are found between 100 and 500 m: 0.22 to 4.25 percent (average 1.85%); toward greater depth contents decrease abruptly to 0.006 percent between 500 and 4,500 m. Here a relationship between organic carbon and P_2O_5-concentrations

has been demonstrated (Emelyanov and Senin, 1973): for less than 1 percent C, P_2O_5 values of 0.03 to 0.1 percent were measured, for 1 to 3 percent C, P_2O_5 is 0.15 to 0.27%, and between 3 and 8.5 percent C exceptionally high P_2O_5 values can be found (one determination of 12.4%, another of 22.9%). It is noteworthy that a positive correlation between carbon and phosphorus was also found along the Congo margin, although the absolute values there are much more modest (Fig. 8); some additional C/P_2O_5-ratios measured on the shelves of Liberia and Morocco point in the same direction. Whatever the nature of phosphatogenesis, one of its conditions (possibly the most important one) is fulfilled.

This phosphatogenesis affects recent, still unconsolidated deposits rich in diatoms, from which amorphous silica disappears as P_2O_5 concentrations increase. Baturin and Dubintchuk (1973) point out that this phosphate is generally amorphous and finely dispersed on frustules as a gel, as "collomorphous" films or as a thin crust around aggregated ooze particles. The authors see indications of transformation from microglobular structures to microcrystalline ones. The last structure is reminiscent of the "phosphatization cells" described by Lamboy (1976) from the Miocene phosphates of the Galician shelf.

All these observations point to the possibility of a rather **rapid phosphatogenesis** during early

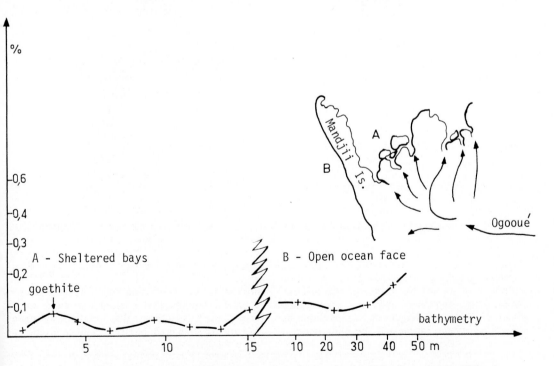

FIG. 6.—Distribution of P_2O_5 in sediments as function of water depth off the Ogooué delta (Gabon).

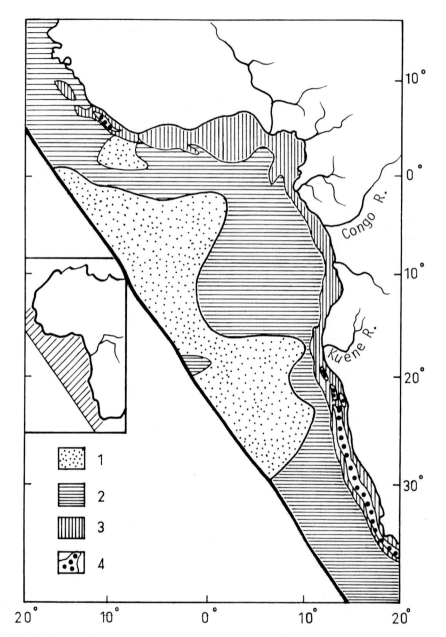

Fɪɢ. 7.—Distribution of phosphorus in the uppermost (0–5 cm) sediment layer off Namibia; simplified after E. M. Emelyanov (1973). 1: <0.05%; 2: 0.05 − 0.10%; 3: 0.10 − 0.20%; 4: >0.20%.

diagenesis. From here on, the degree of phosphatization of a sediment is not necessarily any more a function of its age but rather of the physicochemical environmental conditions. During more advanced stages of diagenesis compaction, dehydration, crystallization and the elimination of foreign matter might progress. According to Soviet authors (Baturin and Dubintchuk, 1974) the possibility of deposition by direct inorganic chemical precipitation has, in this case, to be discarded. A crystallographic growth on an organic support in which bacteria take a prominent

Fɪɢ. 8.—Relationship P_2O_5-C_{org} in the oozes off the Congo shelf (top) and Congo talus (bottom).

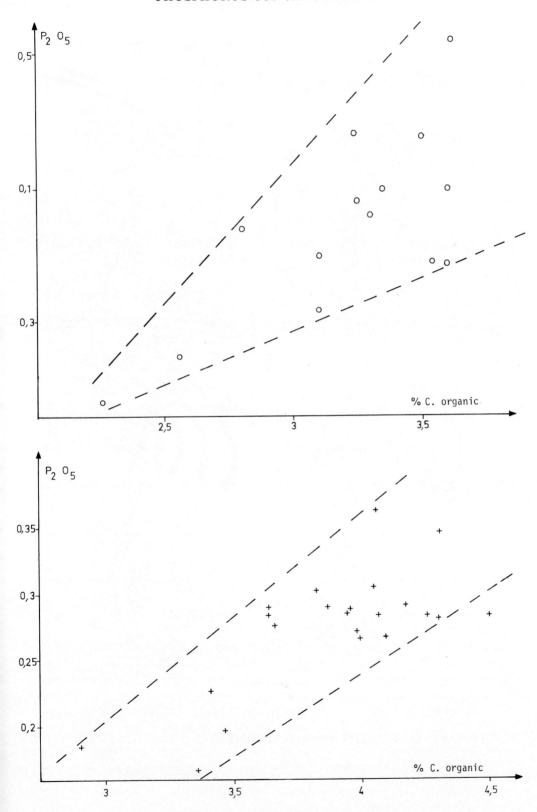

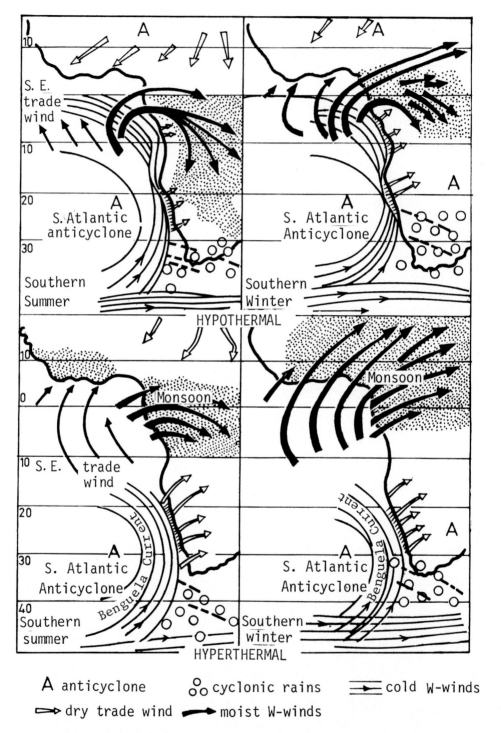

FIG. 9.—Latitudinal displacement of meteorologic and oceanographic zones during glacial (hypothermal) and interglacial (hyperthermal) periods; after E. M. Van Zinderen Bakker (1967), simplified.

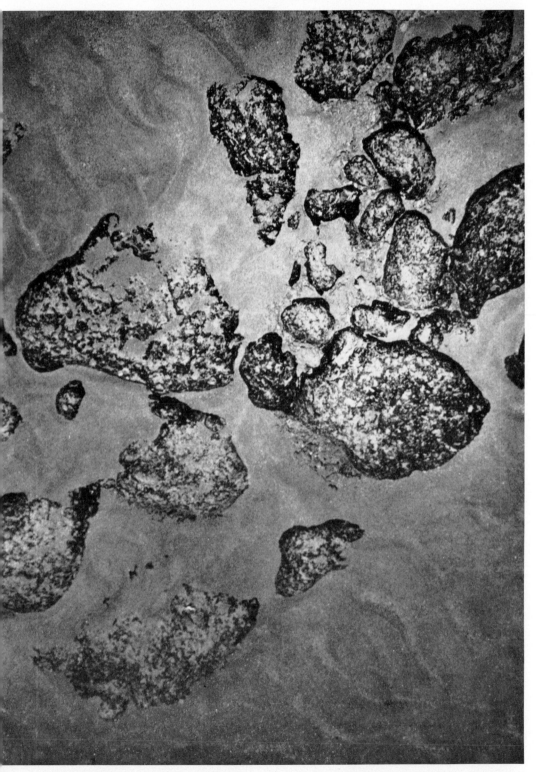

FIG. 4.—Ferromanganese stained and impregnated phosphorite in the northwest Blake Plateau, *Atlantis* II Cruise 266, Lowering 21, location 30°37′ N, 78°30′ W, depth 775 m. (Photo by R. M. Pratt in Stetson, 1961).

A

B

FIG. 5.—Bottom photographs of Fe-Mn-phosphatic pavement from DSRV ALVIN dive on the Blake Plateau, 1966. Equipment in foreground is the submersible's basket and sampling tools. Note rippled globerinid sand, alcyonarian corals growing on thinly covered pavement.

nental shelf immediately to the east, sediment on the plateau is largely well-sorted carbonate sand dominated by globigerinid and pteropod tests, with occasional high concentrations of deep water coral. Previous studies of topography, sediments and bottom currents have indicated that much of the Blake Plateau is now an area of non-depo-

sition or erosion and that these conditions have been maintained by the Gulf Stream since Miocene time (Pratt, 1968). Direct observations by bottom photographs (fig. 4) and by deep submersibles (fig. 5) often show thin layers of well-sorted carbonate sand in transport; these sands evidently cover and uncover the phosphate and manganese deposits in response to local lateral oscillations of the Gulf Stream.

Seismic profiles across the Florida-Hatteras Slope clearly indicate that the westward side of the erosional Blake Plateau surface is buried beneath more recent continental shelf and slope sediments (Emery and Zarudski, 1967; Uchupi and Emery, 1967). Pratt (1966), Ewing et al. (1966) and Zarudzki and Uchupi (1968) have pointed out the probability of intensified erosion during the lowered sea level stages of Pleistocene time, and Manheim (1967) gave evidence that sapping due to intensified submarine discharge of waters during these periods may have helped form the typically karst-like depressions that characterize parts of the Blake Plateau. Some of these depressions expose sediments of Eocene to Late Cretaceous age and are typically covered with rubbly lag deposits of phosphorite and manganese-replaced phosphorites. A sketch of an exposed area of Upper Cretaceous (Campanian-Maastrichtian) strata on the inner margin of the Blake Plateau is given in fig. 6, as detailed by studies made from ALVIN (Milliman et al., 1967). Although evidences of intermittent currents are still strong, the landward part of the rubble-covered Upper Cretaceous limestone is now being covered over with recent and reworked calcareous debris.

In overall aspect, the Blake Plateau deposits show a rather irregular seaward transition from

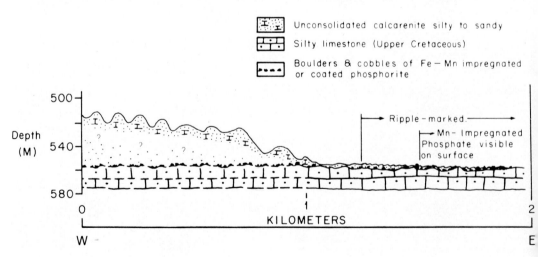

FIG. 6.—Schematic diagram of distribution of phosphatic zone bottom configuration in the inner Blake Plateau; location 30°48' W, 79°12' W; depth 554 m.

Top

End

Bottom

FIG. 7.—Plate of Fe-Mn stained and infiltrated phosphorite, showing smooth top surface and coral holdfasts (white blobs) and pebbly-rubbly bottom surface, frequently encrusted with serpulid worms.

phosphorite nodules partly similar to those observed in deposits on the nearby continent (Malde, 1959), to mixed phosphate-manganese pavements and slabs, and finally to relatively pure manganese-iron concretions having an appearance similar to those found on the deep-sea floor.

Composition and thickness of the continuous pavement areas are poorly known because dredges or other samplers simply bounce off the surface. Only where continuity is disrupted and/or broken fragments occur can they be recovered by conventional oceanographic samplers or the manipulating arm of submersibles. In some areas, underlying sediment has been winnowed away and once-horizontal blocks may be propped almost vertically in depressions (Hawkins, 1969).

Near the edge of the pavement, or in patches within it, loose plates recovered by dredge vary in size from thin sheets to massive blocks weighing hundreds of kilograms. The top of the pavement is generally planed smooth by the scouring effect of loose debris driven by the Gulf Stream, with

TABLE 2.—COMPARATIVE X-RAY DATA FOR PHOSPHORITES. DATA AND MOST INDICES FOR FRANCOLITE ARE FROM McCONNELL (1938). THIS SAMPLE IS A CARBONATE FLUORAPATITE (COLLOPHANE) FROM GRODNO, POLAND (NOW USSR), CONTAINING 51.0% CaO, 5.8% CO_2, 33.5% P_2O_5, 3.5% F, 0.5% MgO, AND 3.2% H_2O. THE FLORIDA SAMPLE IS A LAND PEBBLE FROM THE LAKELAND REGION OF CENTRAL FLORIDA, AND REPRESENTS REWORKED MIDDLE TERTIARY PHOSPHORITE. THE PUNGO RIVER SAMPLE IS FROM THE TEXAS GULF SULPHUR MINE, BEAUFORT COUNTY, NORTH CAROLINA AND CONSISTS OF A MASSIVE WHITISH AGGREGATE. UNIT CELL DIMENSIONS DETERMINED BY DANIEL APPLEMAN, SMITHSONIAN INSTITUTION.

Indices	Francolite (McConnell, 1938) d(Å)	I	Blake phosphorite[1] Sta. 2485 d	I	Phosphatized Manatee rib, Gerda Terrace Sta. 2348 d	I	Phosphorite[2] Bone Valley Formation, Fla. d	I	Phosphorite[3] Pungo River Formation, N.C. d	I
100	ND		8.08	4	8.15	b	8.08	4	8.07	5
101	ND		5.23	4	—	—	5.23	3	5.25	3
200	ND		4.03	4	—	—	4.05	6	4.03	4
111	ND		3.86	6	—	—	3.86	6	3.86	4
002	3.431	2	3.446	43	3.44	41	3.45	46	3.445	42
102	3.157	0.5	3.173	16	3.17	12	3.173	12	3.163	13
120	3.044	2	3.055	18	—	—	3.060	17	3.050	13
121	2.765	>10	2.791	100	2.78	100b	2.793	100	2.785	100
112	—	—	2.688	54	2.695	43b	2.698	58	2.691	51
202	2.618	4	2.622	28	2.622	20	2.625	29	2.621	26
301	2.508	0.5	—	—	—	—	2.514	4	2.502	4
122	2.277	1	2.280	24			2.285	8	2.285	9
130	2.238	3	2.237	21	2.245	18	2.245	24	2.238	20
131	2.127	2	2.127	7	2.125	5	2.137	5	2.123	6
113	2.057	1	2.055	5	—	—	2.062	5	2.057	6
203	1.996	1	1.993	4	1.995	8	2.000	4	1.993	4
222	1.928	3	1.930	21	1.931	17	1.934	25	1.929	20
132	1.876	1	1.877	15	1.88	8b	1.881	13	—	—
123	1.835	3	1.834	25	1.837	21b	1.837	35	1.834	28
231	1.788	2	1.786	10			1.793	13	1.785	10
140	1.762	2	1.760	11	1.764	13	1.766	14	1.760	13
402	1.740	2	1.738	10	—	—	1.744	11	1.740	10
004	1.720	2	1.721	13	1.720	12	1.723	13	1.721	13
232	1.631	0.5	1.630	4	—	—	1.634	6	1.633	9
133	1.601	0.5	1.605	3	—	—	1.604	3	1.602	2
240	1.525	0.5	1.		—	—	1.530	4	1.525	3
331	1.515	0.5	1.515	4	—	—	1.519	4	—	—
124	1.496	0.5	1.500	4	—	—	1.500	4	1.502	4
502	1.462	1	1.462	6	—	—	1.463	9	1.459	6
304	1.453	1	1.452	6	—	—	1.453	8	1.448	7
233	1.441	1	—	—	1.43	6b	—	—	1.438	6
151	1.419	1	1.418	6	—	—	1.422	5	1.416	4
Unit cell a(Å)	9.320		9.314		9.3416		9.345		9.317	

[1] Quartz main peak 3.339;
[2] Quartz main peak 3.345;
[3] Quartz main peak 3.335.
Given values are uncorrected for shifts in this internal standard line.

TABLE 3.—SELECTED MINERAL PARAMETERS OF BLAKE PHOSPHORITE AND STANDARD FLORIDA PHOSPHATE ROCK. (CHEMICAL VALUES IN WEIGHT PERCENT. UNIT CELL (A) DIMENSION DETERMINED BY DANIEL APPLEMAN, SMITHSONIAN INSTITUTION)

	F	CO_2	P_2O_5	F/P_2O_5	Sp. Gravity	Index Refr.	A (Å)
Blake Plateau	2.5	11.4[a]	22.2	0.11	2.9 − 3.1	1.600	9.305
NBS STD 120b	3.84	2.79	34.57	0.111	3.0	1.600 −1.620[b]	—

[a] A portion of the CO_2 is due to physical admixture of calcite.

[b] National Bureau of Standards Phosphate Rock (Florida land pebble). Apatite in isotropic phase with considerable radiation damage has ω and ε = 1.62 (C. C. Woo, oral communication, 1978).

the exception of deep-water corals and sponges that fasten themselves to the surface. The bottom or underside of plates reveal that the pavement is being composed of pebbles and grains of phosphorite cemented together and forming coalescing masses (fig. 7). The shapes of some plates reveal that the phosphorite pebbles of which they are composed apparently filled ripple-like depressions in an underlying carbonate sand. Petrographic examination shows variable cycles of erosion and recrystallization intermingled with episodes of Fe-Mn infiltration and replacement.

MINERALOGY AND PETROGRAPHY

Blake phosphorites occur in the form of pellets, granules, pebbles, homocrystalline replacements and cement in conglomeratic aggregates. The phosphorite aggregates are partly similar to marine phosphorites of middle Tertiary age found in many areas of shallow to intermediate depth around the world: offshore southern California (Dietz et al., 1942; Pasho, 1972); Chatham Rise off New Zealand (Pasho, 1976); northwest Africa (Summerhayes, 1970); Agulhas Bank, South Africa (Parker, 1971); and off Peru-Chile (Burnett, 1974) and Brazil (Guazelli and Corsta, 1978).

The dominant apatite phase in the Blake phosphorite appears to be francolite (carbonate-fluorapatite containing more than 1% F). The apatite in its pure form contains about 3.6% F and on the order of 6% CO_3^{-2}, replacing PO_4^{-3} in the apatite lattice. This conclusion is drawn from the X-ray spacings of typical samples (table 2), chemical data, index of refraction (table 3), and from evidence summarized by McConnell (1973) and references cited. The possibility of small substitutions by silica and sulfur and other elements in the apatite structure must be given consideration. We also acknowledge controversy regarding the size of the unit cell (LeGeros et al., 1967; Lehr et al., 1968; Elderfield et al., 1972) and other uncertainties cited by McConnell (1973).

Most of the apatite is optically pseudo-isotropic under the polarizing microscope (fig. 8), but gives

FIG. 8. Frontispiece—a. Phosphate-mantled, cemented calcareous ooze (left part of slide) in phosphorite slab. Magnification ×43. Sta. 2476, 30°51.8′ N, 79°10.1′ W, 743 m. b. Same slide and magnification, crossed nicols and gypsum plate. Red color indicates isotropic apatite, white and greenish colors refer to calcite, and black is manganese iron oxides. The section shows fragments of foram-coccolith ooze (lithified) which have been mantled by francolite, with interruptions marked by thin manganese coatings. Subsequently, the entire sediment was filled in with fine grained matrix which is now completely converted to francolite, followed by exposure to renewed replacement by manganese. The phosphatization of the inner carbonate may have taken place post-mantling, partial loss of material giving rise to transverse fracturing of mantle (shrinkage cracks). c. Phosphatic conglomerate. No magnification. Sta. 2480, 31°35.9′ N, 79°04.2′ W, 501 m. d. Magnification ×4. Phosphatized erosion surface of Pliocene globigerina ooze, thin manganese-iron oxide rim, infilled with lithified recent-subrecent foram ooze (cement is high magnesian calcite). Sta. 2477, 31°00.5′ N, 79°19.4′ W, 684 m. e. Same section, magnification × 43. f. Same section as e), gypsum plate. Pink-red indicates phosphatized carbonate. Black is manganese. Some of round white areas are quartz grains. g. Same section in phosphatized area, magnification × 220. h. Same as g) with gypsum plate, purple revealing phosphatized carbonate. Note completely phosphatized large globigerina tests outlined by manganese oxide impregnation of pore canals, and phosphatic molds in tests (darker purple). i. Partly phosphatized calcareous sediment containing mixed benthonic and planktonic Oligocene fauna. × 15. Sta. 2438, 25°37.5′ N. 79°54.8′ W, 383 m. (off Gerda Terrace, S. of Palm Beach, Fla.). j. Same as i) with gypsum plate. Note phosphatic mold within test at upper left. k. Same station. Piece of phosphatized dugong bone, magnif. × 15. Prob. Miocene. l. Lithified foram ooze, recent. Test walls are low magnesian calcite; matrix high magnesian. × 15. Sta. 2467, 29°15.5′ N, 79°12.8′ W, 790 m. m. Phosphorite showing dendritic Mn encroachment. Sta. 2438 (see i.) × 15. n. Advanced Mn encroachment. Sta 2478a, 31°08.0′ N, 79°07.5′ W, 649 m. o. From bottom note slightly Mn-encroached phosphorite conglomerate, advanced Mn-Fe replacement (note floating grain) and upper accretional layers of oxide, with high Mg-calcite veinlets. Sta. 2480 (see c.), no magnification.

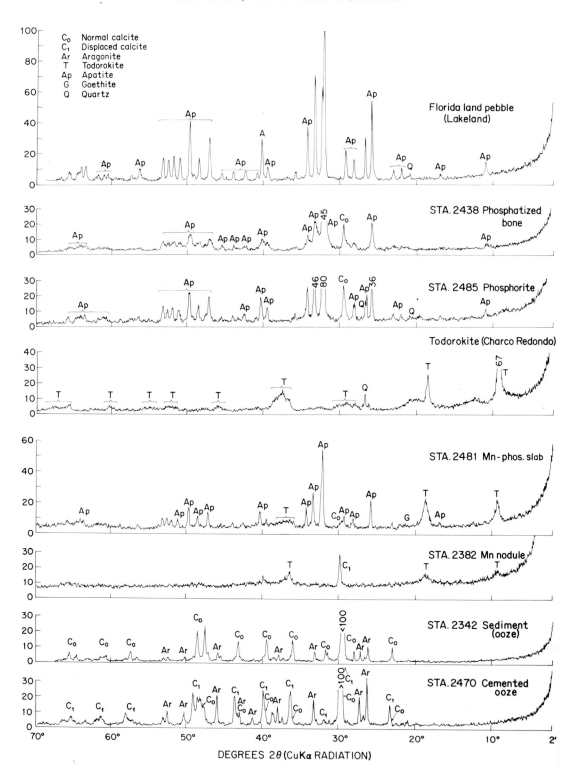

FIG. 9.—X-ray diffractograms for Blake Plateau samples and comparative materials. CuKα radiation with fluorescence from Fe- and Mn-rich phases largely removed by pulse height discrimination.

TABLE 4.—ESTIMATED ABUNDANCE OF MINERAL SPECIES IN THE MAIN ROCK PHASES ON THE BLAKE PLATEAU. ESTIMATES, GIVEN IN UNITS FROM 0 TO 10, UTILIZE X-RAY, OPTICAL AND CHEMICAL DATA, AND SHOULD BE REGARDED AS SEMIQUANTITATIVE.

Mineral Species	Phosphatized bone	Phosphorite (avg.)	Mn-phos. pavement	Cemented ooze[a]
Apatite (undiff.)	10	7	2	(tr.)
Calcite (low-Mg)	tr.	2 1/2	1	3
Calcite (high-Mg)[b]	(tr?)	1/2	1	6
Aragonite	—	—	tr.-2[c]	1
Todorokite (well-crystallized)	—	(tr.)	3	—
Todorokite (poorly crystallized)	—	—	1 1/2	—
Goethite	—	(tr.)	1 1/3	—
Quartz	—	(tr.)	(tr.)	—
Glauconite	—	(tr.)	(tr.)	—
Dolomite	—	(tr.)	(tr.)	—

[a]Refers to ooze with pore spaces nearly filled with matrix or cement.

[b]Refers to calcite having (211) spacing shifted to smaller values due to solid solution of foreign ions. Principle element involved is Mg.

[c]Aragonite occurs in some flat nodules and slabs as thin laminae (McFarlin, 1967), but not in others. An important associated factor in the occurrence of aragonite-bearing concretions seems to be the absence of transverse cracks which may admit calcitic debris into the growing concretion.

a strong X-ray pattern, virtually identical to those of "land pebble" phosphorites in the economically important deposits of central Florida, and also of the Pungo River phosphorites in North Carolina (Kimrey, 1965; Gibson, 1967; Rooney and Kerr, 1967). LeGeros et al. (1967) showed that increasing substitution of CO_3 in the apatite lattice promotes increasingly equidimensional crystallites, as well as decreasing crystal and lattice dimension. The tendency toward poorer crystallinity is partly compensated by the crystallizing effect of F in the solution (Simpson, 1966). Thus, the optically isotropic habit of the Blake phosphorite, like many marine phosphorites, may be explainable by its high CO_3 substitution in the apatite lattice, which under low-temperature conditions leads to formation of an aggregated mass of well-crystallized but minute and equidimensional spherulites. Typical X-ray traces are shown in fig. 9.

In addition to microcrystalline apatite in discrete pellets, grains and pebbles or larger masses, apatite in the form of cement and replacement of carbonate debris is also optically pseudo-isotropic for the most part. The distribution of apatite in discrete microcrystalline pellets and aggregates in mixtures of phosphorite and carbonate is best seen in thin section using the gypsum plate and crossed nicols (figs. 8a and 8b). Under these conditions, the apatite appears purplish red, whereas minerals such as calcite appear white or yellowish. A summary of mineral distribution is provided in table 4.

Except for shark teeth, identifiable organic and biochemically formed apatite such as bone and teeth remains appear to be concentrated in Middle Tertiary outcrops along the Straits of Florida and the Pourtales Terrace. Bone is recognizable in thin sections by characteristic Haversian canals (fig. 8k) and in X-ray diagrams by broadened apatite peaks (fig. 10). Primary apatite and its immediate transformations should be carefully distinguished from phosphatized megafossils, such as phosphatized *Inoceramus-Baculites* (Upper Cretaceous) fauna from off Charleston, S.C., Miocene shark teeth, Recent to Miocene mammalian (manatee) bones, and Oligocene to Pleistocene foraminifera are also identified at various locales.

Carbonates and Their Phosphatization

Calcium carbonate associated with the purer phosphorites is dominated by low magnesian calcite, a large part of which originates from skeletal debris of planktonic foraminifera (fig. 8h). Other forms, such as ostracods, corals, bryozoa and coccoliths, are also noted. Carbonate cement, especially in fine-grained matrix, appears to be largely high magnesian calcite.

In the manganese-phosphorite pavement and slabs, low magnesian calcite (chiefly skeletal debris), aragonite and high magnesian calcite occur, whereas in the round manganese-iron oxide nodules high magnesian calcite is virtually the exclusive carbonate phase.

Unlithified oozes, as well as identifiable debris of planktonic foraminifera and other organisms in cemented globigerina-pteropod ooze, which is very common on the Blake Plateau, are dominated by low magnesian calcite and aragonite. On the other hand, test fillings consist of fine-grained high Mg-carbonate matrix having a relatively constant MgO-content of about 4-5% (10-13 mole%) of $MgCO_3$. These relationships are indicated in microprobe traverses (figs. 10a and b,

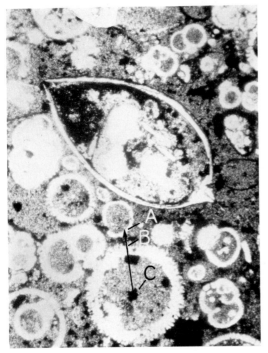

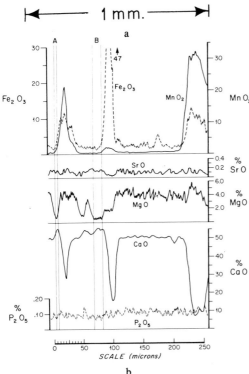

FIG. 10.—(a) Microphotograph of polished thin section of cemented ooze. Location 29°15.5' N, 79°12.8' W; depth 790 m. (b) X-ray microprobe traverse along A-C (in 10 a).

especially crossing intervals "A" and "B").

Phosphatization in varying degrees is illustrated in figs. 8a to 8h. It preferentially affects the fine-grained carbonate matrix within organisms, forming molds. For example, the section of figs. 8i–8j has cut a small mollusc (upper left) near the hinge line to reveal a phosphorite mold within the unphosphatized shell. Where carried to completion, phosphatization obliterates the shell wall, so that aside from outlines of impurities such as iron oxide, good preservation of organism morphology indicates that it has been incompletely phosphatized. This is commonly observed in the case of foraminifera, molluscs, and bryozoa off central and southern Florida, whereas in the northern Blake Plateau only occasional sharply defined molds are found, and carbonate skeletal walls have normally been destroyed.

Aside from the high strontium aragonite provided by deep-water corals such as *Dendrophyllia* (McFarlin, 1967), and the low strontium aragonite contributed by pteropods and other organisms, aragonite is observed in flat plates and slabs of phosphorite partly replaced by manganese and iron. It appears to be a metastable phase in the sense that it has been observed only in those slabs that still retain appreciable phosphate. Aragonite containing slabs are typically black, hard, and vitreous appearing. Slabs which have been so nearly completely replaced by Mn-Fe oxides that they have a dull, earthly and friable character appear also to have lost much of the aragonite they may once have contained. Rarely, later cross-cutting veins of calcite intersect the aragonite systems, which invariably parallel the platy direction of the slabs.

Other Phases

Inspection of typical X-ray diffractograms of manganese-phosphorite pavements as well as nodules from the Blake Plateau reveals that the dominant recognizable manganese mineral is todorokite, whose crystallinity and consequent peak intensity varies widely with respect to well-crystallized standard todorokite (fig. 9). Microprobe studies indicate that on the micron level, the todorokite alternates with an iron-rich phase, apparently goethite (limonite), which is often very poorly crystalline and virtually X-ray amorphous. This occurrence is analogous to deep-ocean forms of iron-manganese (Burns and Burns, 1976).

Manganese and iron oxides occur in two general modes. The first mode, replacement of pre-existing phosphorites and carbonates (figs. 8a and 8n) shows good crystallinity both for todorokite and goethite. The second mode is that of accretion on existing nuclei or tabular or sheet-like bodies (fig. 8o). The accretionary oxides tend to be poorly crystalline, as can be seen in the X-ray pattern

TABLE 5.—COMPOSITION OF BLAKE PLATEAU PHOSPHORITE AND COMPARABLE DEPOSITS.
(UNITS IN WEIGHT PER CENT OF AIR DRY MATERIAL. PARENTHESES INDICATE SEMI-QUANTITATIVE OR UNCERTAIN VALUES)[7]

	A	B[4]	C[5]	D	E
SiO_2	3.7	.20	2.1	4.68	9.31
Al_2O_3	1.1	.51	1.5	1.06	1.29
Fe_2O_3	4.1	2.80	9.2	1.10	1.57
Mn_3O_4[1]	.45	—	17.2	.30	.50
TiO_2	.15	—	.28	.15	.076
CaO	50.0	51.3	31.1	49.40	47.0
MgO	1.2	1.02	2.6	.28	.19
SrO	.18	—	.26	—	(.08)
K_2O	.30	.45	.33	.09	.13
Na_2O[7]	.60	.58	.72	.35	.21
CO_2	11.4	—	16.0	2.79	3.07
F	2.5	3.25	1.1	3.84	3.68
P_2O_5[8]	22.2	25.8	9.9	34.57	32.1
SO_3 (total)[2]	.38	1.52	1.02	—	.60
C_{org}	.4	—	.2	—	(.05)[3]
N	(.01)	—	(.01)	—	—
Ignition loss	14.9	15.2	21.5		$(1.88 - H_2O)$
SUM[6]	101.8	101.7	99.9	98.6	101.7
Less O for F	1.05	1.37	.46	1.61	1.55
TOTAL	100.3	100.3	99.4	97.0	100.2
Ba	.005	—	.20	—	(.008)
B	.005	—	.005		
U	.005	—	≤.001		.015
Ni	.004	—	.27	—	—
Co	≤.01	—	.10	—	—
Mo	≤.001	—	.03	—	—
Cu	.007	—	.09	—	(.003)
Zn	.015	—	.040	—	—
Pb	.005	—	.07	—	—
Nb	≤.001	—	.005		
Ag (ppm)	5.	(4)	—	—	—
Au (ppb)	.3	—	—	—	—
As	—	—	—	—	.008

KEY

A = Blake composite phosphorite (this report).
B = Blake phosphorite nodule (Burnett, 1974).
C = Blake pavement (this report).
D = Florida land pebble (NBS Standard Sample 120b).
E = Bone Valley (Florida) phosphorite; Altschuler et al., 1964.

NOTES

[1] Total Mn.

[2] A sample of phosphatized bone (Gosnold Station 2538), is distinguished from above marine phosphorite by higher organic carbon (1.0%), lower CO_2 (3-5%), and higher total S as $SO_3 = 1.7 - 2.2$.

[3] "organic" only indicated in table of Altschuler et al. (1964).

[4] 10 samples of phosphorites from the inner Blake Plateau, analyzed by the Newport News Shipbuilding & Dry Dock Co. yielded the following analyses (Pilkey, 1967): 20.1, 22.2, 31.9, 27.7, 22.8, 24.8, 22.6, 20.5, 21.6, 26.5% P_2O_5. A sample of whale earbone assayed 31.9% P_2O_5. The phosphorites averaged 24.97% or 52.5% PBL (bone phosphate of lime).

[5] The pavement composite is dominated by ferromanganese oxides, and may not be representative.

[6] Sum is cations plus P_2O_5, total sulfur as SO_3, F, and ignition loss, or where lacking, CO_2, plus H_2O.

[7] Na_2O in Blake samples probably contains significant NaCl.

[8] P_2O_5 concentrations have been reported for many bottom sediments taken during the *Gill* cruises from the southeastern continental margin of the United States (Moore and Gorsline, 1960). These have been used in several subsequent works (e.g. Gorsline, 1963; Uchupi, 1963; Goodell, 1967). Both our analytical values and petrographic estimates for phosphate in shelf areas are much lower than the *Gill* values. For example, much of the inner Florida shelf is indicated to contain more than 3% P_2O_5, whereas our data fail to indicate more than a few tenths of a percent (carbonate background values). Since our data are in general agreement with control analyses performed by the U.S. Geological Survey laboratories in Washington, we have not used the *Gill* data for quantitative purposes.

TABLE 6.—RARE EARTH DISTRIBUTION IN THE BLAKE PLATEAU DEPOSITS AND COMPARABLE FLORIDA PHOSPHORITES, BELIEVED TO HAVE COMMON PRIMARY ORIGIN IN MID-TERTIARY STRATA. (DATA FROM FLORIDA ARE BY ALTSCHULER ET AL. (1967) ON SEPARATED APATITE; BLAKE DATA ARE FROM EHRLICH (1968) DETERMINED BY NEUTRON ACTIVATION. CONCENTRATIONS IN WEIGHT PERCENT. THE SECOND COLUMN FOR EACH SAMPLE REFERS TO DATA NORMALIZED BY RATIO TO CHONDRITES)

Rare Earth	Round Mn-Fe Nodule[1]		Phosphorite Piece From Pavement[2]		Florida Phosphorite	
La	0.0105	349	0.0080	268	0.015	500
Ce	0.0970	1160	0.0140	165	0.012	141
Pr	0.0034	260	0.0015	124	0.003	247
Nd	0.013	230	0.0071	125	0.007	124
Sm	0.0041	207	0.0013	68	0.003	103
Eu	0.0012	170	0.0003	45	0.0004	55
Tb	0.0007	118	0.0002	38	0.0004	78
Dy	0.0034	114	0.0017	58	0.0016	55
Ho	0.0008	114	0.00035	48	0.0004	55
Er	—	—	—	—	0.0021	100
Tm	0.00034	109	0.00015	48	0.0002	65
Yb	0.0023	130	0.00096	57	0.0008	47
Lu	0.00037	120	0.00016	51	0.0003	95
Y	0.0179	90	0.0106	54	0.011	56
TOTAL REE	0.161		0.049		0.059	

[1] Atlantis #266 Sta. 5, 31°56.2' N, 77°15' W, 787 m.
[2] Gosnold #74 Sta. 2390, 31°12.8' N, 78°29.0' W, 648 m.

(fig. 9). Goethite is so poorly crystalline in the round nodules that only weak main lines are indicated on diffractograms, for the most part, although the round nodules contain higher concentrations of iron than many replaced phosphorites.

Other less common mineral species noted are glauconite, quartz, feldspar and heavy minerals. These are entirely detrital relicts, where found in the nodules. As shown by Gorsline (1963), glauconite is particularly characteristic just below the shelfbreak north of 28° N. At least three generations of glauconite may occur on the Florida-Hatteras Slope and Blake Plateau. Residual glauconite from eroded Middle Tertiary* strata is common and is frequently incorporated in nodules in the inner Blake Plateau. Upper Cretaceous glauconite is known in coastal plain strata and may possibly be incorporated as detrital grains in some nodules where Cretaceous strata are exposed. The third type appears to be Recent-Subrecent in origin, as suggested by its association with and presence inside fresh-appearing Holocene-Pliocene planktonic foraminifera; it occurs only on the Florida-Hatteras Slope and innermost Blake Plateau as isolated grains and fragments of grains.

Dolomite grains are found irregularly in phos-

phorite and pebble matrix, and occasionally as discrete fragments. As will be shown later, the dolomite is related to the Miocene strata from which phosphorite was eroded.

A summary of mineral abundances in the Blake Plateau deposits, estimated from all available data, is given in table 4.

CHEMISTRY

The Blake phosphorites differ from Florida and South Carolina land pebble aggregates, which they otherwise resemble, by higher CO_2, Mg and ferromanganese components and associated metals. These differences are largely explained by loss of discrete calcium carbonate (and dolomite in some cases) due to leaching of the Florida and South Carolina phosphorites in the ground water zone, and replacement of the Blake nodules by ferromanganese oxides and their typical associated metals: Ni, Co, Cu, Pb, Zn, Mo and V. Such constituents as SiO_2, Al_2O_3, TiO_2, Na_2O and K_2O are associated with silicate and other detrital minerals. Some Mg, alkalies, as well as silica and sulfur (SO_3), are known to be incorporated in phosphate lattices (McConnell, 1973 and literature cited). However, the bulk of the Na in the Blake phosphorites is probably from residual sea water trapped in the rock prior to drying. Mg is also associated with palygorskite and sepiolite.

Among the trace constituents, only uranium, typically associated with marine phosphorites (Altschuler et al., 1958; Baturin, 1975, and refer-

*Miocene glauconite is generally absent in continental Florida and Georgia, but becomes more abundant in the seaward direction.

ences cited), strontium, and rare earths occur in appreciable concentrations. Silver, present at the 5 ppm level, appears unusually high in concentration and will require rechecking, although such anomalies have previously been noted (Krauskopf, 1955; Smirnov, 1959). Gold is lower in concentration than the 1–3 ppb level found in purified apatite concentrates from Florida (Altschuler and Rowe, 1969). A summary of data obtained on eight phosphorites from the Blake Plateau and comparative analyses are given in table 5.

The concentration of rare earth elements (table 6) in the Blake phosphorites is somewhat lower but otherwise comparable to values obtained for Florida apatites (Altschuler et al., 1967), with due regard to the proportion of apatite in the rock. The sole exception is for Ce, which the above authors showed to be depleted in apatite relative to other crustal materials. On the other hand, Ce is markedly enriched in the ferromanganese phases of nodules (Ehrlich, 1968, and references cited), and the impregnation of the Blake phosphorite with ferromanganese oxides no doubt accounts for the higher Ce in this sampling.

Pavements and slabs show a composition intermediate between phosphorite and round nodules, though they have proportionately greater amounts of Mn, Cu, Mo and Zn than might be expected as a result of straight mixing processes. The replacement mode of Mn-Fe oxides apparently favors enrichment of Mn and its related elements over Fe, as it also tends to be correlated with better crystallinity of the Fe-Mn oxide phase (fig. 9).

AGE RELATIONSHIPS

The drilling of JOIDES drill-holes (JOIDES, 1965) and subsequent analytical studies have shed considerable light on the formation of the Blake phosphorite and ferromanganese deposits. The distribution of carbonate and phosphate, along with a gamma ray log, are depicted in fig. 11 for JOIDES site 1, about 40 km east of Jacksonville, Florida, and in fig. 12 for AMCOR 6002. At these sites on the Atlantic shelf, the phosphatic Middle Miocene strata, equivalent to the Hawthorn strata, are essentially uneroded by the Gulf Stream. Farther seaward on the Blake Plateau, the Gulf Stream and its antecedents in Late Miocene to Holocene time have eroded and winnowed the marly sediments and left only lag deposits of the more insoluble fractions.

The figures indicate that **primary** phosphate

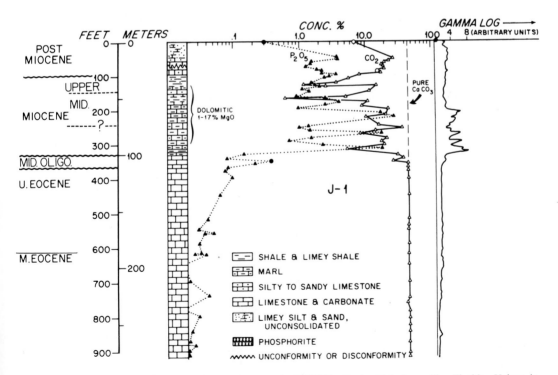

Fig. 11.—Distribution of P_2O_5 and other parameters in JOIDES site 1 off Jacksonville, Florida. Values in weight percent of air dry sediment. For location see fig. 2. Age boundaries corrected by data from C. W. Poag.

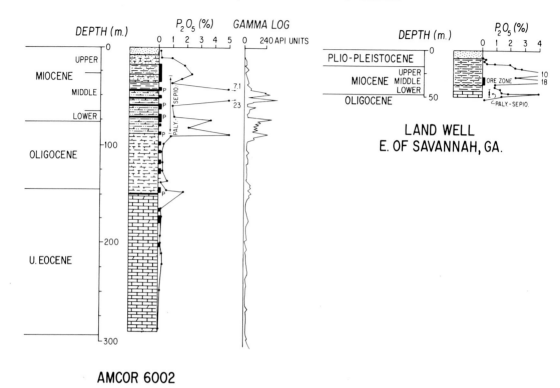

FIG. 12.—Distribution of P$_2$O$_5$ and gamma ray activity in AMCOR site 6002 (location, fig. 2), and a land well cited in Weaver and Beck (1977). Values recalculated from BPL data.

formation began in Oligocene time and reached maxima in Early to Middle Miocene. Phosphate accumulation was accompanied by the uranium enrichment common to marine phosphorites (Baturin, 1975, and references cited). This is sensitively reflected in the gamma ray neutron curves, which have been widely used for phosphate prospecting on the adjacent continent, in Georgia, South Carolina and North Carolina (e.g. Kimrey, 1965; Anonymous, 1969; Weaver and Beck, 1977 and references cited). Time of cessation of primary phosphorite formation is more difficult to establish, not only because it probably occurred gradually or irregularly, but also because overlying sediments and distribution patterns show distinct evidence of reworked earlier phosphatic materials (Emery and Uchupi, 1972).

Once formed, often as replacements or molds of calcareous skeletel debris (Manheim et al., 1975), phosphorite is frequently remobilized and recrystallized, cementing younger debris (fig. 8). As many as four successive cycles of phosphatization have been documented in thin sections of Blake phosphorites. Therefore, the presence of younger organisms in phorphorites should not necessarily be taken as an indicator of age of

primary deposition. The primary Middle Tertiary origin of the southeastern United States land phosphorites has been well established in recent summaries (Cathcart, 1968), but disagreements still exist on paleontologic age questions.

Although interest in modern phosphorite formation has extended to the Atlantic continental margin (Sheldon, 1959; Pevear, 1966; McKelvey and Wang, 1970), and some undoubtedly recent phosphatic formation has been documented as kidney stones in mollusks (Doyle et al., 1978), most authors (e.g. Pilkey and Luternauer, 1967; Emery and Uchupi, 1972, and references cited) have recognized that phosphorite found along the Atlantic continental margin in surficial sediments is of relict origin.

In addition to data provided earlier, other evidences that phosphorite is not forming at present include the following:

1. Most phosphorite occurs in the form of grains, pebbles, and cobbles that are polished, abraded, or show evidence of solution.

2. Except where obviously associated with phosphorite pebbles or other older material, calcareous skeletal debris show no apprecia-

ble evidence of phosphatization, even on the micron level (fig. 10b).

3. No finely dispersed, "primary replacement" type phosphorite is observed in post-Miocene strata, and, in general, Pliocene-Pleistocene-Holocene sediments approach background levels for P_2O_5 (.2% P_2O_5).

Combining present data, mineralogical information on the JOIDES core-holes (Hathaway et al., 1970), and unpublished data, we conclude that the original phosphatic Middle Tertiary (chiefly Lower and Middle Miocene) strata stretched from the southeastern United States continent to the Blake Plateau, gradually diminishing in phosphate content. At the outer edge of the Blake Plateau, minute phosphatic traces may be observed, in the form of replacements and internal fillings of foraminiferal and even bryozoan and other remains. Where the original strata remain uneroded, phosphate is dispersed through thicknesses of up to several hundred meters. Erosion and reworking leaves a phosphate enriched lag rubble only a few tens of cm to many meters in thickness.

Sepiolite-palygorskite clays are widely associated with southeastern United States phosphorites (Weaver and Beck, 1977). Their genesis is apparently related to the abundant amorphous silica of diatom origin, that characterized the organic-rich bottom enrivonment of the phosphatic zone.

Space permits only brief comment on environmental questions. Two important factors are: faunal and floral evidence of relatively cool or cold water associated with phosphatic strata, based on foraminifera, mollusca and diatoms (Gibson, 1967; Malde, 1959; Abbott and Ernissee, 1978). Second, the phosphatic strata are characterized by enrichment in organic matter, especially of diatom origin, and uranium, and impoverishment in oxidate elements such as manganese.

These evidences bespeak a highly productive environmental regime with limited detrital input, and anoxic bottom conditions. Such a regime corresponds well with the concept of formation of phosphorite as a replacement of calcareous matter in an anoxic, organic-rich interstitial water milieu like that now found in Southwest Africa

and off Peru-Chile (Baturin, 1971, 1972, 1975; Veeh et al., 1973; Burnett, 1974; Manheim et al., 1975). Evidence pointing to interstitial replacement as an important process in phosphatization was first provided by Ames, 1959 and has more recently been amplified by Baturin (1972), Martens and Harriss (1970), Price and Calvert (1978), and authors cited. Such a regime could be provided by upwelling and would not be consistent with a fast-moving oxygenated and nutrient-depleted current regime such as characterizes the present Gulf Stream configuration on the Blake Plateau. Absence or strong diminution of the Gulf Stream during Miocene time was already suggested by Vaughan (1910) and appears consistent with regional paleogeographic considerations (Weyl, 1964). Upon reestablishment or establishment of the Gulf Stream in late Miocene and/or subsequent time, the upwelling conditions changed, and a regime of non-deposition or erosion would have made possible ferromanganese accumulation (previously cited publications by Baturin and Manheim et al., 1975). Still remaining to be clarified are the basic paleoceanographic conditions that created massive upwelling phenomena along a large part of the eastern North American continental margin.

ECONOMIC POTENTIAL

Approximate estimates of tonnage of phosphatic deposits on the Blake Plateau (Table 7) have been made on several assumptions. Thickness of the deposits is based on the assumption that phosphorites have not been transported appreciable distances, but that their mass should bear a relation to the total mass contained in original Middle Tertiary strata (i.e. such as are shown in figs. 11 and 12), and gradually diminishes seaward; i.e. we expect continuity in phosphate content between the relatively sparse sampling points. Finally, thickness and distribution of deposits are estimated from bottom photographs, samples recovered by dredge and submersible, and areal distribution as taken from fig. 2.

The present estimate of 2 billion metric tons of phosphorite nodules, which includes 30–40% or perhaps more impurities, may be compared with about 18 billion metric tons of apatite for

TABLE 7.—DISTRIBUTION OF ECONOMIC DEPOSITS ON THE NORTHERN BLAKE PLATEAU

Type of Deposit	Estimated Thickness (cm)	Area (km^2)	Vol. (m^3)	Tonnage
Phosphorite concretions	10	7.4×10^3	7×10^8	2×10^9
Mn-phosphorite pavement and concretions	5	9.4×10^3	4.6×10^8	1.2×10^9
Mn-Fe concretions	2	5.1×10^9	1×10^8	0.25×10^9

the Florida land pebble district (Altschuler et al., 1967), and 65 million metric tons of phosphate nodules in the offshore southern California region (Hess, 1978). Average P_2O_5 is estimated at 22 percent for phosphorite nodules.

Laboratory tests have shown that the offshore phosphorite beds are difficult to beneficiate and free from carbonate and other impurities and are currently non-competitive with land supplies. However, Florida land supplies are becoming depleted, and concern about environmental complications (slimes, radioactive tailings, water pollution) has created increasingly expensive and unfavorable conditions for economic recovery of phosphates on land in the United States. Moreover, new (or revived interest in old) techniques such as direct milling and use of ground phosphorite on soils, particularly in tropical or subtropical areas with heavy rainfall-may create greater potential for marine phosphorites in general, and for the Blake Plateau deposits in particular.

Acknowledgements

We acknowledge assistance with earlier analyses by Susan Kadar, Heidi Richards, Margaret Vieira, Ray Angona, and Karlis Muehlenbachs. Background data were discussed with J. C. Hathaway, P. M. Brown, J. S. Schlee, K. O. Emery, J. D. Milliman, W. A. Berggren, E. Uchupi, E. F. K. Zarudzki, T. Gibson, C. Emiliani, W. Charm, W. A. Sackett, P. C. Valentine and C. Wylie Poag. P. J. Bermudez, Ministry of Natural Resources, Caracas, Venezuela determined the age of some foraminifera in thin sections. We thank R. H. Meade, M. Fleischer, Z. S. Altschuler and J. B. Cathcart for critiques of an earlier manuscript. Financial support for the work was provided largely by the U.S. Geological Survey, supplemented by funds from the U.S. Office of Naval Reaserch (Contract ONR 12196). Early work was conducted during a joint USGS-Woods Hole Oceanographic Institution program led by K. O. Emery.

REFERENCES

ABBOTT, W. H., AND ERNISSEE, J. J., 1978, Biostratigraphy and paleoecology of a diatomaceous clay unit in the Miocene Pungo River Formation of Beaufort County, North Carolina: Smithsonian Contributions to Paleobiology.

ALTSCHULER, Z. S., CLARKE, R. S.,AND YOUNG, E. J., 1958, Geochemistry of uranium in apatite and phosphorite: U.S. Geol. Survey Prof. Paper 314-D, 90 p.

ALTSCHULER, Z. S., BERMAN, SOL, AND CUTTITTA, FRANK, 1967, Rare earths in phosphorites: geochemistry and potential recovery: U.S. Geol. Survey Prof. Paper 575-B, p. 1–9.

——, AND ROWE, J., 1968, written communication.

——, CATHCART, J. B., AND YOUNG E. J., 1964, Geology and geochemistry of the Bone Valley Formation and its phosphate deposits: West Central Florida Guidebook, Field Trip no. 6, Geol. Soc. Am. Convention, Nov. 1964, 68 p.

AMES, L. L., 1959, The genesis of carbonate apatite: Econ. Geol., v. 4, p. 829–841.

AMOS, A. F., GARSIDE, F., HAINES, K. C., AND ROELS, O. A., 1972, Effects of surface-discharged deep-sea mining effluent, *in* D. R. Horn (ed.), Ferromanganese Deposits on the Ocean Floor: Conference, Arden House, International Decade of Oceanogr., Nat. Sci. Found., 293 p.

ANONYMOUS, 1969, Phosphorite: Project Report no. 11, Georgia State Div. Cons., Dept. Mines, Mining and Geology, 165 p.

BARTLETT, J. R., 1883, Deep-sea soundings and temperatures in the Gulf Stream off the Atlantic Coast: American Assoc. Adv. Sci. Proc., v. 31, p. 1–4.

BATURIN, G. N., 1971, Stages of phosphorite formation on the ocean floor: Nature, v. 232, p. 61–62.

——, 1972, Fosfor v ilovykh vodakh osadkov yugo-vostochnoi Atlantiki (Phosphorus in pore waters of sediments in the southeast Atlantic): Okeanologiya, 1972, no. 6, p. 1020–1027.

——, 1975, Uran v sovremennom morskom osadkoobrazovanii (Uranium in Recent marine sediment formation): Atomizdat, Moscow, 151 p.

BREMANIS, E., DEERING, J. R., MEAD, C. F., AND KEYWORTH, D. A., 1967, Elimination of nitrogen and chloride interferences in the iodometric chloride determination of sulfur as sulfur dioxide: Materials Research and Standards, v. 7, p. 459–460.

BRUNDAGE, W., 1972, Patterns of manganese pavement distribution on the Blake Plateau, *in* D. R. Horn (ed.), Ferromanganese Deposits on the Ocean Floor: Nat. Sci. Found., Wash., D.C., p. 221–250.

BURNETT, W. C., 1973, written communication.

——, 1974, Phosphorite deposits from the sea floor off Peru and Chile: radiochemical and geochemical investigations concerning their origin: Hawaii Inst. Geophysics Rept. HIG 74-3, 164 p.

BURNS, R. G., AND BURNS, V. M., 1977, Mineralogy, *in* G. P. Glasby (ed.), Marine Manganese Deposits: Elsevier Pub. Co., Amsterdam-N.Y., p. 185–248.

BUSHINSKII, G. I., 1966, Drevnie fosfority Azii i ikh genezis (Ancient phosphorites of Asia and their genesis): "Nauka" Publ. House, Moscow, 192 p.

CATHCART, J. B., 1968, Phosphate in the Atlantic and Gulf Coastal Plains: Fourth Forum on Geology of Industrial Minerals. Proc., Texas Bureau of Economic Geology, p. 23–34.

DIETZ, R. S., EMERY, K. O., AND SHEPARD, F. P., 1942, Phosphorite deposits on the sea floor of Southern California: Geol. Soc. America Bull., v. 53, p. 815–848.

DOYLE, L. J., BLAKE, N. J., WOO, C. C., AND YEVICH, P., 1978, Recent biogenic phosphorite: concretions in mollusc kidneys: Science, v. 199, p. 1431–1433.

EHRLICH, A. M., 1968, Rare earths in manganese-iron concretions: PhD. dissertation, Dept. Geology and Geophysics, Mass. Inst. Technology.

ELDERFIELD, H., HOLMEFJORD, T., AND SUMMERHAYES, C. P., 1972, Enhanced CO_2 substitution in carbonate-apatite from the Moroccan continental margin: 16th Annual Report, Research Inst. of African Geology, University of Leeds, p. 51–52.

EMERY, K. O., AND UCHUPI, E., 1972, Western North Atlantic Ocean: Topography, rocks, structure, water, life, and sediments: Amer. Assoc. Petrol. Geol., Memoir 17, 532 p.

————, AND ZARUDZKI, E. F. K., 1967, Seismic reflection profiles along the lines of JOIDES drill holes: U.S. Geol. Survey Prof. Paper 581-A, 8 p.

EWING, JOHN, EWING, MAURICE, AND LEYDEN, ROBERT, 1966, Seismic profiler survey of Blake Plateau: Am. Assoc. Petrol. Geol. Bull., v. 50, p. 1948–71.

GIBSON, T. G., 1967, Stratigraphy and paleoenvironment of the phosphatic Miocene strata of North Carolina: Geol. Soc. America Bull., v. 78, p. 631–50.

GOODELL, H. G., 1967, The sediments and sedimentary geochemistry of the southeastern Atlantic shelf: J. Geol., v. 75, p. 665–692.

GORSLINE, D. S., 1963, Bottom sediments of the Atlantic shelf and slope off the southern United States: J. Geol., v. 71, p. 422–439.

————, AND MILLIGAN, D. B., 1963, Phosphatic deposits along the margin of the Pourtales Terrace, Florida: Deep-Sea Research, v. 10, p. 259–262.

GUAZELLI, W., AND CORTA, M. P. DEA., 1978, Occurrencia de fosfato do plato de Ceara: Serie Projecto REMAC, Dinter (Petrobras), Rio de Janeiro (in press).

HATHAWAY, J. C., 1971, Data file: Continental Margin Program, Atlantic coast of the United States, Woods Hole Oceanographic Institution, Ref. no. 71, v. 2, 495 p.

————, McFARLIN, P. F., AND ROSS, D. A., 1970, Mineralogy and origin of sediments from drill holes on the continental margin off Florida: U.S. Geol. Survey Prof. Paper 581-E, 26 p. with maps.

————, SCHLEE, J. S., POAG, C. W., VALENTINE, P. C., WEED, E. G. A., BOTHNER, M. H., KOHOUT, F. A., MANHEIM, F. T., SCHOEN, R., MILLER, R. E., AND SCHULTZ, D. M., 1976, Preliminary Summary of the 1976 Atlantic Margin Coring Project of the U.S. Geological Survey: U.S. Geol. Survey Open-File Rept. 76-844, 218 p.

HAWKINS, L. K., 1969, Visual observations of manganese deposits on the Blake Plateau: J. Geophys. Res., v. 74, p. 7008–7017.

HEEZEN, B. C., AND HOLLISTER, C. H., 1971, The Face of the Deep: Oxford Univ. Press, Oxford-New York, 659 p.

HERSEY, J. P., BUNCE, E. T., WYRICK, R. F., AND DIETZ, F. T., 1959, Geophysical investigation of the continental margin between Cape Henry, Virginia and Jacksonville, Fla.: Geol. Soc. America Bull., v. 70, p. 437–466.

HESS, H. D., 1978, written communication.

JOIDES (Joint Oceanographic Institutions' Deep Earth Sampling Program), 1965, Ocean drilling on the continental margin: Science, v. 150, p. 709–716.

KIMREY, J. O., 1965, Description of the Pungo River Formation, Beaufort County, North Carolina: N. C. Dept. Conservation & Devel., Div. Mineral Resources, Bull. 79, 131 p.

KRAUSKOPF, K. B., 1955, Sedimentary deposits of rare metals: Econ. Geol., 50th Anniv. Volume, p. 411–463.

KU, TEH-LUNG, AND BROECKER, W. S., 1968, Radiochemical studies on manganese nodules of deep sea origin: Deep-Sea Research, v. 16, p. 625–637.

LANDERGREN, STURE, MULD, WILLIAM, AND RAJANDI, BENITA, 1964, Analytical methods, *in* Landergren, Sture: On the Geochemistry of Deep Sea Sediments: Repts. Swedish Deep Sea Expedition, v. 10, Spec. Inv. no. 5, p. 148–151.

LeGEROS, R. Z., TRAUTZ, O. R., LeGEROS, J. P., AND KLEIN, EDWARD, 1967, Apatite crystallites: effects of carbonate on morphology: Science, v. 155, p. 1409–1411.

LEHR, J. R., McCLELLAN, G. H., SMITH, J. P., AND FRAZIER, A. W., 1968, Characterization of apatites in commercial phosphate rocks: Bull. Soc. Chim. France, v. 2, p. 29.

MALDE, H. E., 1959, Geology of the Charleston phosphate area, South Carolina: U.S. Geol. Survey Bull., 1079, 105 p.

MANHEIM, F. T., 1965, Manganese-iron accumulations in the shallow marine environment: Symp. Marine Geochemistry, Occ. Publ. no. 3-1965, Narragansett Marine Lab., Univ. Rhode Island, p. 217–276.

————, 1967, Evidence for submarine discharge of water on the Atlantic Continental Slope of the southern United States, and suggestions for further search: N. Y. Acad. Sci. Trans., v. 29, p. 839–853.

————, 1971, Chemical analysis, major and minor elements, *in* Hathaway, J. C. (ed.): Data File, Continental Margin Program, Atlantic Coast of the United States, v. 2: Woods Hole Oceanographic Institution Rept. 71-15, p. 437–449.

————, AND COMMEAU, J. A., 1978, Chemical composition of rocks from the AMCOR drill holes on the United States Continental Shelf: Geol. Soc. Am. Abs. with Programs, v. 10, p. 450.

————, Rowe, G., and Jipa, D., 1975, Marine phosphorite formations off Peru: J. Sed. Petrol., v. 45, p. 243–251.

Markel, S., 1967, Newspaper accounts of *Aluminaut* passage on the Blake Plateau: Reynolds Submarine Services, Richmond, Va.

Martens, C. S., and Harriss, R. C., 1970, Inhibition of apatite precipitation in the marine environment by magnesium ions: Geochim. et Cosmochim. Acta, v. 34, p. 621–625.

McConnell, Duncan, 1938, A structural investigation of isomorphism of the apatite group: Am. Mineralogist, v. 23, p. 1–19.

McConnell, D. W., 1973, Apatite, its crystal chemistry, mineralogy, utilization, and geologic and biologic occurrences: Springer Verlag, N. Y., 111 p.

McFarlin, P. F., 1967, Aragonite vein fillings in marine manganese nodules: J. Sed. Petrology, v. 37, p. 68–72.

McKelvey, V. E., and Wang, F. H., 1970, World subsea mineral resources; preliminary maps: U.S. Geol. Survey, Misc. Geol. Inv. Map I-632, 17 p.

Mero, J. O., 1965, The mineral resources of the sea: Elsevier, Amsterdam-New York, 312 p.

Milliman, J. D., Manheim, F. T., Pratt, R. M., and Zarudzki, E. F. K., 1967, ALVIN dives on the continental margin off the southeastern United States: Woods Hole Oceanographic Institution Ref. 67–80 (umpubl.), 47 p.

Moore, J. E., and Gorsline, D. S., 1960, Physical and chemical data for bottom sediments, South Atlantic Coast of the United States: U.S. Fish and Wildlife Service, Spec. Sci. Rept. no. 366, 84 p.

Murray, John, 1885, Report on the specimens of bottom deposits: Harvard Mus. Comp. Zoology Bull., v. 12, p. 37–61.

Parker, R. J., 1971, The petrography and major element geochemistry of phosphorite nodule deposits on the Agulhas Bank, South Africa: South African National Committee for Oceanographic Research, Marine Geology Programme, Bull. no. 2, 94 p.

Pasho, D. W., 1972, Character and origin of marine phosphorites: Univ. Southern California, Report USC Geol. 72-5, 188 p.

————, 1976, Distribution and morphology of Chatham Rise phosphorites: New Zealand Oceanogr. Inst. Memoir 77, 28 p.

Pevear, D. R., 1966, The estuarine formation of United States Atlantic coastal plain phosphorite: Econ. Geol., v. 61, p. 251–256.

Pilkey, O. H., 1967, written communication.

————, and Luternauer, J. L., 1967, A North Carolina shelf phosphate deposit of possible commercial interest: Southeastern Geology, v. 8, p. 33–51.

Pratt, R. M., 1963, Bottom currents on the Blake Plateau: Deep-Sea Research, v. 10, p. 245–249.

————, 1966, The Gulf Stream as a graded river: Limnology and Oceanography, v. 11, p. 60–67.

————, 1968, Deep-sea topography and sediments off the Atlantic coast: U.S. Geol. Survey Prof. Paper 529-B, 44 p. with map.

————, and McFarlin, P. F., 1966, Manganese pavements on the Blake Plateau: Science, v. 151, p. 1080–1082.

Price, N. B., and Calvert, S. E., 1978, The geochemistry of phosphorites from the Namibian Shelf: Chem. Geol., v. 23, p. 151–170.

Rooney, T. P., and Kerr, P. F., 1967, Mineralogic nature and origin of phosphorite, Beaufort County, North Carolina: Geol. Soc. America Bull., v. 78, p. 731–748.

Schopf, T. J. M., and Manheim, F. T., 1967, Chemical composition of Ectroprocta (Bryozoa): J. Paleo., v. 41, p. 1197–1225; Addenda, J. Paleo., v. 42 (in press).

Schroeder, E., 1963, Serial atlas of the marine environment: Folio 2, North Atlantic Temperatures at a depth of 200 m: Amer. Geographical Soc., 9 plates.

Sheldon, R., 1964, Paleolatitudinal and paleogeographic distribution of phosphorite: U.S. Geol. Survey Prof. Paper 501-C, p. 106–113.

Simons, F., and Altschuler, Z. S., 1968, Gold in marine phosphorites: Unpublished memorandum, U.S. Geol. Survey, Wash., D.C.

Simpson, D. R., 1966, Apatite and octa-calcium phosphate: effects of carbon dioxide and halogens on formation: Science, v. 154, p. 1660–1661.

Smirnov, A. I., 1959, Novye dannye po elementarnomu sostavu fostoritov basseina Karatau (New data on the composition of Karatau phosphorites): Doklady Akad. Nauk, SSSR, v. 125, p. 177–181.

Stetson, T. R., 1961, Report on Atlantic Cruise 266: Woods Hole Oceanographic Institution Ref. No. 61-35 (unpubl.), 24 p.

Summerhayes, C. P., 1970, Phosphate deposits of the Northwest Africa continental shelf and slope: PhD. thesis, University of London.

Uchupi, Elazar, 1963, Sediments on the continental margin off eastern United States: U.S. Geol. Survey Prof. Paper 475-C, p. 132–137.

————, and Emery, K. O., 1967, structure of continental margin off Atlantic coast of the United States: Am. Assoc. Petroleum Geologists Bull., v. 51, p. 223–234.

————, 1967, The continental margin south of Cape Hatteras, North Carolina: shallow structure: Southeastern Geology, v. 8, p. 155–177.

Vaughan, T. W., 1910, A contribution to the history of the Floridian Plateau: Carnegie Inst. Wash. Publ. Co. no. 133, p. 99–185.

VEEH, H. H., BURNETT, W. C., AND SOUTAR, A., 1973, Contemporary phosphorites on the continental margin of Peru: Science, v. 181, p. 844–845.

WEAVER, C. E., AND BECK, K. C., 1977, Miocene of the southeastern United States: a model for chemical sedimentation in a peri-marine environment: Sed. Geology, v. 17, 234 p.

WEYL, R., 1964, Die paläogeographische Entwicklung des Mittelamerikanisch-Westindischen Raumes: Geol. Rundschau, v. 54, p. 1213–1240.

ZARUDZKI, E. F. K., AND UCHUPI, ELAZAR, 1968, Organic reef alignments of the continental margin south of Cape Hatteras: Geol. Soc. America Bull., v. 79, p. 1867–1870.

SEPM SPECIAL PUBLICATION No. 29, P. 139–148, NOVEMBER 1980

DISTRIBUTION, COMPOSITION AND AGE OF SUBMARINE PHOSPHORITES ON CHATHAM RISE, EAST OF NEW ZEALAND

DAVID J. CULLEN

New Zealand Oceanographic Institute, Department of Scientific
and Industrial Research, P.O. Box 12-346, Wellington
North, New Zealand

ABSTRACT

A belt of nodular phosphorite deposits can be traced on the sea floor for some 480 km along the crest of Chatham Rise between longitudes 177°E and 177°W, mostly at depths less than 400 m. Their economic potential is being investigated, particularly near the 180° meridian where concentrations of phosphorite in the order of 75–80 kg/m^2 have been measured. Although the surface distribution is patchy, and the thickness of the deposit limited, appreciable sub-surface continuity of the phosphorite is indicated. Bioturbation plays an important role in localized redistribution of the nodules and their exposure on the sea floor surface.

The phosphorus content of nodules varies between 15 and 25% P_2O_5, the higher values tending to occur in the smallest-sized particles. Analyses of uranium and rare earth element concentrations in the Chatham Rise phosphorites reveal a comparable relation to particle size.

The nodules rest on a bored and eroded surface of lowermost Oligocene chalky and chert-bearing limestone. They consist mainly of Lower and lower Middle Miocene limestones from horizons not now locally exposed, and are typically coated by greenish-black glauconite which is provisionally dated as Late Miocene or Early Pliocene. Phosphatization, erosion and nodule formation are therefore attributed to Middle-Late Miocene events. There is no evidence of subsequent phosphatization on Chatham Rise.

INTRODUCTION

At the present time the Chatham Rise, east of New Zealand, is of particular interest in that it is one of the very few areas (perhaps the only area) in the world where assessment of submarine phosphorites is being actively pursued with a view to possible commercial exploitation.

The present comprehensive survey of the Chatham Rise phosphorites was instigated by a growing awareness of the rapid depletion of New Zealand's existing sources of rock-phosphate on Nauru and Ocean Island, in the western Pacific, and Christmas Island, in the eastern Indian Ocean. Moreover, a massive increase in the price of Moroccan rock-phosphate in 1973 (Morocco is the world's largest exporter of this commodity) raised concern over the possibility of future instability of rock-phosphate prices on the world market. The dependence of New Zealand's agriculture-based economy on supplies of fertilizer materials is undeniable, and, in the virtual absence of usable internal terrestrial resources of phosphate, the advisability of investigating the Chatham Rise phosphorite deposits as a potential resource is self-evident.

Distribution

The presence of nodular phosphorite on Chatham Rise was first reported by Reed and Hornibrook in 1952, when they described some rather meager material collected by R/V *Discovery II*. Subsequent descriptions of samples from Chatham Rise by Norris (1964), Cullen (1975), and Pasho (1976) provided additional data on the phosphorite deposits, but, prior to the beginning of the present investigation, no really detailed information was available on their distribution and thickness, or on their field relationships, age and chemical composition. It is now known that the phosphorites are widely distributed on the sea floor on Chatham Rise, and there is a growing fund of evidence as to their geological and geochemical nature.

Occurrences of nodular phosphorite have now been traced over a distance of some 480 km along the crest of Chatham Rise, between longitudes 177°E and 177°W, within an E-W belt that varies in width up to about 40 km. The largest-known accumulations occur in the vicinity of the 180° meridian, in water depths between 350 m and 450 m (fig. 1).

Underwater photography (Cullen and Singleton, 1977) has shown that, even in areas of maximum concentration (fig. 2), exposures of phosphorite nodules on the sea floor surface are inclined to be quite patchy. The patches occur at varying scales measured in centimeters, in tens or hundreds of meters, and in kilometers, with the smaller patches conglomerating to form larger spreads. In the intermediate range, individual patches appear to extend to about 200 m across in a N-S direction. As most sampling and photography was effected along N-S traverses, their E-W extent is as yet unknown. In view of the

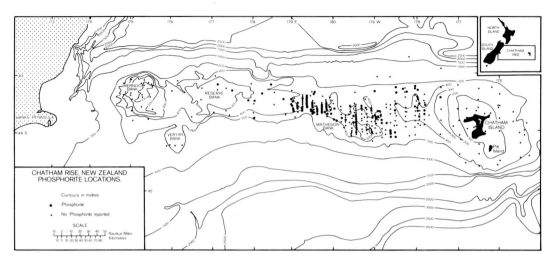

FIG. 1.—Map showing location of stations and distribution of phosphorite deposits on Chatham Rise (after Pasho, 1976). Note the concentration of phosphorite about the 180° meridian. Westward, glauconitic sands and muds prevail.

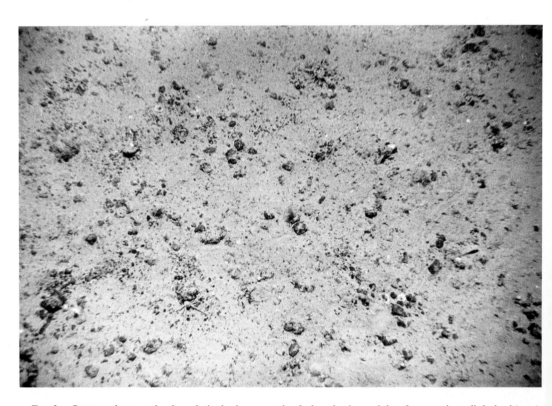

FIG. 2.—Bottom photograph of a relatively dense patch of phosphorite nodules (large and small dark objects) with associated pale sandy mud at station H956. Note the galatheid shrimp (bottom left), the cidarid echinoid (top center) and the animal trail (right). The base of the photograph represents approximately 1 meter.

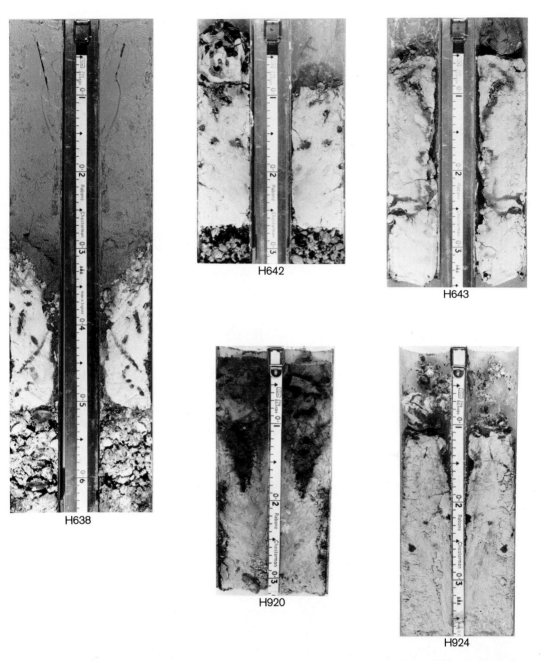

FIG. 3.—Piston cores demonstrating the surficial stratigraphy of central Chatham Rise. The most complete sequence (core H638) shows a basal phosphorite layer, a 20 cm layer of white ooze with burrows overlain by a second phosphorite layer and 30 cm of glauconitic sandy mud. The other cores show less complete sequences. Scale in meters.

regional E-W trend of geological and morphological features on Chatham Rise, however, it may be that the patches also are elongated in that direction.

Some continuity of the phosphorite, at shallow depth beneath the sea floor in the intervening "barren" areas, is indicated by two lines of evidence. Firstly, in both piston and box cores (Cullen, 1978a), phosphorite nodules often occur beneath a variable thickness of fine superficial

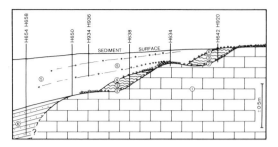

F<small>IG</small>. 4.—Schematic representation of the surficial stratigraphy of central Chatham Rise. 1. Oligocene chalk "basement"; 2. Basal phosphorite layer; 3. White foraminiferal ooze; 4. Upper phosphorite layer; 5. Glauconitic sandy mud with scattered (mostly small) phosphorite nodules; 6. Laminated sandy mud with ash layers (on flanks of Rise).

sediments—mostly foraminiferal ooze and glauconitic sandy mud—down to at least 0.7 m below the sea floor surface (fig. 3). A schematic reconstruction of the superficial stratigraphy of central Chatham Rise, based on data from piston cores, is presented in fig. 4. It also attempts to explain the presence at certain localities of two distinct layers of phosphorite nodules, and of scattered nodules in the superficial "blanket" of glauconitic sandy muds.

Sub-surface continuity of the phosphorite can also be inferred from bottom photography in the "barren" areas. There, small isolated nodule patches—usually less than 0.5 m across, and containing only the smallest phosphorite particles—are almost invariably associated with evidence of burrowing by macrobenthic organisms (especially crabs), and it is clear that these nodules have been carried up to the sediment surface from a subjacent phosphorite layer at shallow depth.

N877

F<small>IG</small>. 5.—Side (top left), front (top right) and surface views of box core N877, showing abundant phosphorite nodules within and upon the upper surface of the core. Compare surface with bottom photograph (fig. 2). This core represents a phosphorite concentration of 82 kg/m^2 in the 10–12 cm immediately below the sea floor.

10cm

N879

Fig. 6.—Side (top left), front (top right) and surface views of box core N879, showing abundant phosphorite nodules beneath a barren surface. This core represents a phosphorite concentration of 77 kg/m^2 in the 10–12 cm immediately below the sea floor.

Indeed, the photographs suggest that bioturbation is an important factor in the exposure of phosphorite nodules in the present sedimentary regime on the crest of Chatham Rise. The absence of current-induced structures such as ripple-marks, together with the survival of completely unconsolidated, very fine grained sediment in association with the phosphorite, indicates an essentially low-energy hydrological environment. It is suggested that bioturbation plays a role in exposing the nodules, not only by physically transporting them upward to the sediment surface, but also by raising into suspension the associated fine sediment which can then be dispersed by such gentle bottom currents as do operate in the region.

The core samples (Cullen, 1978) indicate that individual phosphorite layers are of limited thickness, the maximum so far encountered being 0.15 m (N.Z. Oceanographic Institute Stations H638, H920). As mentioned previously, however,

two distinct phosphorite layers can be recognized in certain areas, with nodules also dispersed in some of the associated sediments. A phosphorite layer at station N877, penetrated to a depth of only 0.12 m by a box corer (fig. 5) which obviously did not reach the base of the layer, was found to represent a concentration of phosphorite of 82 kg/m^2 for the 0.12 m immediately underlying the sea floor. The distribution of phosphorite nodules, as seen on the surface of this core, can be compared with that apparent in the bottom photograph from station H956 (fig. 2), and in this way correlation of photographic and coring data has been attempted for assessment purposes. Even more illuminating perhaps is the analysis of box core N879 (fig. 6). Despite its completely barren surface, this core was found to contain only slightly less phosphorite—representing a concentration of 77 kg/m^2—for a comparable depth of penetration. This emphasizes the poten-

Fig. 7.—Submarine erosion of phosphorite nodules from station H667, involving stripping-off of the dark glauconite pellicle and pitting of the subjacent phosphatized limestone.

tial quantity of phosphorite, buried at shallow depth beneath superficial sediments, in areas that appear otherwise barren.

General Characteristics and Composition of the Phosphorite Nodules

The phosphorite occurs on Chatham Rise as a nodular, remanié-type deposit, formed by the erosion and dissolution of pre-existing limestone horizons, and the partial replacement of carbonate in the remnant fragments by phosphate. No evidence exists on Chatham Rise of purely accretionary phosphorite particles or of pelletal varieties.

The nodules range in size from a few millimeters across, up to 150 mm or more, with size frequency peaking between 20 mm and 40 mm. Typically, nodules are sub-angular to sub-rounded. The markedly irregular shapes of many of the larger nodules reflect the influence of close-spaced borings and tubular burrows, most of which seem to have formed before final induration of the nodules.

Internally, nodule colors range from yellowish grey (5Y 7/2)* to moderage yellowish brown (10YR 5/4) and greyish olive (10Y 4/2). External surfaces of the vast majority of nodules are very dark ranging from olive grey (5Y 3/2) to olive black (5Y 2/1), and frequently have a smooth, glossy texture. These characteristics betray the almost ubiquitous presence of glauconite, as a thin pellicle, coating the nodules. Glauconite also occurs as discrete grains scattered within the phosphatized limestone fabric of the nodules, and, in this case, is clearly part of the original sediment from which the nodules formed.

Erosion of the glauconite pellicle and superficial pitting of nodules (fig. 7) is a prominent feature in a few localities, and has been attributed by Pasho (1976) to subaerial weathering following Plio-Pleistocene uplift. However, in the case of the Chatham Rise phosphorites, this interpretation is not unequivocally supported by available evi-

*Rock color code advanced by the Rock-color Chart Committee (1975).

TABLE 1.—TYPICAL CHEMICAL ANALYSES OF CHATHAM RISE PHOSPHORITE NODULES*

| | Station H955 (Sample 1) | | | | | Station H955 (Sample 2) | | |
	1	2	3	4	5	6	7	8
	%	%	%	%	%	%	%	%
P_2O_5	23.8	23.0	23.0	21.3	23.7	23.0	21.9	19.5
CO_2	5.4	9.2	10.9	14.5	5.9	9.7	12.3	16.8
H_2O+	3.5	3.2	3.1	2.4	3.6	3.2	3.0	2.5
H_2O-	0.44	0.33	0.32	0.37	0.53	0.41	0.32	0.42
SiO_2	11.2	7.4	4.5	4.0	11.2	7.4	4.0	3.9
Al_2O_3	1.0	0.55	0.48	0.50	0.99	0.62	0.44	0.47
FeO	0.49	0.32	0.23	0.17	0.51	0.27	0.15	0.14
Fe_2O_3	5.2	4.7	3.8	2.8	5.5	5.2	5.4	3.2
TiO_2	0.03	0.02	0.01	0.04	<0.01	0.01	<0.01	0.01
MnO	0.01	0.01	0.01	0.02	0.01	0.01	0.02	0.02
CaO	41.9	44.0	46.2	47.6	40.6	44.3	45.8	47.5
MgO	1.4	1.0	0.86	0.76	1.4	1.0	0.76	0.71
K_2O	1.5	1.1	0.72	0.59	1.7	1.0	0.56	0.59
Na_2O	0.97	0.88	0.89	0.81	0.92	0.91	0.86	0.77
SO_3	1.9	1.8	1.7	1.6	1.8	1.6	1.6	1.5
F	3.0	2.9	2.9	2.7	3.0	3.0	2.9	2.6
Cl	<0.1	<0.1	<0.1	<0.1	<0.1	<0.1	<0.1	<0.1

Columns 1, 5 : particles less than 6.5 mm
Columns 2, 6 : particles 6.5–13.0 mm
Columns 3, 7 : particles 13.0–26.0 mm
Columns 4, 8 : particles 26.0–52.0 mm
*Analyses by W. Kitt, Chemistry Division, New Zealand Department of Scientific and Industrial Research.

dence on the oxidation state of the uranium present—the criterion used by Burnett and Gomberg (1977) for recognition of subaerial erosion of phosphorites on submerged terraces off the Florida coast. The dominance of tetravalent over hexavalent uranium in typical specimens of the Chatham Rise phosphorites—the former averages 80% of the total uranium according to Kolodny and Kaplan (1970) and Burnett and Veeh (1977)—means that subjection of this deposit to widespread subaerial weathering is not likely to have happened.

Phosphate replacement of the original limestone, as indicated by dark color-zonation where calcium carbonate has been substituted by carbonate-fluorapatite (francolite), tends to be somewhat irregular. It is generally most intense towards the periphery of the nodules, with (especially in the larger nodules) a decreasing phosphate/carbonate ratio towards the interior. This is reflected in the overall phosphate contents of different sized particles. Large, incompletely replaced nodules (>64 mm) may have P_2O_5 values as low as 17–18%, whereas particles less than 6 mm across contain up to 24% P_2O_5 (table 1). An average value for the P_2O_5 content of nodules would probably be in the region of 21–22%.

In an account of the uranium content of the Chatham Rise phosphorites, Cullen (1978b) lists four reasons for the quantitative determination of this element. These include:
(1) Checking the amounts of potentially harm-

TABLE 2.—TRACE ELEMENT CONCENTRATIONS IN TYPICAL CHATHAM RISE PHOSPHORITE NODULES.*

| | Concentration in ppm | | | |
	N877	N879(1)	N879(2)	N879(3)
U	58	100	92	170
Th	2.7	<1.0	<1.0	<1.0
Pb	23	35	53	38
Hf	<2.0	<2.0	<2.0	<2.0
Yb	<1.0	3.5	1.6	1.6
Er	<0.6	3.7	1.5	1.7
Ho	<0.3	1.4	0.53	0.53
Dy	<0.7	4.8	1.7	2.1
Tb	<0.3	1.2	0.44	0.44
Gd	<1.0	9.0	3.8	3.2
Eu	<0.5	1.0	<0.5	<0.5
Sm	<1.0	8.2	3.6	3.9
Nd	11	18	7.2	7.0
Pr	3.2	4.7	1.9	1.9
Ce	25	26	9.2	9.0
La	20	38	21	15
Ba	200	120	230	120
Cs	3.2	4.3	2.1	0.93
I	>200	>200	>200	30
Nb	2.9	1.4	<1.0	<1.0
Zr	160	48	31	36
Y	35	84	48	37
Sr	700	>1000	900	1000
Rb	60	>100	>100	14

(1) 1.16–6.35 mm size range
(2) 6.35–16.64 mm size range
(3) 16.64–64.0 mm size range
*Analyses by P. Rankin and J. Hunt (Soil Bureau, New Zealand Department of Scientific and Industrial Research) using spark-source mass spectrometry.

ful radionuclides that would be added to farm land if the phosphorite were eventually to be used for fertilizer production.

(2) Investigating the possibility of uranium being present in the phosphorite in exploitable amounts. In fact, the uranium levels encountered are such as could be of commercial interest in a terrestrial deposit.

(3) Enquiring into the practicability of using the uranium-series radiometric dating method to detect evidence of possible Quaternary phosphatization. This line of investigation has not, as yet, been pursued.

(4) Determining the feasibility of using the inherent radioactivity of the phosphorites as a means of mapping their areal extent with a deep-towed scintillation counter. Uranium levels in the phosphorites far exceed those in the associated sedimentary components (including pelletal and encrusting glauconite) and in sea-water, so that such a technique could have local application.

The uranium contents of the Chatham Rise phosphorites were found, from neutron activation analyses carried out by the Australian Atomic Energy Commission (Cullen, 1978b), to be highly variable with values ranging from 9 ppm up to 434 ppm uranium. Kolodny and Kaplan (1970)

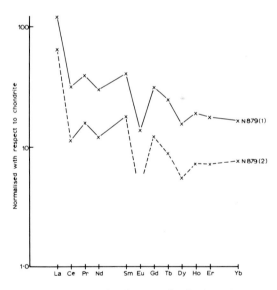

Fig. 8.—Rare-earth element distributions in two phosphorite sub-samples of different particle size (upper curve 1.16–6.35 mm: lower curve 6.35–16.64 mm) from station N879. Note the depletion in cerium and europium, and the higher concentrations characteristic of the smaller particles. Analyses by P. Rankin and J. Hunt, Soil Bureau, New Zealand Department of Scientific and Industrial Research.

quote a maximum value of 524 ppm uranium for samples of Chatham Rise phosphorite earlier analyzed by alpha-particle spectroscopy, and the average of all 21 analyzed samples from the area (Kolodny and Kaplan, 1970; Cullen, 1978b) is 200 ppm uranium.

Cullen (1978b) also noted that, while variations in the uranium and phosphate contents of the nodules on Chatham Rise are not strictly correlative, the uranium contents are broadly size-dependent with maximum values occurring in nodules in the 10–30 mm size range.

The limited number of rare earth element analyses of Chatham Rise phosphorites so far available (P. Rankin, personal communication) suggest that concentrations of these elements are significantly higher in the smaller sized nodules (<6.35 mm) than in the larger (table 2). Plotting of the analytical data (fig. 8), obtained by spark-source mass-spectrometry and normalized with respect to chondrite, produces a fairly regular curve showing a depletion in cerium, and a marked deficiency in europium.

Age of the Phosphorite

The majority of nodules on Chatham Rise are composed of phosphatized foraminiferal limestones that have been dated micropaleontologically as Lower Miocene (lower Altonian) and lower Middle Miocene (Altonian-Clifdenian). The younger of these limestones are characterized by the presence of *Globorotalia miozea* (N. de B. Hornibrook, personal communication), which is absent from the limestone of Early Miocene age. Actual outcrops of Miocene rocks are rare on Chatham Rise, and are only definitely known to occur towards the eastern end of the Rise. Airgun records show formations, provisionally interpreted as Miocene beds, buried beneath thick sediment accumulations on the southern flank of the Rise (see fig. 9).

At certain localities in both central and eastern Chatham Rise, phosphatic nodules have been recovered consisting of Lower Oligocene (lower Whaingaroan) limestone, distinguished by a foraminiferal assemblage containing *Chiloguembelina* and *Globigerina* cf. *angiporoides*. These nodules are clearly derived from the white chalk formation with layers of concretionary flints, that today forms the Tertiary "basement" beneath thin superficial deposits along the crest of much of central and eastern Chatham Rise.

It would thus appear that, in this area, the earliest possible date for the formation of most nodular phosphorites from bedded limestone deposits would have been fairly early in Middle Miocene times. The possibility of transformation of some Oligocene limestone to phosphorite nodules late in the Oligocene epoch cannot be

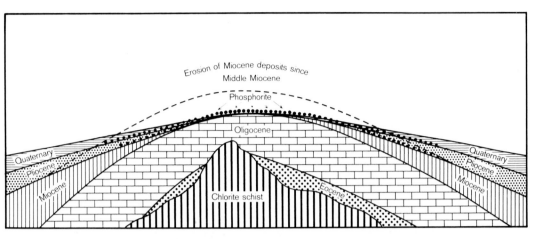

FIG. 9.—Schematic structural representation of formations occurring on central Chatham Rise, showing the postulated derivation of the remanié phosphorite from Lower Miocene and Oligocene limestone horizons.

excluded positively, but the close morphological and chemical correspondence of nodules, irrespective of the ages of their parent limestones, would seem to imply that nodule formation was essentially restricted to a single episode of erosion and phosphatization—after the beginning of the Middle Miocene. Nowhere on Chatham Rise have clasts of Oligocene phosphatic limestone been encountered in Miocene sediments, and this also militates against pre-Miocene phosphatization of the Oligocene chalk.

The minimum age of the phosphorite is indicated by the almost ubiquitous coatings of greenish-black glauconite on the nodules, mentioned earlier. Although the coatings of this mineral are too thin to provide sufficient material for direct radiometric dating, greenish-black *pelletal* glauconite, representative of that in the interstitial fine-grained sediment, has been dated by the K-Ar method as 5.6 ± 1 m.y. (Cullen, 1967). Mineralogically, these two types of glauconite are indistinguishable, and it would seem not unreasonable to suppose that they formed contemporaneously,

either very late in Miocene times or early in the Pliocene.

It is thus surmised that the Chatham Rise nodular phosphorites were formed by the erosion and phosphatization, in the interval between the beginning of the Middle Miocene and the end of the Late Miocene (15-5 m.y. B.P.), of both recently deposited (but already consolidated) Early Miocene limestone, and much older Oligocene chalk which must have been locally exposed on the sea floor at that time. The accretion of the glauconite coating, late in Miocene times or very early in the Pliocene, marked the termination of nodule formation. The subsequent history of the phosphorite nodules has involved burial, relatively slight reworking by gentle current action and/or bioturbation, and some submarine chemical erosion involving re-solution, resulting locally in stripping-off of glauconite pellicles and superficial pitting of nodules. There is no evidence on Chatham Rise of post-Miocene phosphorite formation.

REFERENCES

BURNETT, W. C., AND GOMBERG, D. N., 1977, Uranium oxidation and probable subaerial weathering of phosphatized limestone from the Pourtales Terrace: Sedimentology, v. 24, p. 291–302.
———, AND VEEH, H. H., 1977, Uranium-series disequilibrium studies in phosphorite nodules from the west coast of South America: Geochim. Cosmochim. Acta, v. 41, p. 755–764.
CULLEN, D. J., 1967, The age of glauconite from the Chatham Rise, east of New Zealand: N.Z. J. Mar. Freshwat. Res., v. 1, p. 399–406.
———, 1975, Petrology, distribution and economic potential of phosphorite deposits on Chatham Rise, east of New Zealand: Oceanogr. Summary N.Z. Oceanogr. Inst., v. 8, 6 p.
———, 1978a, The distribution of submarine phosphorite deposits on central Chatham Rise, east of New Zealand. 2. Sub-surface distribution from cores: Oceanogr. Fld. Rept. N.Z. Oceanogr. Inst., v. 12, 29 p.
———, 1978b, The uranium content of submarine phosphorite and glauconite deposits on Chatham Rise, east of New Zealand: Marine Geology, v. 28, p. M67–M76.
———, AND SINGLETON, R. J., 1977, The distribution of submarine phosphorite deposits on central Chatham

Rise, east of New Zealand. 1. Surface distribution from underwater photographs: Oceanogr. Fld. Rept. N.Z. Oceanogr. Inst., v. 10, 24 p.

KOLODNY, Y., AND KAPLAN, I. R., 1970, Uranium isotopes in sea-floor phosphorites: Geochim. Cosmochim. Acta, v. 34, p. 3–24.

NORRIS, R. M., 1964, Sediments of Chatham Rise: Mem. N.Z. Oceanogr. Inst., v. 26, 39 p.

PASHO, D. W., 1976, Distribution and morphology of Chatham Rise phosphorites: Mem. N.Z. Oceanogr. Inst., v. 77, 27 p.

REED, J. J., AND HORNIBROOK, N. DE B., 1952, Sediments from the Chatham Rise: N.Z. Jl Sci. Technol., v. 34B, p. 173–188.

ROCK-COLOR CHART COMMITTEE, 1975 (reprinted), Rock-color chart: The Geological Society of America, Boulder, Colorado.

SEPM SPECIAL PUBLICATION NO. 29, P. 149–152, NOVEMBER 1980

MINERALOGICAL AND GEOCHEMICAL STUDIES OF THE PHOSPHATIC FORMATIONS IN SOUTHEASTERN TURKEY (MAZIDAĞI-MARDIN)

JACQUES LUCAS,[1] LILIANE PRÉVÔT,[1] GÜROL ATAMAN[2] AND NIYAZI GÜNDOĞDU[2]
[1] Laboratoire de Géologie de l'Université Louis Pasteur
de Strasbourg, France, Centre de Sédimentologie et
Géochimie de la Surface, CNRS
1 Rue Blessig, 67000 Strasbourg, France
[2] Hacettepe Universitesi, Yerbilimleri Enstitüsü
Beytepe-Ankara, Turkey

This work presents the results of a short petrographical, mineralogical and geochemical study of the phosphorites of Mazidaği (Southeastern Turkey). This deposit is situated near the border of Syria (fig. 1) and was deposited during the Turonian and Senonian epochs of the Cretaceous.

Locally, the following stratigraphic units are distinguished: Karababa 1, Taşit and Karababa 2, belonging to the Turonian series; Kasrik, Şemikan and Karabogaz, belonging to the Senonian series; and Akras corresponding to the upper part of the Senonian and the basal part of a very reduced Paleocene series. It should be noted that the Turonian occurrence is one of the earliest known in the Middle East and in North Africa. Elsewhere in these areas, the phosphorites appear later, during the Campanian or Maastrichtian.

This sequence is composed mainly of carbonate rocks, in which four levels of phosphorites have been recognized in the Taşit, Kasrik, Şemikan and Akras Formations, respectively (fig. 2). The first, situated near the middle of the Turonian sequence, is a thin precursory phosphatic layer, separated from the Kasrik Formation by 100 meters of more or less argillaceous limestones. The Kasrik and Şemikan Formations are of Coniacian-Santonian age and contain the main phosphatic strata, which are associated with limestones, marls and cherts. These two phosphorite units appear closely together within the geological section, or even in continuity. The Akras Formation, the youngest one here discussed, is separated from the underlying one by more than 200 meters of the thick calcareous Karabogaz Formation of Late Maastrichtian age.

Since the discovery of the Mazidaği deposit by Sheldon in 1964, its only detailed study is the very interesting one of Heimbach et al. (1974) which, however, only deals with the Şemikan Formation. Our present aim is to complete the study of Ataman and Gündoğdu (1976) and to obtain information on the entire rock sequence, by a study of samples from outcrops and galleries.

The major minerals of all these rocks are calcite, dolomite, apatite and clays. Apatite is concentrated mainly in the phosphorite layers mentioned above, but occurs in small amounts also in some of the intercalated limestones; it is, however, apparently absent from the Karabogaz Formation. It is a fluor-carbonate-apatite with the following mean values: $CO_2 = 3.85\%$, $1.33 < CaO/P_2O_5 < 1.50$, $F/P_2O_5 = 0.11$. This apatite is similar to that described by Lucas et al. (1979a and c) from the Sidi Daoui deposit in the Khouribga area, Morocco, which has been interpreted as a product of gentle weathering. The entire sequence is calcitic, with the exception of the Akras Formation, in which dolomite is the dominant carbonate mineral present.

Clay minerals from marls and phosphorites are smectite and palygorskite (attapulgite) which are both common minerals of phosphorites. The smectite is frequently badly crystalline and associated with complex mixed-layer clay minerals. This clay assemblage resembles those of soils in the Mediterranean regions (Yaalon et al., 1966; Paquet, 1969; Desaunettes, 1971; Paquet and Millot, 1973), as well as that of the Sidi Daoui phosphorites. Kaolinite is always present in variable amounts, while glauconite is abundant in the Akras Formation.

All the phosphatic beds of the Mazidaği area show textures indicative of reworking with more

FIG. 1.—General location.

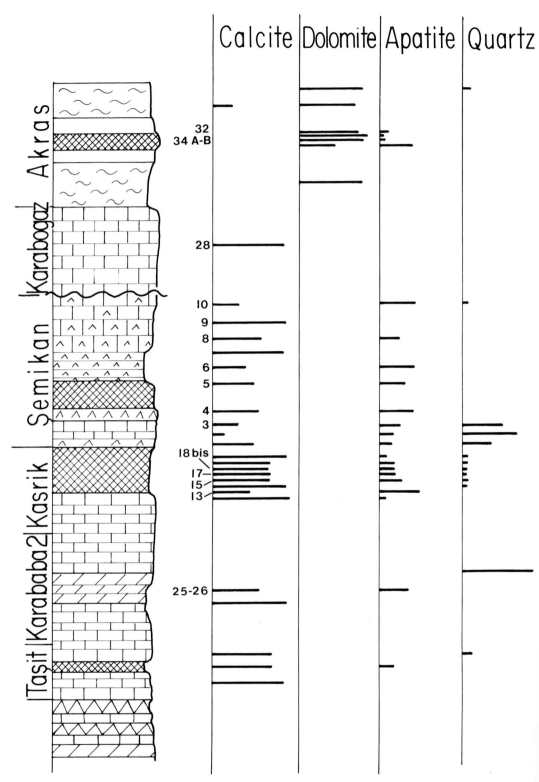

FIG. 2.—Schematic distribution of minerals in the stratigraphic sequence (thicknesses not to scale).

TABLE 1.—CHEMICAL COMPOSITION OF SOME PHOSPHORITES FROM THE MAZIDAĞI DEPOSIT. THE SAMPLE NUMBERS CORRESPOND TO THOSE OF FIGURE 2, EXCEPT NUMBER 11 WHICH IS A RED CLAY FROM RECENT WEATHERING.

Sample Number	SiO_2	Al_2O_3	MgO	CaO	Fe_2O_3	Mn_3O_4	TiO_2	Na_2O	K_2O	P_2O_5	Loss at $1000°$ C	Sum	F
3	64.9	0.3	0.08	19.5	0.3	<0.10	<0.02	0.17	0.10	8.5	6.62	100.5	
4	1.5	<0.2	0.20	56.9	<0.1	<0.10	<0.02	0.18	<0.05	21.7	18.56	99.3	
5	1.7	0.4	0.22	55.8	0.2	<0.10	0.02	0.14	<0.05	20.4	19.53	98.26	2.4
6	6.5	1.6	0.32	52.4	0.6	<0.10	0.08	0.17	<0.05	20.0	17.35	99.01	
8	6.3	1.5	0.33	48.4	0.8	<0.10	0.07	0.18	<0.05	13.9	25.51	97.14	
9	1.2	<0.2	0.36	53.2	<0.1	<0.10	<0.02	0.06	<0.05	1.1	42.41	98.64	
10	10.3	2.0	0.41	47.2	1.1	<0.10	0.11	0.29	<0.05	21.5	14.19	97.14	2.6
11	36.0	16.0	1.34	18.7	8.5	0.64	0.58	0.15	0.93	2.1	14.45	98.83	
13	1.1	0.2	0.24	53.7	0.1	<0.10	<0.02	0.25	<0.05	23.3	16.85	95.83	2.7
15	0.5	<0.2	0.20	53.7	<0.1	<0.10	<0.02	0.12	<0.05	12.2	31.19	98.22	
17	4.3	1.1	0.28	53.2	0.4	<0.10	0.06	0.15	<0.05	10.1	28.65	98.25	1.4
18bis	26.7	11.7	1.25	29.4	6.0	0.49	0.34	0.46	0.83	14.3	7.85	98.87	
25	5.2	<0.2	0.22	53.8	<0.1	<0.10	<0.02	0.29	<0.05	15.6	22.74	98.06	2.4
26	1.3	<0.2	0.20	54.9	<0.1	<0.10	<0.02	0.46	<0.05	28.6	11.06	96.79	
28	1.4	0.3	0.27	54.8	<0.1	<0.10	<0.02	0.07	<0.05	0.5	41.94	99.28	
32	4.9	1.2	16.7	29.0	5.7	0.18	0.19	0.16	0.43	1.6	39.25	99.13	
34A	9.3	2.7	5.38	33.9	14.7	0.30	0.30	0.78	0.70	12.3	17.34	97.40	2.0
34B	11.7	3.1	7.57	26.3	17.0	0.29	0.40	0.51	1.39	8.4	20.01	96.51	

detrital bone fragments than pellets and nodules. Quartz and other detrital minerals, however, are absent. The only silica is that of the silicifications. These observations make it probable that the phosphorites are the result of local reworking of pre-existing deposits by winnowing.

These phosphorites are inhomogeneous granular rocks in which phosphate occurs as bone fragments of different sizes (from several millimeters to a fraction of a millimeter in diameter), as pellets, as homogeneous collophanitic micro-nodules and as transparent cement. The pellets range in size from 0.10 to 0.20 mm. No sorting can be observed, but the bone fragments frequently belong to two size groups, indicating different origins. The usually pseudo-oolitic pellets result from autochthonous sedimentation, while nodules and cement are signs of diagenesis.

Here, as in many other phosphorites, both silicification and calcitization are common. Some bone fragments, even some of the larger ones, are completely calcitized. Calcitization affects all forms of apatitic material, including nodules, pellets and matrix. The presence of large calcitized and of small non-calcitized bone fragments in the same sample is indicative of an earlier stage of calcitization. The large fragments could have been eroded and transported from a previously calcitized phosphatic layer. In other samples, all the elements of the rock, including even secondary silica, are affected by a calcitization which seems to be more recent. Thus, calcitization seems to have operated at different stages in the history of the phosphorites.

Chemical compositions (table 1) confirm the homogeneity of the different facies. The phosphorites contain 52 to 56 percent CaO, with the exception of those from the Akras Formation which are rich in Mg from dolomite and in Fe from glauconite. The CaO-content remains constant and is independent of the apatite content. This is not surprising as the transformation of calcite into apatite and vice versa occurs without modification of the CaO content (Lucas et al., 1978). Likewise, Sr* remains constant at about 1000 ppm through phosphatization, calcitization and silicification.

It is concluded from these observations that the Mazidaği phosphorite deposit is the result of several processes which include: (1) erosion of more or less calcitized previous deposits and redeposition of this detrital material in a phosphatizing environment, (2) phosphatization of this detrital material, and (3) weathering which results in the characteristic mineralogy of the apatite (average CO_2-content, see Lucas et al., 1979c) and of the clay minerals, causing an enrichment of the ores. Heimbach et al. (1974) have indeed observed that the richest phosphorites are always situated near the present surface under a cover of less than 15 meters.

Weathering and calcitization had opposite effects: weathering enriched the phosphorites, calcitization depleted them. The present grade of the phosphorites appears to be the result of the interplay of these two processes.

*Data on trace elements are given in a more detailed publication (Lucas et al., 1979b).

Acknowledgements

Thanks are due to the society Etibank Fosfat Tesisleri and its director who gave us permission to visit and sample the Mazidaği deposit.

W. Heimbach of the Bundesanstalt für Bodenforschung kindly offered us his results for which we want to thank him greatly.

REFERENCES

ATAMAN, G., AND GÜNDOĞDU, N., 1976, Mardin-Mazidaği Fosfat yataklari kil mineralogisi ve fosfat sedimentasyonu ortaminin analizi: Yerbilimleri, Ankara, v. 2, p. 6–11.

DESAUNETTES, J. R., 1971, Sols rouges fersialitiques sur micaschistes en Grèce: Science du Sol, v. 2, p. 37–49.

HEIMBACH, W., SHOUKAY, B., AND STEINER, S., 1974, Die Phosphat-Lagerstätte Mazidagi, SE-Türkei: Bundesanstalt für Bodenforschung, unpubl.

LUCAS, J., PRÉVÔT, L., AND LAMBOY, M., 1978, Les phosphorites de la marge nord de l'Espagne; chimie, minéralogie, genèse: Oceanol. Acta, v. 1, p. 55–72.

————, ————, AND EL MOUNTASSIR, M., 1979a, Les phosphorites rubéfiées de Sidi Daoui; transformation météorique locale du gisement de phosphate des Ouled Abdoun (Maroc): Sci. Géol. Strasbourg, Bull.

————, ————, ATAMAN, G., AND GÜNDOĞDU, N., 1976b, Etude minéralogique et géochimique de la série phosphatée du Sud-Est de la Turquie (Mazidaği-Mardin): Sci. Géol. Bull., v. 32, (in press).

————, FLICOTEAUX, R., NATHAN, Y., PRÉVÔT, L., AND SHAHAR, Y., 1979c, Different aspects of phosphorite weathering: 10th Intern. Congr. Sedim., Jerusalem.

PAQUET, H., 1969, Evolution géochimique des minéraux argileux dans les altérations et les sols des climats méditerranéens et tropicaux à saisons contrastées: Thèse Sci. Strasbourg et Mém. Serv. Carte Géol. Als. Lorr., v. 30, 1970, 210 p.

————, AND MILLOT, G., 1973, Geochemical evolution of clay minerals in the weathered products and soils of Mediterranean climates: Proc. Intern. Clay Conf. Madrid, p. 199–206.

SHELDON, R. P., 1964, Exploration for phosphorite in Turkey. A case history: Econ. Geol., v. 59, p. 1159–1175.

YAALON, D. H., NATHAN, Y., KOYUMDJISKY, H., AND DAN, J., 1966, Weathering in soils and various parent material in Israel. Proc. Intern. Clay Conf. Jerusalem, v. 1, p. 187–198.

SEPM Special Publication No. 29, p. 153–165, November 1980

THE PETROGRAPHY OF ISRAELI PHOSPHORITES AS RELATED TO THEIR BENEFICIATION

S. AXELROD*, A. METZER** and V. ROHRLICH**
*Fertilizers and Chemicals Ltd., P.O. Box 1428 Haifa, Israel
**Geotechnical and Mineral Engineering Dept., Technion I.I.T., Haifa, Israel

ABSTRACT

The marine phosphorites of Campanian age that are presently exploited in Israel are composed of apatite grains (ovulites and/or skeletal) in a calcite (rarely siliceous) matrix, grain to mud supported. The chemical composition of the apatite, especially the substituted CO_3^{-2}, is the limiting factor in the quality of the concentrate obtained by physical methods. The average composition of the Israeli apatite is: 35.5% P_2O_5, 3.6% CO_2, 4% F. The unit cell has on the average the following dimension: a = 9.337 Å and c = 6.890 Å. The CO_2-content of apatites from different areas varies, as the degree of CO_3^{-2} substitution in skeletal grains is different from that in ovulites.

The apatite grains are poorly to very poorly sorted; they are fine sand with the following graphic parameters (Folk and Ward, 1957): mean 1.5 – 3.3 phi, sorting 1.3 – 1.9 phi, mode between 1 and 3 phi. The mode and sorting of the apatite component as opposed to the mode(s) and sorting of the calcite gangue, will determine if concentration based on sizing is possible.

The possibility of freeing the individual components ("liberation") in order to separate them depends on the character of the matrix (micritic or sparitic) and on the nature of the boundary between the apatite grains and the matrix. These textural properties will determine the efficiency of any physical concentration process.

The porosity, specific gravity and shape of the apatite as compared with the calcite matrix, could influence possible separation techniques based on surface properties (flotation) or on differential settling (gravity separation). There are differences in the above properties between the highly porous skeletal grains, in which the fine structure of the bone (including the Haversian system and canaliculi) is still discernible, spheroidal ovulites and non porous but lighter calcite.

All those properties, resulting from the sedimentary environment of the phosphorite are examined in detail for the Hor Hahar deposit and are related to the concentration process at present in use at the Nahal Zin plant.

INTRODUCTION

The phosphate deposits of the Negev play an important role in the economic development of Israel. At present, four deposits are exploited, with a total production capacity of over 3 million tons. Most of the rock mined is exported after beneficiation, while a relatively small amount is converted to phosphoric acid and phosphatic fertilizers for local use. Total measured reserves of phosphorite are approximately 350 million tons, of which 140 million contain over 27% P_2O_5 and 35 million tons over 30% (Shiloni & Soudri, 1976). Indicated reserves are much larger.

The concentration processes presently in operation are designed to increase the phosphorus content to 31–32% P_2O_5, which is required for commercial phosphates, and also to remove soluble chlorides which are corrosive to the materials used in the construction of phosphoric acid plants. This is done by washing the phosphorite with brackish water and by removing a fine fraction (of slimes) which is poor in P_2O_5. However, not all types of rock are amenable to this treatment and a detailed study of their petrography was undertaken to help improve present methods and develop new ones.

Previous petrographic studies dealt with the Oron deposit, the first to be exploited in Israel (Altschuler, 1957; Axelrod, 1966) and at Arad (Gross, in Würzburger et al., 1963 and Shiloni, 1966a). Geological surveys of the various phosphate deposits generally include a short chapter on petrography (e.g. Shiloni, 1966b, Shiloni and Shahar, 1969). A general summary of the known phosphorite deposits in Israel was published in 1968 by Würzburger.

GEOLOGICAL SETTING AND GENERAL PETROGRAPHY

The phosphorites in Israel occur in almost all the synclinal regions of the Negev in the upper part of the Mishash Formation of Late Campanian age. They belong to the North African—Middle East phosphate province, which extends from Morocco to Turkey (Campanian to Eocene age). In Israel many areas of phosphatic rocks are known. Nine of them were investigated in detail (Shiloni and Soudri, 1976); four are presently exploited (fig. 1). Most deposits contain several high grade (>27% P_2O_5) and medium grade (22–27% P_2O_5) phosphorite layers, interbedded with flint, chalk and low grade phosphorites.

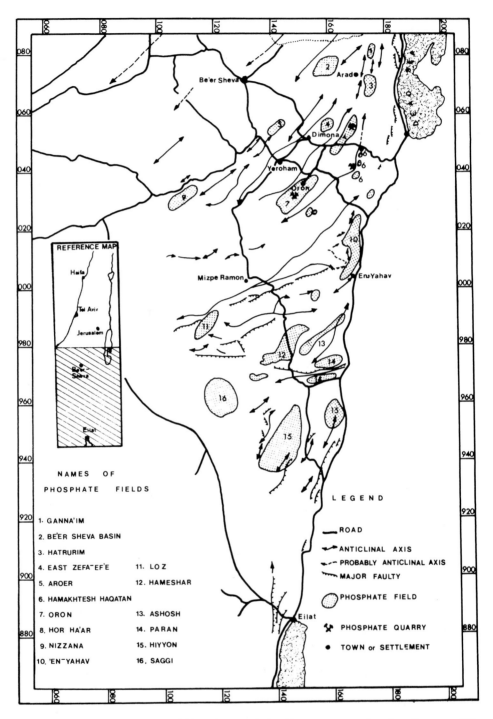

FIG. 1.—Location of Israeli phosphate fields and their relationship to structure. Based on Bentor and Vroman (1954), Picard and Greenberg (1964), Zohar (1958), Würtzburger (1968).

TABLE 1.—MINERALOGICAL COMPOSITION OF MEDIUM AND HIGH GRADE PHOSPHORITES FROM ISRAEL
(in weight percentages)

Locality	Apatite	Calcite	Gypsum	Halite	Quartz	Clay
Hor Hahar	78–89	7–12	2–5	1	1–3	0–1
Oron*	56–70	15–32	3–4	1	n.d.	1
Arad**	58–88	2–22	4–12	0–1	n.d.	n.d.
Arad north***	70–90	1.3–25	3–10	1	1–3	n.d.

*Bentor, 1952
**Würzburger et al., 1963
***Shiloni, 1966a.

The phosphorites have a clastic texture and consist of a matrix and a granular component, the latter comprising apatite grains (pseudo-oolitic or ovulitic, skeletal, bone and teeth fragments, coprolites, irregular lumps) together with some gypsum, calcareous fossils (mostly foraminifera) and flint fragments. The matrix may be calcitic (micritic to sparry), apatitic (fine apatite) or sili- ceous (micro-quartz). Fine gypsum is sometimes present. Calcite and gypsum veins often criss- cross the rock.

According to the prevailing matrix the following types of phosphorites are distinguished:
1. Friable phosphorite
2. Friable chalky phosphorite
3. Cemented calcareous phosphorite

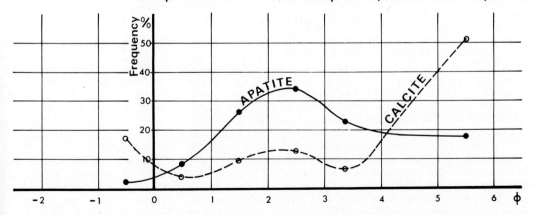

FIG. 2.—Grain size frequency distributions of apatite and calcite in Israeli phosphorites.

TABLE 2.—CHEMICAL COMPOSITION OF SOME APATITES
(Weight percentages)

Locality	CaO	P_2O_5	F	CO_2	Na_2O	MgO	CaO/P_2O_5	F/P_2O_5
Hor Hahar 1	49.4	34.1	4.0	4.2	0.88	0.17	1.45	0.12
Hor Hahar 2	51.4	35.3	4.0	4.1	1.22	0.15	1.46	0.11
Hor Hahar 3	51.9	36.7	4.2	3.0	0.66	0.1	1.41	0.11
Hor Hahar 4	50.3	35.2	4.3	3.4	0.66	0.1	1.43	0.12
Oron 2*	52.0	34.0	4.1	3.2	n.d.	0.11	1.53	0.12
Oron 3*	52.4	34.5	4.1	2.5	n.d.	0.06	1.52	0.12
Oron**	52.1	35.0	3.8	3.3	0.48	0.28	1.49	0.11
Arad top layer	52.5	34.6	4.0	3.9	1.2	n.d.	1.52	0.12
Arad bottom layer	52.4	34.6	4.0	4.0	1.3	n.d.	1.57	0.12
Jordan***	52.8	35.3	4.1	4.1	0.01	0.01	1.50	0.12
Morocco**	53.5	34.8	4.3	4.6	0.72	0.47	1.54	0.12
Morocco**	53.7	37.9	4.3	2.3	0.28	0.8	1.42	0.11
Tunisia+	51.9	33.5	4.1	5.5	0.8	0.7	1.55	0.12
Oron, calcined	55.1	39.4	n.d.	0.4	n.d.	n.d.	1.40	—
Kola, USSR**	52.4	38.3	3.2	0.4	0.36	0.4	1.37	0.08

*Altschuler, 1957
**McClellan and Lehr, 1969
***Reeves and Saadi, 1971
+Smani et al., 1975

4. Cemented siliceous phosphorite
5. Cemented ferruginous phosphorite.
Type 1 is a high-grade phosphorite, type 2 is medium grade, and types 3 to 5 are medium to low grade.

Each of the five phosphorite types can further be subdivided according to the main apatite component into skeletal (called also bone), ovulitic or coprolitic phosphorite. The mineralogical composition of some high to medium grade phosphorites is given in table 1.

CHARACTERISTICS OF THE APATITE GRAINS

Pure apatite grains are the best concentrate obtainable by physical treatment. The chemical composition of the apatite will therefore be the limiting factor in the quality of the concentrate. The granulometry of the apatite component and its relation to that of the gangue minerals (in our case mainly calcite) will determine if concentration based on sizing is possible (fig. 2). Other properties such as specific gravity and porosity of the grains also determine the choice of the separation techniques.

Apatite grains were separated from the rocks by prolonged soaking in Silverman's solution (Silverman et al., 1952) until no residual carbonates were detected by microscopic examination. Soluble salts and gypsum were dissolved in water and clay minerals (size less then two microns) decanted after sedimentation. The apatite grains, thus separated, were examined under the optical and scanning electron microscope, their grain size distribution was obtained by sieving, and their chemical composition, porosity and specific gravity were determined.

Chemistry of Apatite Grains

Typical chemical analyses of some Israeli apatites (and other apatites for comparison) in terms of the six major apatite constituents (McClellan and Lehr, 1969) are given in table 2. Minor constituents such as $(SO_4)^{-2}$ and $(SiO_4)^{-4}$ which replace phosphate and trace constituents which are substituting for calcium in addition to Na and Mg, occur in Israeli apatites but were not analyzed systematically. (See the article by J. Nathan in this volume).

The composition of the apatites in Israeli phosphorites varies from field to field and within the same field between layers. The most constant is the CaO-content and the most variable is the CO_2 (variation up to 25%). The fluorine and phosphorus contents of the apatites vary up to 10 percent. This is in agreement with the formula for sedimentary apatites given by McClellan and Lehr (1969):

$$(Ca_{10-a-b}Na_aMg_b)(PO_4)_{6-x}(CO_3)_xF_{0.4x}F_2$$

The average composition of the Israeli apatite, taking into account all published (Axelrod, 1978; McClellan and Lehr, 1969) and unpublished data (by the authors; Altschuler, 1957; Ish-Shalom et al., 1968; Shiloni, 1966a) is: 35.5% P_2O_5; 3.6% CO_2 : 4% F, and the average unit cell has accordingly a = 9.337 Å and c = 6.890 Å.

A statistical analysis of the concentration of CO_2, CaO and P_2O_5 in 47 different apatites is summarized in table 3. It is clear that the degree of substitution by CO_3^{-2} differs in skeletal and ovulitic apatites. The latter generally have less CO_2 (and more P_2O_5). Analysis of variance shows

TABLE 3.—P_2O_5, CO_2, AND CaO-CONTENTS OF APATITES FROM ISRAEL

Locality	No. of samples	CO_2 mean	CO_2 St. dev.	P_2O_5 mean	P_2O_5 St. dev.	CaO mean	CaO St. dev.	CaO/P_2O_5 mean	CaO/P_2O_5 St. dev.	CO_2/P_2O_5 mean	CO_2/P_2O_5 St. dev.	Prevailing grains
Oron	15	3.1	0.5	35.5	1.2	52.3	0.9	1.5	0	11.4	1.6	Ovulitic
Arad*	14	4.0	0.1	34.8	1.0	52.7	0.8	1.5	0	8.5	0.3	Skeletal
Hor Hahar layers 1 and 2	13	4.0	0.1	34.1	0.6	52.8	0.6	1.5	0	8.7	0.3	Skeletal
Hor Hahar Layers 3 and 4	5	3.1	0.3	36.2	0.5	51.3	0.9	1.4	0	11.7	1.2	Ovulitic

*Axelrod, 1978

that there are systematic differences between Arad (skeletal) and Oron (ovulitic) phosphorites in CO_2-content on the 99% confidence level and in the P_2O_5 on the 90% confidence level. Similar results were obtained for the Hor Hahar deposit. Layers 1 and 2 which are skeletal have on the average 4.0% CO_2, whereas layers 3 and 4 (ovulitic) have 3.1%.

Those differences can be seen also in the CO_2/P_2O_5 ratio, which is not surprising, as $(CO_3)^{-2}$ replaces phosphate. This substitution is coupled with calcium subtitution by various metals (to balance to some extent the charge difference between carbonate and phosphate). As a result, we have an almost constant ratio of CaO/P_2O_5 of approximately 1.5. A full multivariate statistical analysis is in progress.

It should be noted that the two types of apatite grains differ in the size of the apatite crystallites as well as in chemistry. Measurements made by TEM (Axelrod, 1978) and x-rays (Isch-Shalom et al., 1968 and McClellan and Lehr, 1969) show that the crystallites in ovulites measure 300–1000 Å and 200–600 Å in skeletal fragments. In mammalian bones, the crystallites measure 200–400 Å.

Grain Size Distribution

The size distribution of apatite grains (which themselves are aggregates of crystallites 200–1000 Å in size) from Hor Hahar, Oron, Arad and Hamakhtesh Haqatan are shown in figs. 2 and 3. Their graphic textural parameters, calculated after Folk and Ward (1957) and Inman (1952), are given in table 4.

The apatite grains are medium to very fine sand size (mostly medium to fine), moderately to poorly sorted. 70–80 percent of the grains are in the sand size range (0.074–2 mm). This, together with their mode in the range of 1–3 phi (as opposed to the coarser and finer modes of calcite grains), enables apatite to be concentrated by sieving. The size distribution also determines the maximum recovery of phosphate by this method. From 13–30 percent of apatite may be in the silt and clay range (mostly silt sized, although there is apatite also in the less then two microns size range) and up to 10 percent are more than 2 mm in size.

There is no recognizable difference between the distribution of ovulitic and skeletal grains (samples 1 and 2 as opposed to 3 and 4 in the Hor Hahar deposit), but there is a slight difference between the grain size distribution of samples from different deposits. There are not enough data available to determine variations, if any, in textural parameters in different parts of the same field or in relation to the structural characteristic of the fields (synclinal axis, etc.).

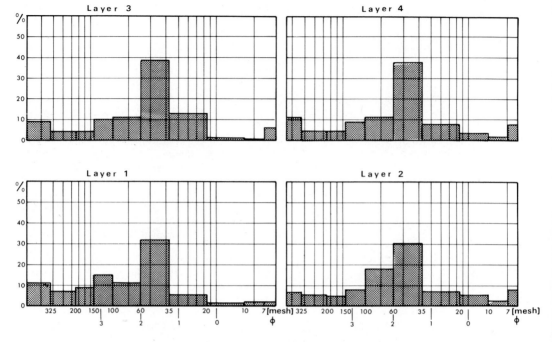

Fɪɢ. 3.—Grain size distribution of apatites from the Hor Hahar deposit.

TABLE 4.—Gʀᴀɪɴ sɪᴢᴇ ᴘᴀʀᴀᴍᴇᴛᴇʀs ᴏꜰ ᴀᴘᴀᴛɪᴛᴇs ꜰʀᴏᴍ Isʀᴀᴇʟ

	after Folk and Ward			after Inman		
Sample	median	mean	sorting	mean	sorting	skewness
Oron 1	3.15	3.3	1.4	3.43	1.35	0.21
Oron 2	2.75	2.8	1.3	2.78	1.33	0.02
Oron 3	2.9	3.0	1.3	3.05	1.05	0.14
Arad 10—III	2.2	2.1	1.6	2.05	1.35	−0.1
Arad 15—III	2.75	2.8	1.3	2.85	1.35	0.09
Arad 9—I	2.1	2.3	1.8	1.9	1.6	−0.1
Hamakhtesh Haqatan 501	2.1	2.2	1.7	2.25	1.75	0.09
Hamakhtesh Haqatan 503	3.0	3.3	1.9	3.45	2.55	0.25
Hor Hahar 1	2.2	1.9	1.5	1.75	2.25	−0.26
Hor Hahar 2	2.2	1.9	1.5	1.75	1.5	−0.3
Hor Hahar 3	1.7	1.5	1.9	1.13	2.13	−0.27
Hor Hahar 4	1.8	1.7	1.4	1.62	1.6	−0.1

PLATE 1.—Porosity, shape and structure of apatite grains

FɪɢURE 1.—Hor Hahar, layer 2; fraction 35/65 mesh; various shapes of skeletal apatite.

FɪɢURE 2.—Enlargement of fig. 1. Porous and less porous skeletal grains, an ovulite.

FɪɢURE 3.—Enlargement of a prorous skeletal grain.

FɪɢURE 4.—Hor Hahar, layer 2; Internal structure of an apatite grain. The Haversian canal is seen.

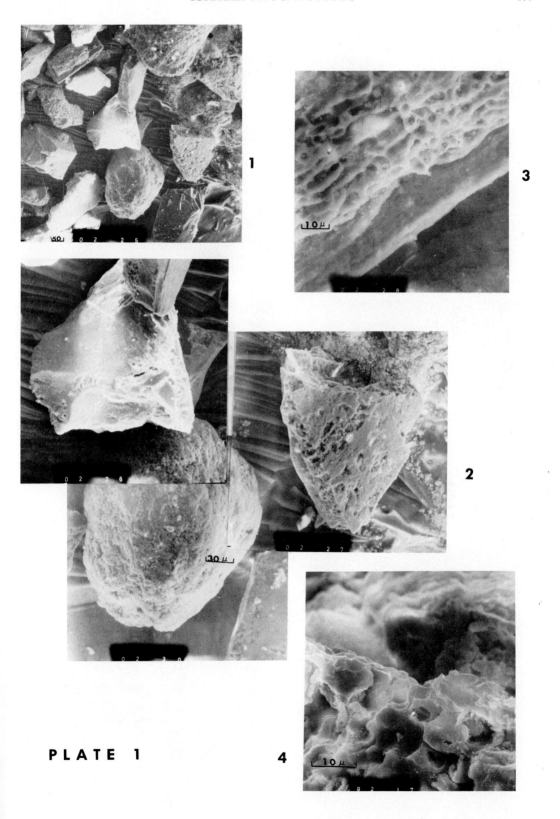

PLATE 1

PLATE 2

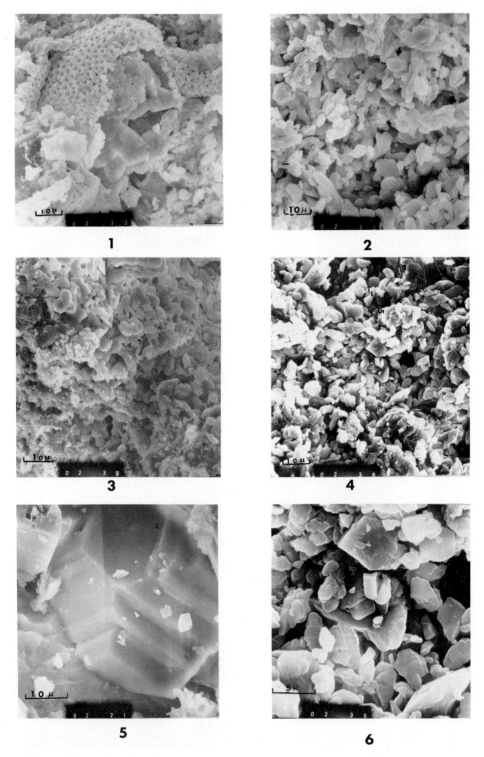

The similar distribution of skeletal and ovulitic grains, the skewness of which is negative to slightly positive and which according to Lacey and Carrozzi (1967) is characteristic of allochthonous oolites, and the variability from field to field, suggest current transported apatite grains. The current was not very strong and the distance of transport not long as shown by the poor sorting.

Porosity, Specific Gravity and Shape

The specific gravity of apatite is known to vary from 3.17 to 3.23 as a result of its variable chemical composition. The difference between the density of apatite and the lighter calcite (ca. 2.7) can also be used for separation.

The specific gravity and porosity of separated apatite grains from the Hor Hahar deposit was measured by the method of Innes (1956). The results are variable and cannot be correlated with the type of phosphorite (skeletal or ovulitic). The specific gravity is in the expected range and the porosity is around 30 percent (effective porosity). The overall porosity as seen by SEM (plate 1) is different in different types of grains. Skeletal apatite has often retained the original bone structure, including Haversian canals and canaliculi, and is as a result very porous (plate 1, fig. 3, 4). Parts of skeletal apatite are almost compact (plate 1, fig. 1) depending which part of the bone it is. Ovulitic grains are generally of intermediate porosity. Calcite grains (plate 2) are practically without porosity (figs. 2, 4) except foraminiferal tests (fig. 1) and other fossil fragments.

The porosity of the apatite grains, which implies a relatively large surface area, should have a bearing on separation processes such as flotation and agglomeration, as well as on the kinetics of dissolution of soluble salts during washing. The last process, as practiced in two plants (Nahal Zin and Oron), is known to be relatively slow as would be predicted from porosity considerations.

The shape of the apatite grains which influences their sinking velocity and settling characteristics, is also seen on SEM photographs (plates 1 and 2). Ovulitic apatite is elliptical, whereas skeletal

grains are angular (elongated, platy or irregular). Calcite grains are mostly angular and irregular, rarely euhedral. Gypsum is often fibrous.

Solubility

The solubility of apatite in mild organic acids was determined as this is an important factor in the direct application of phosphorites as fertilizer in acid soils. The results show differences between skeletal and ovulitic grains. The solubility of the mainly skeletal layer 2 of Hor Hahar in 2 percent formic acid is about 55 percent of the total P_2O_5, whereas that of apatite from the predominantly ovulitic layers (3 and 4) of the same deposit is around 45 percent of the total P_2O_5. In skeletal apatite grains from Arad, the solubility is mainly

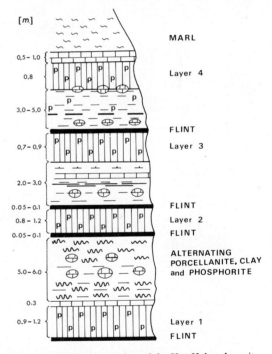

FIG. 4.—Columnar section of the Hor Hahar deposit. (After Nahmias et al., 1976).

PLATE 2.—Porosity, structure and type of calcite grains: Types of matrix in Hor Hahar phosphorites.

FIGURE 1.—Hor Hahar, layer 4; A forminiferal test filled with sparry calcite.

FIGURES 2 and 4.—Hor Hahar, layer 4; loose micritic calcite.

FIGURE 3.—Hor Hahar, layer 3; dense packed calcite.

FIGURE 5.—Hor Hahar, layer 3; Halite crystal formed by evaporation in vacuum.

FIGURE 6.—Enlargement of fig. 2 b; The shape of the calcite grains and their loose packing are seen.

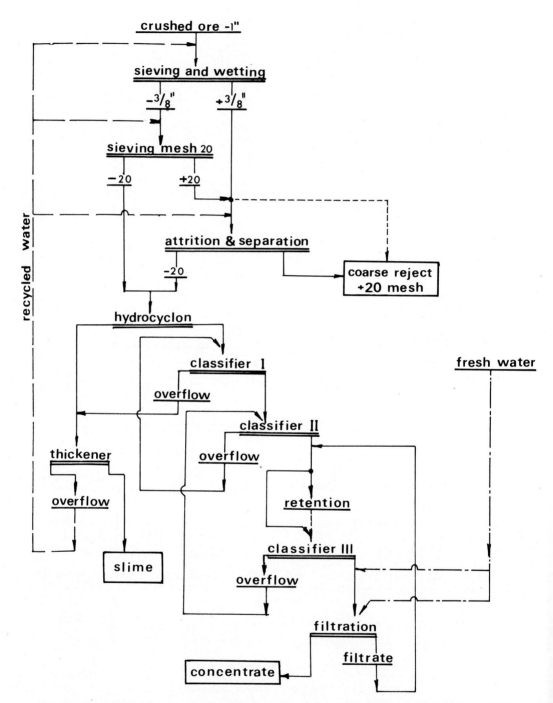

FIG. 5.—Flow sheet of the concentration process in Hor Hahar. (After Hainman and Pregerson, 1976).

in the range of 56–62 percent of the total P_2O_5. The solubility is related to the CO_2-content which varies in the different grain types. Their porosity and the size of the crystallites may also influence the solution kinetics.

RELATION GRAIN—MATRIX AND THE PROBLEM OF LIBERATION

When the friable types of phosphorites are comminuted, fracture takes place preferentially along the grain boundaries. As a consequence, the apatite grains are liberated by detachment from the calcite matrix. In the softer types of phosphorite the matrix is quickly disintegrated into fine particles, which can then be separated from the coarser apatite grains by sizing.

In some cases this operation produces concentrates containing 95 percent apatite. The liberation is, however, generally not complete and apatite grains may be coated with adhering matrix material and small apatite grains may be aggregated by the matrix.

In hard cemented phosphorites liberation is more difficult. The main problem of the siliceous phosphorite is the intimate mixture and the strong cohesion between micro-quartz and apatite. The siliceous matrix penetrates into cracks in apatitic ovulites and bone fragments. Multiple cracks in skeletal apatite cause them to "overcomminute," if grinding is prolonged.

The nature of the matrix is thus one of the factors controlling liberation. A high-grade phosphorite is generally grain supported with a high grain-micrite ratio and very little sparitic cement, whereas in intermediate and low grade phosphorites, the grain-micrite ratio is lower, and there is often more sparry calcite. Most of the low-grade phosphorites are mud supported. The texture of the phosphorite is not always homogeneous and several textural variations may be found in one horizon (on a mircro- and macro-scale) causing part of the grains to be easily liberated and others to remain sticking together. The micritic matrix (plate 2) can be loose or dense. In siliceous phosphorites the matrix is dense, fine grained and more or less homogeneous.

A CASE HISTORY

The Petrography of the Hor Hahar Deposit Related to the Concentration Process

The Hor Hahar Deposit—The Hor Hahar deposit is part of the Nahal Zin synclinal belt and is located 70 km from Beer Sheba and 10 km from the Oron deposit. The columnar section (fig. 4) shows four main layers of high-grade phosphorite. Layers 1 and 2 are friable skeletal phosphorite, whereas layers 3 and 4 are friable ovulitic phosphorite. Their mineralogical composition is

given in table 1. The P_2O_5-content varies between 28–30 percent and the reserves are estimated at 80 million tons (Nahmias et al., 1976). A beneficiation plant started to treat the open-cast mined ore in 1978.

The Concentration Process and the Petrography of its Products—Process Petrography—The size distribution of the apatite in the phosphate and its relation to the size distribution of the calcite gangue, the friable nature of the ore and its relative ease of disintegration into components, make a beneficiation process based on sizing feasible (Altschuler, 1957). To achieve a concentrate with 32% P_2O_5 and to reduce the chlorine content to minimum a process whose flow-sheet is given in fig. 5 and which is based on sizing and washing of the phosphate was decided upon (Hainman and Pregerson, 1976).

Laboratory simulation of this process was carried out in the mineral processing laboratory of Negev Phosphates and later in the Technion. The grain size distribution of the crushed and washed ore, the liberation of particles in each size fraction, the mineralogic composition of the concentrate and the rejects and the compressive strength of the coarse reject were investigated.

The grain size distribution is given in fig. 6 and the liberation summarized in table 5. Comparison of the above figures with the grain size distribution of apatite in the same sample

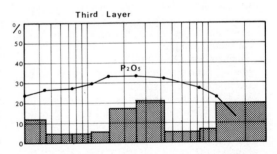

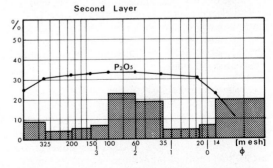

FIG. 6.—Grain size distribution and P_2O_5-content of crushed phosphorite from Hor Hahar.

TABLE 5.—LIBERATION OF CRUSHED ORE FROM HOR HAHAR
(in visually estimated percents)

Layer/Fraction	Liberated apatite	Aggregates	Adhering calcite as % to total calcite
Second			
+20 mesh	60	10	10
20/35 mesh	70	—	30
35/60 mesh	80	—	18
60/100 mesh	93	—	5
Third			
+20 mesh	20	60	20
20/35 mesh	50	25	25
35/60 mesh	68	5	25
60/100 mesh	80	—	15

(fig. 3) and the liberation permit the following conclusions:
1. 75 percent of the apatite grains are in the range 10–200 mesh and approximately 15 percent are smaller than 200 mesh. The maximum possible recovery of the process will thus be 75 percent.
2. The actual recovery is smaller because liberation is not complete and rock fragments containing apatite grains (i.e. apatite cemented by calcite) are rejected with the coarse fraction.
3. Good liberation is achieved below the size of 55 mesh.
4. There is almost no comminution of apatite during the process and the quantity of apatite grains in the fine reject is approximately the same as in the minus 200 mesh range of the untreated sample.
5. The concentrate contains 90 percent or more apatite. The remainder consist of calcite particles adhering to apatite, calcite grains in the sand size range (foraminifera, sparry calcite and aggregates of micrite) and some gypsum.
6. The rock fragments in the coarse reject have a compressive strength of 2,500 − 3,500 PSI (i.e. in the range of siltstones), higher than those of chalk but much lower than limestone.

The above conclusions are all pertinent to the improvement of the concentration process and the increase in the recovery of phosphorus and should serve as guide lines in future mineral concentration studies.

SEDIMENTARY ENVIRONMENT AND ITS INFLUENCE ON
THE ECONOMY OF THE PHOSPHORITES

Many of the characteristics of the phosphorites mentioned in the previous chapters as pertinent to the production of a marketable concentrate are a direct result of the sedimentary environment.

The phosphorites were deposited in long narrow semi-enclosed basins (Bentor, 1953). The thickness of the phosphorite bearing strata, their dilution with carbonatic or siliceous gangue and their content of organic matter (an important factor in phosphoric acid production), may be connected with their position within these basins.

The grain size distribution is influenced by the energy and current action in the environment as well as by its physico-chemical character (in case of chemical deposition). It is generally supposed that the ovulites are chemical precipitates (Tooms et al., 1969) or diagenetically formed pellets (Price and Calvert, 1977), although others (e.g. Reeves and Saadi, 1971) believe them to be reworked and rounded skeletal grains.

One can only speculate as to the cause of the difference in CO_2-content in ovulites and skeletal apatite. Do the skeletal grains and ovulites represent different facies in the sense of Gulbrandsen (1970) or is it the result of disequilibrium resulting from higher initial CO_2 in fish teeth and bones? Price and Calvert (1977) show 5.3 percent CO_2 in teeth and bones from the Namibian shelf, whereas pelletal phosphorite found together with the teeth has only 3.9 percent. More data are needed in order to show how the sedimentary environment determines the P_2O_5 and CO_2-content of the optimal concentrate—the pure apatite.

The solubility of apatite and in consequence the possibility of direct application of phosphorites is in our experience also related to the type of apatite grain (skeletal or ovulitic) and thus to the sedimentary environment.

Many other factors influencing the economic evaluation of a phosphorite deposit (such as depth of burial, thickness of the phosphate bearing strata and their alternation with other rocks) are determined by the sedimentary environment. They are generally connected with the mineability of the deposit and are not discussed here, as this is beyond the scope of this article.

Acknowledgement

Thanks are due to Israel Chemical Ltd. and Negev Phosphates Ltd. for permission to publish data from the research they sponsored; to B. Pregerson and J. Nahmias for their help and cooperation. We are grateful to N. Finkelstein and U. Würzburger for critically reviewing the manuscript.

REFERENCES

ALTSCHULER, Z. S., 1957, The Petrography and Beneficiation of Negev Phosphates: Report Technical Assistance, New York, 62 p.

AXELROD, S., 1966, Lithostratigraphy of the main phosphorite member in the Oron syncline (in Hebrew): M.Sc. Thesis, Hebrew University, Jerusalem, 87 p.

————, 1978, Phosphate for direct application: Paper presented at the seminar of "Phosphate rocks for direct application," Haifa, Israel, 36 p.

BENTOR, Y. K., 1953, Relations entre la tectonique et les dépôts de phosphates dans le Negev Israelien: Proc. 19th Intern, Geol. Congress, Alger, Sec. 11, p. 93–101.

————, 1952, Origin of the mineral deposits of the Negev (Southern Israel): Geol. Survey Israel, Jerusalem, 93 p.

FOLK, R. L., AND WARD, W. C., 1957, Brazos River Bar—a study in the significance of grain size parameters: Jour. Pet. v. 27, p. 3–26.

GULBRANDSEN, R. A., 1970, Relation of Carbon Dioxide content of Apatite of the Phosphoria Formation to Regional Facies: U.S. Geol. Survey Prof. Paper *700*-B, p. B9–B13.

HAINMAN, W., AND PREGERSON, B., 1976, Beneficiation of Hor Hahar phosphates by washing: 3d Mineral Engineering Conference, Beer Sheba, p. 1-7-1-1-7-11.

INMAN, D. I., 1952, Measures for describing the size distribution of sediments: Jour. Sed. Pet., v. 22, p. 125–145.

INNES, W. B., 1956, Total Porosity and Particle Density of Fluid Catalysts by Liquid Titration: Analytical Chemistry, v. 28, p. 332–334.

ISCH-SHALOM, M., LEIBOWITZ, J., GOREN, S., AND JOURAVIN (LUMINEITZ), E., 1968: Oron phosphate rock Final report, Israel Ceramic and Silicate Inst., Haifa. 44 p.

LACEY, J. E., AND CAROZZI, A. V., 1967, Critères de distinction entre oolithes autochtones et allochtones, Application au calcaire de Sainte-Geneviève (Viséen) d'Illinois, U.S.A.: Bull. Cent. Res. Pau. 1, p. 279–313.

MCCLELLAN, G. H., AND LEHR, J. R., 1969, Crystal Chemical Investigation of Natural Apatites, Min. v. 54, p. 1374–1391.

NAHMIAS, J., SOURDRI, D., AND SHILONI, Y., 1976, Geological considerations on exploitation of phosphorite fields in the area of Nahal Zin: 3d Mineral Engineering Conference, Beer Sheba, (in Hebrew), p. 1-41-1-4-11.

PRICE, N. B., AND CALVERT, S. E., 1977, The geochemistry of phosphorites from the Namibian shelf: Grant Inst. of Geology, Edinburgh, 38 p.

REEVES, M. J., AND SAADI, T. A. K., 1971, Factors controlling the Deposition of some Phosphate Bearing Strata from Jordan, Economic Geology, v. 66, p. 451–465.

SHILONI, Y., 1966b, The Phosphate Field of Hamakhtesh Haqatan: Geol. Surv. Israel, Unpublished report No. 176/66 (in Hebrew), 73 p.

————, 1966a, Zefa-Ef'e phosphate deposit: Report no. 2, Geol. Surv. Israel, Unpublished report no. 154/66, 29 p.

————, AND SHAHAR, Y., 1969, The phosphate field of Ein Ofarim, Geol. Surv. Israel, Unpublished report no. 196/69 (in Hebrew), 17 p.

SILVERMAN, S. R., PUYAT, R. K., AND WEISER, J. D., 1952, Quantitative Determination of Calcite Associated with Carbonate-Bearing Apatites: Am. Min., v. *37*, p. 211–222.

SMANI, M. S., BLAZY, P., AND CASES, J. M., 1975, Beneficiation of Sedimentary Moroccan Phosphate Ores: Trans. Soc. AIME, v. *253*, p. 168–184.

TOOMS, J. S., SUMMERHAYES, C. P., AND CRONAN, D. S., 1969, Geochemistry of marine phosphate and manganese deposits: Oceanogr. Mar. Biol. Ann. Rev., v. 7, p. 49–100.

WÜRZBURGER, U., LASMAN, N., GROSS, S., AND SHILONI, Y., 1963, The Zefa-Ef'e Phosphate Deposit: Geol. Survey of Israel, Unpublished report no. 126/62, 39 p.

————, 1968, A Survey of Phosphate Deposits in Israel: Mineral Resources Development Series no. *32*, United Nations, 14 p.

SEPM Special Publication No. 29, p. 167–192, November 1980

THE INITIATION OF PHOSPHATIC CHALK SEDIMENTATION—THE SENONIAN (CRETACEOUS) OF THE ANGLO-PARIS BASIN

IAN JARVIS

Department of Geology The University G12 800, Glasgow Scotland

ABSTRACT

Field studies and review of the nineteenth century literature have led to a new model for the conditions of formation of Senonian phosphorites of the Anglo-Paris Basin.

All Chalk phosphorites are floored by a well developed hardground. Its formation was a direct result of increased current activity which eroded troughs of up to 1 km in length within the underlying white chalk and also produced, by winnowing, a coarser sediment more susceptible to sea-floor lithification.

A prolific biota developed within these cuvettes. This biota concentrated phosphorus from sea-water and produced an organic-rich substrate, predominantly of fecal pellets, suitable for early diagenetic phosphatization.

The increase in current activity and the ubiquitous nature of shiny phosphate veneers, which are of potential algal origin, suggest that the late Santonian to early Campanian was a period of shallowing of the Chalk sea. These distinctive sediments may be related to major changes in oceanic circulation.

INTRODUCTION

The phosphatic chalks of Picardy in northern France have been described in a large volume of literature written by numerous French authors during the late nineteenth and early twentieth centuries. The most famous of these authors were L. Cayeux, J. Gosselet, A. de Grossouvre, H. Lasne and M. Leriche. Despite this prolific literature, however, little description filtered into the English language and consequently much of this rich and important work has been overlooked by contemporary geologists.

It is not my purpose to review this vast literature, but rather to propose a genetic model for the formation of these Senonian phosphorites. The richest and most accessible deposits were mined out at the beginning of the century; consequently my conclusions are based on a combination of an extensive literature survey and my own field observations of the now sadly limited number of extant exposures of phosphatic chalk in the Anglo-Paris Basin.

A phosphatic chalk is regarded here as being a pelletal chalk containing in excess of 5% P_2O_5. The term does not include phosphatized lithified chalks such as those which form the top surfaces of many hardgrounds.

The phosphatic chalks considered in this paper provide the thickest and most concentrated reserves of economic phosphate in NW Europe. The deposits commonly occur in isolated troughs up to 1 km in length, 250 m in width and 30 m deep in the soft white chalks of the late Coniacian to early Campanian (fig. 1) of northern France and southern England. These troughs have been described as phosphate cuvettes by numerous authors (e.g. de Grossouvre, 1901 p. 80)

and the term is retained here.

The original distribution and extent of these cuvettes cannot now be determined, since the majority occur as isolated erosional outliers of late Santonian to early Campanian age surrounded by older chalks, while much of the outcrop in the southern and central area of the Paris Basin has a thick Tertiary cover.

All the cuvettes have an erosional origin and truncate the bedding of the immediately underlying chalk. This erosional relationship can best be seen at Hallencourt quarry and has been noted elsewhere by e.g. Lasne (1892), de Grossouvre (1901), Raguin (1926) and Broquet (1973).

The base of all the cuvettes is marked by a strongly lithified and mineralized hardground, here termed the basal hardground. This hardground has developed in a winnow coarsened sediment of late Coniacian to early Santonian (e.g. Beauval, Hallencourt pit) or late Santonian (e.g. Hallencourt quarry) age.

On top of the basal hardground there rests up to 15 m of phosphatic chalk containing a prolific and distinctive fauna, especially at its base. Other cycles based by hardgrounds and containing phosphatic chalk may overlie the initial one, although the axis of the cuvette may become displaced laterally. The final phosphatic chalk development is no younger than early Campanian age and usually contains distinctive bands of *Offaster pilula* (Lamarck) and *Gonioteuthis quadrata quadrata* (Blainville).

The History of Phosphatic Chalk Research

In 1849, Buteux described the occurrence of a bed of 'grey' chalk containing numerous grains of phosphate at Beauval, a small village south

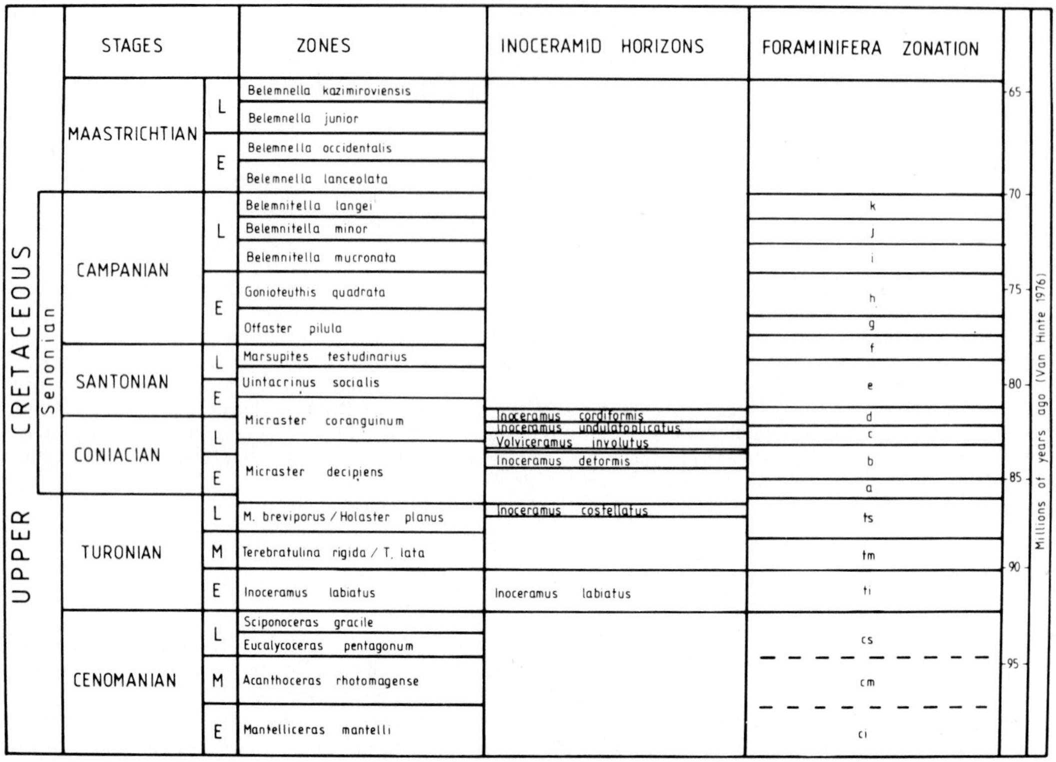

STAGES			ZONES		INOCERAMID HORIZONS	FORAMINIFERA ZONATION	Age
UPPER CRETACEOUS	Senonian	MAASTRICHTIAN	L	Belemnella kazimiroviensis			65
				Belemnella junior			
			E	Belemnella occidentalis			
				Belemnella lanceolata			
		CAMPANIAN	L	Belemnitella langei		k	70
				Belemnitella minor		j	
				Belemnitella mucronata		i	
			E	Gonioteuthis quadrata		h	75
				Offaster pilula		g	
						f	
		SANTONIAN	L	Marsupites testudinarius			
			E	Uintacrinus socialis		e	80
		CONIACIAN	L	Micraster coranguinum	Inoceramus cordiformis	d	
					Inoceramus undulatoplicatus	c	
					Volviceramus involutus		
			E	Micraster decipiens	Inoceramus deformis	b	85
						a	
	TURONIAN		L	M. breviporus / Holaster planus	Inoceramus costellatus	ts	
			M	Terebratulina rigida / T. lata		tm	90
			E	Inoceramus labiatus	Inoceramus labiatus	ti	
	CENOMANIAN		L	Sciponoceras gracile			
				Eucalycoceras pentagonum		cs	95
			M	Acanthoceras rhotomagense		cm	
			E	Mantelliceras mantelli		ci	

(right-hand axis: Millions of years ago (Van Hinte, 1976))

FIG. 1.—Correlation diagram of Upper Cretaceous zonation schemes in the Anglo-Paris Basin. The vertical scale is based on absolute age (Van Hinte, 1976). The macrofaunal zonation is that in general use in England. The inoceramid horizons provide a correlation with the German stratigraphy. The French foraminiferal Zones are based on the work of Monciardini in the new series 1:50,000 French geological maps (e.g. Monciardini in Mennessier et al., 1974).

of Doullens (Somme, France). Between 1863 and 1867 de Mercey published descriptions of similar beds at Breteuil near Hardivillers (Oise) and Hallencourt (Somme).

By 1886, the discovery of secondarily enriched phosphate sands at Beauval, containing in excess of 35% P_2O_5, led to the realization of the economic potential of these deposits as a source of agricultural phosphate. There followed a rapid expansion of the industry with the discovery and description of similar beds at Orville, Terramesnil, Beauquesne, Raincheval and Puchevillers in the department of Somme, followed by Toutencourt and Ribemont near Peronne and the deposits in the Somme river valley at Curlu, Bray-sur-Somme, Vaux-Eclusier and Templeux-la-Fosse. It was soon realized that the rich phosphate sands which had originally led to the exploitation of these sites were a Tertiary weathering phenomenon, a decalcification product of the underlying phosphate-bearing chalks first described by Buteux (1849) at Beauval. These rich solution pockets were resting on poorer primary phosphatic chalks

containing between 5 and 20% P_2O_5.

Between 1888 and 1896 the literature on phosphatic chalks reached its peak, a reflection of the rapid expansion in the industry. Gosselet in particular, produced a large amount of descriptive literature. Numerous new phosphate localities were described during this period including Auxi-le-Château in 1891 and Marcheville and Gorenflos in 1893.

After 1900, the number of new publications on the subject fell rapidly and since 1914 only a handful of papers have been published, the most important being Cayeux's review in his 'Les phosphates de chaux sédimentaires de France' (1939–1950). The industry never recovered between the two wars or afterwards and today (1979) only two workings are exploiting phosphatic chalk—Nurlu (Somme) and Hallencourt pit (Somme). Exposures still remain at Beauval, Ribemont, Orville, Faucouzy, Hardivillers and St. Martin-du-Tertre. Less permanent exposures are present at Hallencourt quarry, Hem-Monacu, Villers-devant-le-Thour and Marcheville. An

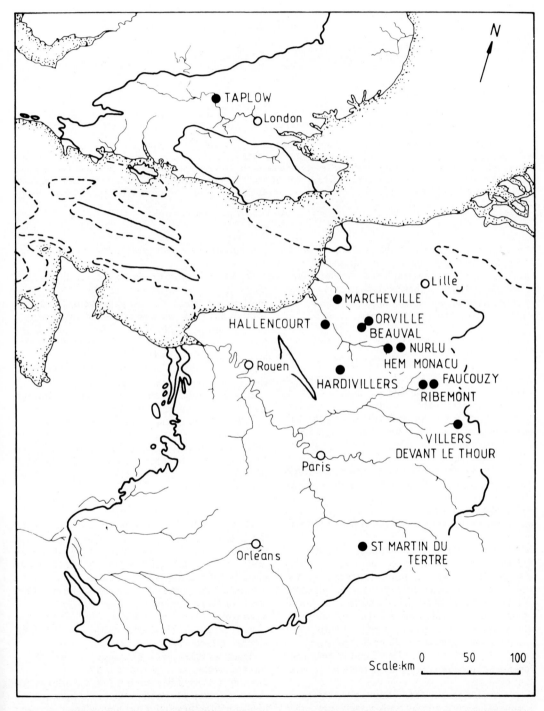

Fig. 2.—Distribution of extant phosphatic chalk exposures (solid symbols). The heavy solid and dashed lines mark the base of the Upper Cretaceous. The majority of sites, no longer exposed, lie in the department of Somme on a line between Marcheville and Faucouzy.

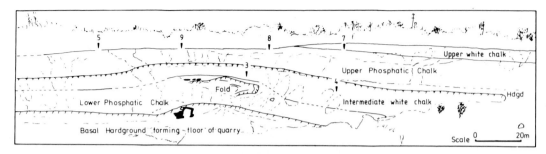

FIG. 3.—Sketch of Beauval quarry, a view looking SW. The diagram illustrates a number of important features:—(a). The presence of a basal hardground which forms the floor of the quarry, as it acts as a natural base to phosphatic chalk extraction, (b). The occurrence of intraformational folding of the basal hardground, which does not affect the overlying white chalk, (c). A second, later, hardground/phosphatic chalk sequence overlying the earlier phase. The numbers indicate the positions of measured sections utilised in the construction of fig. 4.

exposure is also present in the south of England at Taplow, but although this is potentially economic, it has never been exploited for phosphate.

It is examination of these extant exposures (fig. 2) that has provided much of the evidence for the model postulated in this paper.

LITHOSTRATIGRAPHY AND BIOSTRATIGRAPHY

General

All the exposures have a large number of features in common but Beauval quarry (figs. 3, 4), at present being exploited for chalk from below the basal hardground, provides the most complete assemblage of features believed to be typical of phosphatic chalk deposits.

These features are:—

(1). The occurrence of a cuvette cutting into the underlying white chalk and delimiting the area of phosphate deposition.

(2). The presence of a basal hardground which acts as the lower boundary to the phosphatic chalk unit.

(3). Demonstrable and frequently visible topography on the basal hardground, on a variety of scales, from a few millimetres to several metres.

(4). The occurrence of a distinctive intraclast pebble lag, here termed the basal lag, on top of the basal hardground (particularly in depressions), which contains a prolific, varied and highly distinctive fauna typified by '*Terebella*' *phosphatica* Leriche (a worm tube) and *Diblasus arborescens* Parent (a compound coral) patch reefs with abundant oysters.

(5). A phosphatic chalk unit up to 15 m in thickness having a rapidly transitional, sometimes sharp upper limit returning to normal soft white chalk deposition.

(6). Folding and thrust dislocation of the basal hardground after deposition of the overlying

phosphatic chalk, but prior to the return of white chalk deposition.

(7). A repetition or repetitions of phosphatic chalk deposition with the same sequence of basal hardground, basal lag and phosphatic chalk. No folding has been seen or described from second or later units of phosphatic chalk, nor are the later deposits affected by the synsedimentary fracturing seen in the initial sequence.

(8). A ubiquitous faunal sequence occurring in the upper part of the youngest phosphatic chalk unit and typified by beds of *Offaster pilula* and *Gonioteuthis quadrata quadrata*.

The features to be further considered in this paper are those related to the initial formation of an environment suitable for the formation and deposition of phosphatic chalks, but not later, post-formational, tectonic effects.

The Cuvette

Only very limited information is available on the gross morphology of phosphatic chalk cuvettes, and at the present time (1979) exposure is too poor to add anything to the descriptions in the literature, although Hallencourt quarry (fig. 5) exposes a sequence which displays the erosional origin of these structures. Cuvette cross-sections have been drawn by several authors (fig. 6), but only Broquet (1973) describes the three dimensional characteristics of a cuvette.

Broquet (1973) gives a detailed account of the three cuvettes of Hallencourt pit, the only remaining site to utilize subterranean workings for the extraction of phosphorite. The phosphatic chalks within these cuvettes have all been worked for phosphate although only the uppermost of the three is at present being exploited. All three cuvettes trend north-south (figs. 6, 7) and display the following features:—

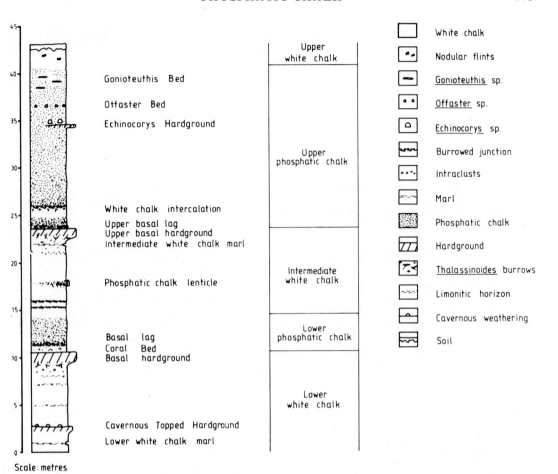

Scale: metres

FIG. 4.—Beauval quarry; a composite lithostratigraphy. The main features are:—(a). The presence of two phosphatic chalks, each with an underlying basal hardground and basal lag, (b). A major phosphatic chalk lenticle within the intermediate white chalk, (c). A white chalk intercalation occurring near the base of the upper phosphatic chalk. The lower white chalk is probably of early *Micraster coranguinum* Zone age and the lower phosphatic chalk of middle and late *M. coranguinum* Zone age. *Uintacrinus socialis* occurs within the middle white chalk. Much of the upper phosphatic chalk is clearly assignable to the *Offaster pilula* Zone (see text). *Marsupites testudinarius* has not been found, and consequently the presence of that zone within the quarry cannot be confirmed. It is possible that the *Marsupites* Zone has been removed prior to the formation of the upper basal hardground, but this is not confirmed by the micropalaeontological zonation (Tabatabaï, 1977). The sediment log has a weathering profile.

(1). The oldest cuvette contains sediment of mid to late Santonian age [French foraminifera Zone e (Monciardini in Broquet, 1973; Monciardini in Mennessier et al., 1974)] but rests on chalk of the earliest late Coniacian (Monciardini in Broquet, 1973). The phosphatic chalk is 4–4½ m thick and contains 6–13% P_2O_5.

(2). This unit is truncated by a second smaller cuvette of similar age which contains 3 m of phosphatic chalk with 10–19% P_2O_5.

(3). The third cuvette, the one being now exploited, lies slightly to the north and has 12 m of phosphatic chalk with 8–18% P_2O_5. It contains sediment dated as early Campanian [French fora-

minifera Zone f–g (Monciardini in Broquet, 1973; Monciardini in Mennessier et al., 1974)] and rests on lower Santonian at its centre.

These three cuvettes, which vary in age from mid Santonian to early Campanian, all have the same axial trend and are all developed in the same area. They are up to 250 m wide, 30 m deep and 1 km in length (Broquet, 1973; Mennessier et al., 1974) and are floored by a basal hardground.

The Basal Hardground

Detailed morphology of the basal hardground varies from exposure to exposure and between

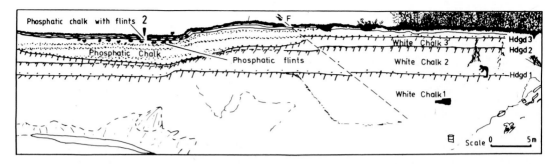

FIG. 5.—Diagram of Hallencourt quarry. A general view of the base of the phosphatic chalk cuvette. Three hardgrounds (1,2,3) cut into parallel bedded white chalks of late Santonian (*Uintacrinus socialis* and *Marsupites testudinorius* Zones) age. The third hardground is the basal hardground. The phosphatic chalk contains *Gonioteuthis quadrata quadrata* and is assigned to the early Campanian *O. pilula* Zone.

cuvettes, but all show a majority of features in common. These are:—

(a). A highly lithified top, up to 30 cm in thickness, passing down into—

(b). Less indurated lower levels with lithification becoming poor or absent around 60 cm below the top of the hardground.

(c). Vertical penetration of the hardground by numerous *Thalassinoides* burrow systems (fig. 8) which were open at the time of lithification

and were subsequently filled with the richly phosphatic basal lag which rests on the hardground surface. The burrow systems penetrate beneath the lithified portions of the hardground (figs. 8A,8B) and may commonly be traced 3 m, and sometimes as much as 5 m below the hardground surface.

(d). Mineralization is concentrated in the upper portions of the hardground and is typified by phosphatization and glauconitization of the lithi-

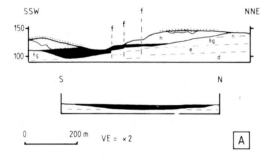

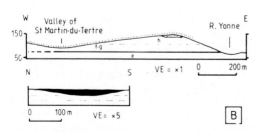

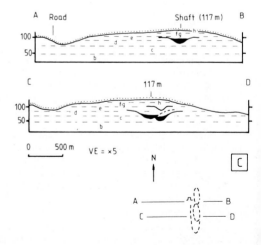

FIG. 6.—Phosphatic chalk cuvette structures. (A). Hardivillers; cross-sections based on Lasne (1892) and de Grossouvre (1901). (B). St. Martin-du-Tertre; cross sections based on Negre (1913) and Raguin (1926). (C). Hallencourt pit; cross-sections and plan view based on Broquet (1973). Black = phosphatic chalk; White = white chalk; Stipple = Tertiary cover; Dash = chalk bedding; Small lettering = foraminifera zones; f = fault. Note the similarity in dimensions.

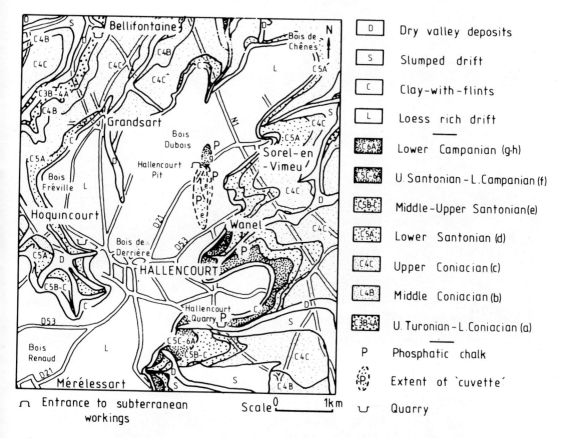

Dry valley deposits

Slumped drift

Clay-with-flints

Loess rich drift

Lower Campanian (g·h)

U. Santonian - L. Campanian (f)

Middle - Upper Santonian (e)

Lower Santonian (d)

Upper Coniacian (c)

Middle Coniacian (b)

U. Turonian - L. Coniacian (a)

P   Phosphatic chalk

Extent of 'cuvette'

Entrance to subterranean workings

Scale 0   1km

Quarry

FIG. 7.—Geological map of the Hallencourt area. Cuvette morphology has been mapped in some detail during the exploitation of the Hallencourt pit subterranean workings. An exposure is present at Hallencourt quarry (fig. 5.). The area shown lies 20 km south of Abbeville (Somme) and is represented on the French 1:50,000 geological map, (Mennessier et al., 1974).

fied chalk, downwards from the surface and outwards from burrow walls (fig. 8C). The top of the hardground is invariably coated by a thin (<1 mm) shiny phosphate skin, which extends down into the upper portions of the burrow systems and may be encrusted by an unphosphatized epifauna.

(e). The hardground top is frequently extensively bored. Borings are of a great variety of types and may be attributed to sponges, sipunculid worms, polychaete worms (fig. 9C) and pholadid bivalves (fig. 10B). The walls of these borings are invariably extensively phosphatized. The borings themselves have usually been infilled by intraclasts and their tops sealed off by an overlying shiny phosphate veneer complex (fig. 10B).

(f). The hardground sediment itself contains both mineralized and unmineralized intraclasts and shell debris, which have been incorporated into the main body of the hardground (fig. 10) and plastered on top during the later stages of

accretionary lithification (fig. 9C).

(g). During the later stages of hardground formation, the incorporation of intraclastic material into the hardground top has often led to the sealing of the upper passages of the *Thalassinoides* systems (fig. 9C) and the stenomorphism or restriction (Bromley, 1975) of others (fig. 9A). The lag, where it has been lithified early diagenetically, is frequently overlain by '*Terebella*' *phosphatica* patch reefs, and phosphate skin complexes.

(h). This final stage of hardground formation was followed by mantling with a coarse intraclastic lag containing bored and otherwise bioeroded fragments of hardground, all coated by the same ubiquitous shiny phosphate patina that coats the hardground top. Other components of the lag include phosphatized fecal pellets, shell fragments and bone debris all similarly coated, floating in an unmineralized, unlithified soft white chalk.

(i). Coral patch reefs were formed prior to the

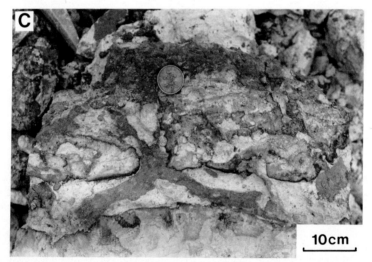

Fɪɢ. 8.—Basal hardground *Thalassinoides* burrow systems. (A). Nurlu; crowded idiomorphic *Thalassinoides* burrows penetrate the basal hardground for a distance in excess of 2½ m from the top. (B). Nurlu; a polished block taken 1 m below the hardground surface. The white chalk has repeatedly been burrowed from the basal hardground surface and the later burrows infilled by phosphatic chalk from above the hardground. All burrows are of the *Thalassinoides* type, but there is a complex of smaller diameter reburrowing, picked out by different generations of phosphatic chalk. Intense burrowing of this type is typical below basal hardgrounds, where burrow systems spread horizontally after being vertically constrained (stenomorphed) within the hardground. (C). Beauval; the hardground top. A filigree surface has developed, largely due to boring by sponges, but also to the isolation of the top by large *Thalassinoides* burrows. The burrow shown has been infilled by the poorly phosphatic chalk of the Coral Bed, which has, in turn, been later reburrowed and infilled with phosphatic chalk. Phosphatization, glauconitization and limonitization of the lithified chalk, have spread outwards from the burrow walls. Glauconitization and goethitic crusts are concentrated on the top surfaces of the burrows.

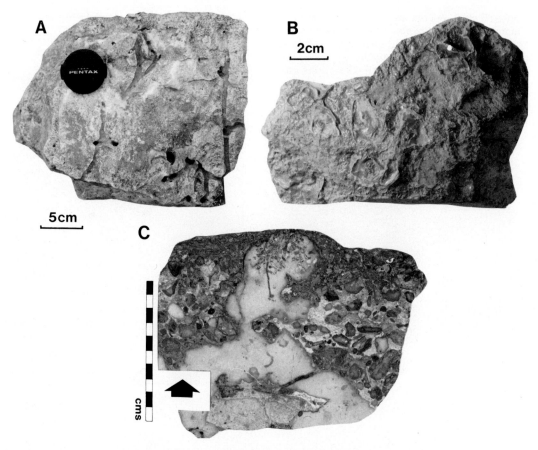

FIG. 9.—Phosphatic chalk hardgrounds. (A). Faucouzy; the Gonioteuthis Hardground. The block displays good examples of stenomorphed (restricted) *Thalassinoides* burrows. (B). Hardivillers; the basal hardground. A rare example of an oyster-encrusted basal hardground. The oysters are encrusting a typical irridescent phosphate skin, which is, in turn, coating the oysters. (C). Nurlu; the basal hardground. A combination of large idiomorphic *Thalassinoides* burrows and possible erosion by organisms has resulted in the isolation of a boss above the main surface of the hardground. The depressions on either side of the boss have been infilled with an early diagenetically hardened intraclast pebble lag, which has later been coated by a complex of phosphate skins. It is noticeable that only the top of the boss has been bored (by spionid worms). The intraclasts show varying degrees of phosphatization with the more heavily phosphatized examples also being the most extensively bored.

deposition of the phosphatic chalk, since the Coral Bed is only poorly phosphatic, although it is frequently reworked into the basal lag.

Where the basal hardground is extensively exposed i.e. Beauval and Nurlu, the nature of the hardground can be seen to vary greatly laterally. At Beauval, it is composed of a complex of converging and diverging hardground surfaces (fig. 11), superimposed one on top of the other. Nevertheless, present-day exposure and lateral control are insufficient to trace a basal hardground from a cuvette axial- to a cuvette marginal facies. However, Gosselet (1893, 1896, 1897, 1900) describes the lateral changes in both phosphatic chalk and basal hardground during the exploitation

of Flour's quarry at Fresnoy-le-Grand (Aisne). The descriptions demonstrate that as the phosphate content of the basal phosphatic chalk decreases, lithification of the basal hardground becomes less pronounced (fig. 12). This is here interpreted as being the transition from an axial to a marginal facies and as such suggests a connection between the amount of white chalk eroded and the degree of lithification of the basal hardground.

The Basal Lag

Like the basal hardground, the nature of the basal lag varies laterally. In general, it consists of a concentration of phosphatized and/or glauconitized chalk pebble intraclasts surrounded by a matrix of sand-grade phosphate and micrite (fig. 13). The lag may become cemented on top of the hardground (see above). The intraclasts are commonly bored with *Entobia*-like forms predominating.

The fauna of the basal lag is typified by two elements:—

(1). *'Terebella' phosphatica*
(2). *Diblasus arborescens*

'T' phosphatica is a sinuous worm tube (fig. 14) composed of oriented shell fragments, teeth,

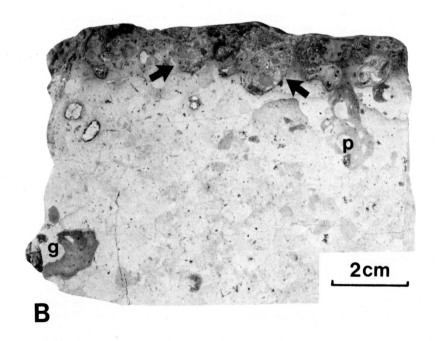

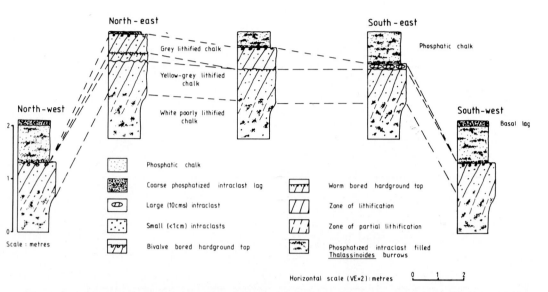

Fig. 11.—Lateral variation in the basal hardground, Beauval. Five sections have been drawn at 5 m intervals from a small exploration pit. The following features are displayed:—(1). The thickness of the lithified portion of the basal hardground apparently increases towards the NE, where, (2). It contains three distinct surfaces. (3). Towards the NW and the south the three surfaces converge and become superimposed. (4). The grey lithified chalk unit goes through an intermediate stage of large, recemented intraclasts, before finally becoming superimposed. (5). A poor phosphatic chalk, the lateral equivalent of the Coral Bed (fig. 4), overlies the youngest surface at all five exposures. These observations demonstrate that basal hardground formation was not a single event, and that the cuvette was probably the result of a series of progressively deeper-cutting erosive events, similar to those seen at Hallencourt quarry (fig. 5).

intraclasts and particularly fecal pellets, cemented by phosphate. Where found *in situ* the tubes are invariably cemented to an early diagenetically lithified portion of the basal lag but pass upwards into an uncemented phosphatized calcarenite substrate. Comparable tubes have been described from the present day and are attributed to sabellariid worms (Kirtley and Tanner, 1968).

D. arborescens is a scleractinian compound coral found in the poorly phosphatic chalk which occurs in patches on top of the basal hardground but beneath the basal lag (fig. 15). Beauval is the only site where the patch reef is exposed (1979) *in situ* but the coral is ubiquitous to all basal lags, into which it is reworked.

Thick shelled oysters, *Lopha semiplana*

(Sowerby), are abundant while cirripeds, *Scalpellum sp.*, aragonitic bivalves, gastropods, vertebrate remains which include elasmobranch teeth, teleost otoliths and bone fragments, echinoderms, asteroid ossicles, cidarid spines and fragments of *Micraster* tests, are all common.

The Phosphatic Chalk

The phosphatic chalk is readily distinguished from white chalk by its coarse pelletal phosphate content which gives it a deep chocolate brown color when wet. Phosphatized material within the phosphatic chalk lithofacies falls into two categories:—

(1). lithified carbonate, including hardground surfaces and associated intraclasts.

Fig. 10.—Examples of basal hardground sediment. (A). Hallencourt quarry; a polished block from 10 cm below the top of hardground 3. The sediment consists of a lithified micrite, rich in coarse silt to sand grade carbonate particles, many of which have been glauconitized and/or phosphatized. Larger glauconitized (g), and phosphatized (p), intraclasts, have had their interiors excavated by *Entobia*-like sponge borings. A stenomorphic (restricted) *Thalassinoides* burrow (arrowed) has become further restricted by repeated layers of shiny phosphate skins, which also line the *Thalassinoides* burrow at the top of the block. (B). Beauval; the basal hardground top. The sediment is similar to that at Hallencourt but contains a higher proportion of recognizable white chalk intraclasts. The hardground surface, which has been phosphatized, contains truncated pholadid bivalve borings (arrowed). These borings have subsequently been infilled by a complex of intraclasts and phosphate skins. The truncation may be indicative of significant bioerosion during the final stages of hardground formation.

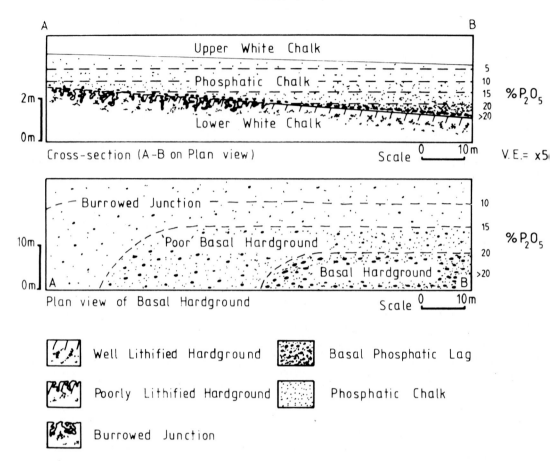

Fig. 12.—Schematic diagram of Flour's quarry 1893–1900, Fresnoy-le-Grand (Aisne), 15 km NE of St. Quentin (an interpretation of data in Gosselet, 1893, 1896, 1897, 1900). The diagram illustrates the positive correlation between the degree of lithification of the basal hardground, and the P_2O_5 content and thickness of the overlying phosphatic chalk.

(2). material with an initially high phosphate content, including fecal pellets and bioclasts.

All of these components are important within the phosphatic chalk *sensu stricto* except the hardground surface which is excluded by definition.

Tabatabaï's (1977) quantitative work on the phosphatic chalks of Hardivillers, Nurlu and Beauval has demonstrated that significant compositional changes occur within the phosphatic chalk during the evolution of the cuvette (fig. 16). Near the basal hardground, phosphatized coprolites comprise a large proportion of the recognizable elements of the sediment. Benthic foraminifera dominate over planktic and echinoderm and bone fragments are common. Sponge spicules and inoceramid prisms, on the other hand, are less frequent than farther above the hardground. As the infilling of the cuvette proceeded the percentage of coprolites, echinoderm, bone fragments and benthic foraminifera decline. All fragments return to a low level on the resumption of white chalk deposition. The most phosphatic sediments are generally the coarsest, but the phosphatic chalk directly above the hardground is coarser than that of equally phosphatic sediment higher in the sequence.

Macrofauna is prolific in the basal lag and in the directly overlying phosphatic chalk but is infrequent within the bulk of the remaining phosphatic chalk, within which oysters are the only abundant macrofossil. Despite this lack of preserved fauna, bioturbation is intense (fig. 17) throughout the entire sequence. In the upper portion of the youngest phosphatic chalks, however, a distinct faunal sequence may be discerned. In all suitable exposures examined, a bed of belemnites occurs just below the highest phosphatic chalk; *Gonioteuthis quadrata quadrata* with rare *Belemnitella* ex gr. *praecursor* Stolley.

This band overlies, but is separated from, a bed of *Offaster pilula.* The occurrence of *Echinocorys truncata* (Griffith and Brydone) in the latter bed indicates that it corresponds to the "lower belt of *Offaster pilula,* Subzone of abundant *O. pilula*" (Brydone, 1914). Rare *Echinocorys cincta* (Brydone) occur above the *Offaster* Bed indicating that the age of the youngest phosphatic chalk is probably within the *E. cincta* level of Brydone (1914). Tabatabaï (1977) dates the final period of phosphatization as being within the French foraminifera Zone h. This suggests at least a partial correspondence between the *O. pilula* Zone and Zone h.

DISCUSSION

Lithification and Winnowing

The coarse, commonly intraclastic nature of the lithified sediment contained within the basal hardground is clearly of significance both to the

processes of lithification and to the overall environment of deposition.

Ordinary white chalks have a high porosity of 35–50 percent (Scholle and Kennedy, 1974; Scholle, 1977) but a low permeability—1–8 md (Scholle, 1974); hardground chalks on the other hand have a much reduced porosity, 10–20 percent (Scholle and Kennedy, 1974) or less. This large reduction in porosity is due to the introduction of cement, a process which is difficult to envisage in a sediment with such a low permeability. However, the permeability will be considerably enhanced if the finer fraction of the sediment is removed by winnowing and the mean grain size increased. It is suggested here that such an increase in permeability acts as a substantial aid to lithification. Increased grain size is not the only requirement, however, since not all coarse grained chalks become hardened. Similarly, elsewhere, not all hardened chalks are coarse grained.

Nevertheless, in a continually winnowed en-

FIG. 13.—(A). The surface of the basal hardground, Beauval. Gulley erosion by rainwater has exposed the hummocky surface of the hardground. Hummocks vary in size from a few mm to 1 m, an intermediate variety is shown in the photograph. (B). An intraclast pebble lag, Gonioteuthis Hardground, Faucouzy. A thick bed of phosphatized and occasionally glauconitized 0.1–50 mm intraclasts rest on the hardground surface. Phosphatic chalk rests directly on top of the intraclast bed with no apparent gradation. The intraclasts are cut by a variety of borings, polychaete worm bores predominating.

A

cms

B

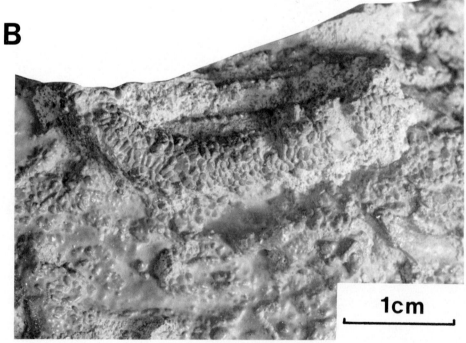

1cm

FIG. 15.—The Coral Bed, Beauval. The Bed contains abundant sand-grade phosphate as well as silicified fragments of inoceramid shell (i) and bored glauconitized intraclasts (g). The coral *Diblasus arborescens* Parent is found in two modes of preservation; (d) in which the walls of the corallum have been silicified and the septae phosphatized and (s), in which the outer portion of the walls are preserved in calcite and the septae are only occasionally seen, as calcitic or limonitic ghosts.

vironment, the top few centimetres of sediment would be too mobile to allow cementation, while at greater depths, interaction with fresh sea-water is lacking and the pore water reaches equilibrium with the surrounding grains. Between these two extremes, there must lie a zone where particle movement is sufficiently slight to allow cementation but there is sufficient replacement of pore water to provide the necessary amount of calcium carbonate. It is by such a flushing action by currents and possibly burrowing organisms, as suggested by Bromley (1967, 1975), that sufficient cement could be introduced into a sediment with such an initial high porosity.

It is suggested therefore, that cementation occurred a few centimetres below the sediment/

water interface in a winnowed sediment of increased permeability. Cementation probably occurred by the overgrowth of calcitic particles, but was prevented in the areas of the *Thalassinoides* burrows which remained open, and in the top few centimetres of sediment, which were in motion. The original mineralogy of the cement is uncertain although Kennedy and Garrison (1975) favor magnesium calcite. The calcite in the upper portions of the basal hardgrounds at Beauval and Nurlu contains up to 1400 ppm Mg, compared with 900 ppm in the underlying soft white chalk. Although this observation is not conclusive, it may reflect an initially higher Mg content in the basal hardground cements.

The winnowed nature of the hardground sedi-

FIG. 14.—'*Terebella' phosphatica* Leriche. (A). A general view of the surface of the basal hardground, Beauval, encrusted by '*T' phosphatica*. (B). Close-up of a single tube (arrowed in A), which consists predominantly of fecal pellets cemented by phosphate and oriented with their long axes normal to the direction of growth. The fossil is intimately associated with a complex of phosphate skins.

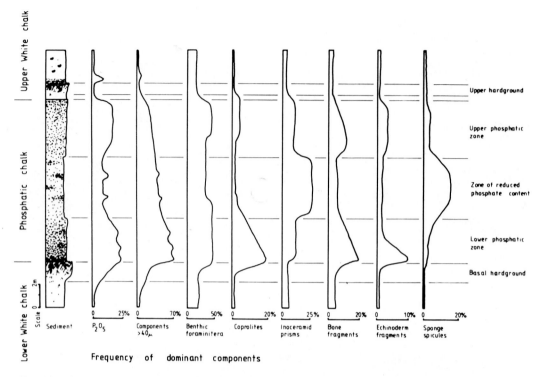

FIG. 16.—Component analysis of an idealized phosphatic chalk; based on Tabataba'i (1977) and personal observation. The tailing-off of components below the basal hardground, rather than a sharp cut-off, is due to bioturbation. The sediment log has a weathering profile.

ment is clear evidence of the existence of a stronger current regime. The erosion of the chalk which produced the cuvettes prior to basal hardground formation, the occurrence of a fauna including corals and sabellariid worms which are favored by high current activity, and in the case of the sabellariids, require it, all corroborate the evidence provided by the hardground itself.

The Phosphatic Chalks

Once the hardgrounds had formed they provided a special environment within the Chalk sea. The number of potential ecological niches was considerably increased by the formation of mixed hard and soft substrates. Thus the hard surfaces were colonized by a community which included corals, tube-worms and oysters and an infaunal community, including bivalves and echinoderms,

inhabited the mobile calcarenite which locally covered the hardground.

This fauna, its associated flora, and the pelagic biota, concentrated phosphorus from sea-water and, on death, produced an organic-rich substrate. Decomposition of organic matter released PO_4 into the surrounding pore water and overlying bottom water, thereby providing a local concentration of dissolved phosphorus. There followed the selective mineralization of material of an initially high phosphate content, such as bone fragments, fecal pellets and bioclasts, and of lithified carbonate, including the hardground surface and its associated intraclasts.

The occurrence of phosphatized fecal pellets in the virtual absence of unmineralized examples, suggests that the phosphatization process was intrinsic to their preservation. Under normal

FIG. 17.—Phosphatic chalks. (A). Nurlu; bioturbation is intense throughout. 30 cm long, narrow (0.5–1.5 mm), straight, white chalk-filled burrows (arrowed) are common. These are representatives of the ichnogenus *Trichichnus*. Burrows with white chalk rinds and phosphatic chalk fills are also common. (B). A polished block from Faucouzy demonstrates the occurrence of *Meunsteria*-like meniscus-fill burrows. White chalk rind burrows, *Thalassinoides* and *Chondrites* are also common.

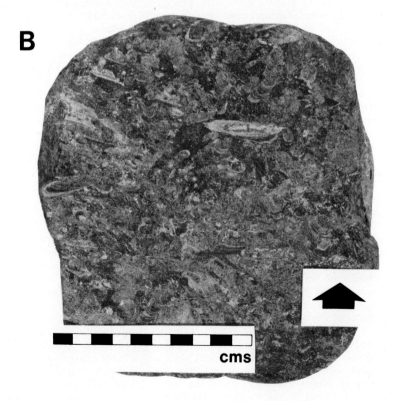

marine conditions fecal pellets are destroyed rapidly (e.g. Bayer et al., 1977), their conservation therefore indicates that mineralization was relatively fast. Furthermore, if the pellets did not have carbonate cemented precursors, they must have resulted from a combination of replacement of the enclosed micrite and cementation by phosphate, probably by the syntaxial overgrowth on existing grains. Since calcite may act as a surface for the nucleation of apatite (Stumm and Morgan, 1970), cementation may pre-, post-date, or be concurrent with, replacive phosphatization.

The preferential phosphatization of lithified carbonate has been discussed by Kennedy and Garrison (1975) who suggest that if the hardground cement was high Mg-calcite or aragonite, it would dissolve more easily and therefore be more susceptible to mineralization than the surrounding and enclosed low Mg-calcite. The presence of phosphatized, originally aragonitic, shells of gastropods and bivalves demonstrates that phosphatization preceded aragonite dissolution, a sea-floor or early post-burial phenomenon (Jefferies, 1962; Bromley, 1965; Kennedy and Garrison, 1975). Aragonite replacement, therefore, provides further evidence of the early diagenetic nature of the phosphatization process.

The hardground surface and the majority of the overlying phosphatized components are invariably covered by a shiny phosphate veneer. In thin section, this skin is composed of laminated coatings of fine, elongate crystals having their long axes normal to the surface which they mantle. Unfortunately, SEM studies have so far been unable to resolve individual crystals, so their detailed morphology remains unknown.

It has been suggested (Bromley, 1965; Kennedy and Garrison, 1975) that these veneers result from the direct precipitation of phosphate from seawater. An alternative hypothesis is that they are the product of the phosphatization of algal mucilage and other organic matter that coats ooliths and peloids in carbonate sediments at the present day (Bathurst, 1976). That similar organic material can become phosphatized is demonstrated by the phosphatized worm tube cements which were originally organic (Kirtley and Tanner, 1968). Such a flourishing algal growth would act as a major concentrator of phosphorus on the sea-floor (Charles, 1953), and could, on decay, induce the precipitation of phosphate within the microenvironment formed by the mat or, alternatively, result in the phosphatization of the organic material itself, or the contained and underlying micrite.

A combination of winnowing and both mechanical and biological erosion, together with a continual process of mineralization and degradation, resulted in the concentration of the most phosphatic material on the hardground surface.

As the process continued the coarsest and densest sediment (the phosphatized component), was transported into the centre of the cuvette by downslope movement, thus amassing the richest phosphorite into this area. As the cuvette evolved, production of material suitable for phosphatization was able to continue both in the newly formed phosphatic chalk and on the basal hardground of the still uncovered sides. In the deeper parts of the cuvette, the biological communities gradually became limited to calcarenite-associated faunas such as certain infaunal bivalves, asteroids and echinoids, but with some other material being derived laterally. Intense bioturbation occurred throughout the entire sequence and destroyed almost all original bedding lamination.

Interpretation of the trends observed within phosphatic chalks (fig. 16) is not as clear cut as it might be for a clastic sediment. It would appear that a progressively waning current regime is the logical mechanism to produce this type of sequence. However, other factors must also be considered.

Fecal pellets are an important factor in the observed sediment coarsening near the hardground surface. The majority of pellets are of the simple ovoid variety (fig. 14), Wilcox's (1953) type D. They are invariably coated with a shiny phosphate patina and consist of a phosphatized, foraminifera-bearing micrite. Wilcox (1953) suggests that this type of fecal pellet could be attributed to either detritus feeders or the boring worms which penetrate hardground surfaces. If the latter is the case, the pellets are primarily the result of a hardground-tied fauna and such pellets would have to be derived laterally from the exposed hardground on the sides of the cuvette, after occlusion of a significant area of hardground surface by phosphatic chalk. Much of the intraclastic material which rests on top of the hardground is eroded hardground sediment; its abundance markedly increases the grain size of the sediment, yet its origin was probably due to bioerosion and does not necessarily reflect any hydrodynamic effects.

If the processes of early diagenetic phosphatization were solely related to the prolific biota which developed on the hardground, then as the hardground became mantled in sediment, less and less fecal material would be produced and therefore preserved, also the amount of organic matter being supplied to the sediment would be greatly reduced.

All of the above factors; energy levels, the supply of material suitable for phosphatization and the concentration of dissolved phosphate, are closely related and interdependent. Undoubtedly all three contributed to the final composition of the lithofacies.

It is suggested that phosphatization was directly

linked to the proliferation of organic debris which must have accompanied the formation of these sediments. Cornet (1905) has shown that the brown coloration of the Ciply phosphatic chalk (Maastrichtian, Belgium), a deposit sedimentologically identical to, but younger than, the Anglo-Paris Basin phosphorites, is a weathering phenomenon. Examination of phosphatic chalk from boreholes and in deep quarry sections, demonstrates (Cornet, 1905) that the brown color is due to the oxidized state of the enclosed iron minerals, and that fresh, unoxidized material collected from below the water table is grey-blue in color and contains abundant disseminated pyrite. The occurrence of pyrite and reduced iron are clear indications of anaerobic conditions within phosphatic chalk sediments. Tabatabaï (1977) records up to 0.3 percent organic carbon in Anglo-Paris Basin phosphatic chalk, although values of 4.5 percent are obtained from the acid insoluble fractions of the same rocks. Tabatabaï (1977) considers that the clay minerals associated with this organic matter aid in it's preservation. It is proposed that the organic content of the clay fraction may be applicable to the whole rock in it's unoxidized form, and that subsurface weathering of phosphorite above the water table has subsequently reduced the carbon content.

In modern environments, decaying organic matter may raise the pH within the sediment (Berner, 1969) because of the formation of NH_4 and other nitrogenous bases. This environment of high pH and high alkalinity is required for phosphate replacement and precipitation (Senin, 1970; Cook, 1976) at the present day. Evidence from Recent sediments further suggests that phosphatization occurs in diatomaceous muds a few centimetres below the sediment/water interface (Baturin, 1969, 1971; Senin, 1970; Romankevich and Baturin, 1972; Burnett, 1977; Price and Calvert, 1978), and it is suggested that a similar subsurface environment might also provide suitable geochemical conditions in the carbonate muds of the phosphatic chalk lithofacies.

The rich fauna which is associated with the basal hardgrounds clearly indicates that the bottom water and sediment were oxygenating for most of the period of hardground formation, but above this, macrofauna is rare except for pelagic elements such as belemnites. Benthic foraminifera, an important component in all phosphatic chalks, flourish in, and adjacent to, the oxygen minimum layer (the layer in the oceans vertical profile in which dissolved oxygen is at its minimum) off the Peru coast at the present day (Frankenberg and Menzies, 1968; Bandy and Rodolfo, 1964), indicating that they are facultative anaerobes; similarly some species of worm can also tolerate intermittent anoxia.

The occurrence of less versatile fauna, including octocorals and echinoderms, and the presence of a varied infauna, however, demonstrate that the sea-floor and probably the surface sediment were aerobic for much of the time. These two trends are not necessarily mutually exclusive, for it is possible to envisage a sea-floor where aerobic and anaerobic conditions alternate beneath the sediment surface but where previous anaerobic phases are destroyed by the bioturbation of the next aerobic phase. Another possibility is that anaerobia only occurred within the microenvironments provided by fecal pellets, beneath algal(?) and other organic coatings, and within shells.

Transgression and Regression

Apparently, phosphatic chalk cuvettes only formed during a relatively short period of geological time—mid Santonian to early Campanian. One possible mechanism for this temporal control involves a eustatic change of sea level. It has been suggested (e.g. Cooper, 1977) that during a regressive period in basinal areas away from a sediment source, lowering of sea level may result in submarine erosion of topographic highs and the development of hardgrounds. Such a link between regression and the development of hardgrounds has been proposed by Bromley (1965, 1967).

Indications of marine transgression during early and mid-Santonian times comes from such widely spaced areas as Ireland, Sweden, Madagascar and Australia (Cooper, 1977). The late Santonian to early Campanian, on the other hand, appears to have been a period of lowering of sea level (Hancock, 1975; Cooper, 1977) which resulted in widespread disconformity in the North Sea (Ziegler, 1978). The next transgressive episode has been dated in southern Sweden as uppermost Lower Campanian (Christensen, 1975).

The phosphatic chalk lithofacies itself provides some evidence for shallow-water conditions. Small borings associated with skeletal fragments included into the basal hardground and within the phosphatic chalks may be attributable to thallophytes. The presence of such algal or fungal(?) borings would imply deposition within the photic zone i.e. <150 m even for clear water such as that to be expected in the Chalk sea. Such borings have been described from other hardground horizons (Bromley, 1965, 1970; Kennedy, 1970; Kennedy and Garrison, 1975). Other structures of probable algal origin are the phosphate skins which coat the hardground surfaces and the majority of the phosphatized intraclasts, fecal pellets and skeletal material in the main body of the phosphatic chalks. Such algal structures are totally lacking in normal white chalks (Kennedy and Garrison, 1975) and therefore suggest a lower stand of sea level.

A

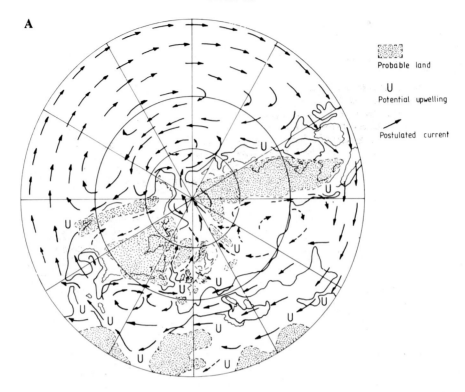

Probable land

U
Potential upwelling

Postulated current

B

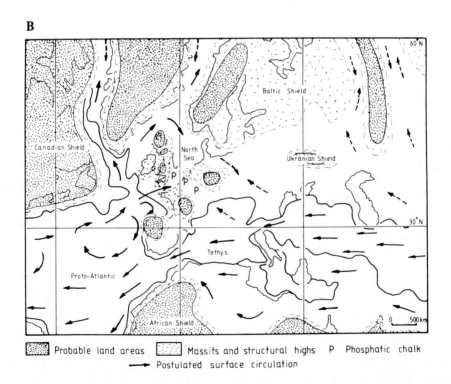

Probable land areas   Massifs and structural highs   P   Phosphatic chalk
Postulated surface circulation

Currents and Cuvettes

Although the extent to which increased current activity was directly responsible for the increased grain size of phosphatic chalks is uncertain, it is clear that current activity was persistent and strong during the initial formation of the phosphatic chalk lithofacies. Evidence for this is provided by the coarseness of the hardground lithified sediment, the erosion of appreciable thicknesses of white chalk prior to hardground formation and the establishment of a current-requiring fauna of sabellariid worms and scleractinian corals. Much of the concentration of phosphatic chalks must relate to the cessation of chalk sedimentation or continual winnowing of fines by the currents.

Shepard (1973) and Johnson (1978) divide ocean currents, apart from those related to breaking waves in the surf zone, into those produced by:—

(1). wind stress on the surface of the ocean,
(2). tidal forces,
(3). differences of water density.

Wind induced currents are of two types. The first, related to local climatic conditions, reaches depths of only up to 50 m from the water surface. Estimated depths for the Chalk sea are generally between 100 and 600 m (Hancock, 1975), although shallower depths, possibly as little as 50 m, have been suggested for some horizons, such as the Chalk Rock (Kennedy and Garrison, 1975). It seems unlikely that, even with depths of 50 m, this type of current would be sufficient to erode such large scale features just within the limit of its depth range.

The second form of wind induced currents are permanent surface currents, maintained by the Earths prevailing wind systems. These currents, and the underlying bottom current systems which are directly related to them, can move at considerable velocities and be erosive to depths in excess of 1000 m (Heezen and Hollister, 1971). This type of current is therefore a clear candidate for the mechanism of erosive scour which produced phosphatic chalk cuvettes.

Tidal currents have a larger effect on the shallow sea-floor than permanent currents, but depend upon restriction of flow between straits to achieve their erosive potential. Such currents are unlikely to have been pronounced in the broad, generally unrestricted, epicontinental sea inferred for northwest Europe during Santonian to Campanian times (fig. 18B). The possible range of shelf depths involved, however, means that they cannot be entirely discounted.

The most significant form of erosive density currents are turbidity currents, which are well known contributors to many clastic sequences. Such flows require potential energy for their initiation and it seems unlikely that the necessary slopes would be present on the continental shelf sea-floor prior to cuvette formation. Furthermore, none of the basal sediments exhibit characteristics one would normally expect of a turbidite.

The Hallencourt pit cuvettes may provide some clue to the type, since currents which produced the cuvettes must have been operating in the same position for over 4 million years (mid-Santonian to early Campanian) and yet maintain the same trend.

Of the three current types considered, only a permanent current would be expected to produce such a constant orientation. Newton et al. (1973), in their study of the continental shelf off the Spanish Sahara, report what they consider to be longitudinal erosional 'windows' of over 200 m in width and 1 km in length for the larger forms. These 'windows,' which are up to 20 m deep, have their long axes parallel to the isobaths and occur in water depths of between 50 and 80 m. The authors consider that these structures were produced by erosion by the Canary current. Clearly, these features might be considered comparable to phosphatic chalk cuvettes.

Oceanic Circulation

Erosion by a permanent ocean current may provide the mechanism for cuvette formation, while regression may be necessary for it to achieve significant erosional effects (therefore providing a temporal control), but neither mechanism explains why deposition of phosphatic chalks took place on such a wide scale within the Anglo-Paris Basin (and elsewhere, e.g. in Belgium [Leriche, 1935]) during the mid-Santonian to early Campanian. Furthermore, conditions appear to have continued to be favorable for phosphate deposition during the late Campanian to Maastrichtian in the Middle East (Würzburger, 1968) and Belgium (Cornet and Briart, 1878) and into the Eocene in North Africa (Salvan, 1960). All these deposits appear to be of the same general type, being composed of thin (rarely >3 m) beds of pelletal phosphorite. Prior to this, Cretaceous pelletal

Fig. 18.—Late Santonian—Campanian palaeogeography. The palaeocontinents have been reconstructed by Smith and Briden (1977). Palaeoceanography has been constructed by analogy to present-day surface ocean-current circulation, and incorporates data from Freas and Eckstrom (1968), Luyendyk et al. (1972) and Gordon (1973). Thick continuous lines are the breaks of slope along the continental shelf areas or pre-collision boundaries (e.g. N. Italy). The fine continuous lines mark present day landmasses. (A). Northern hemisphere, the map is drawn on a north polar stereographic projection, (B). Europe, based on a Mercator projection.

phosphorites were rare and poorly developed, e.g. in the mid-Turonian of Lewes (Strahan, 1896) and in Cambrai (Leriche, 1909). Perhaps some major change in oceanic régime occured prior to the mid-Santonian which resulted in the deposition of the phosphatic chalk lithofacies.

Studies of Recent phosphate formation in the off-shore areas of Peru-Chile (Baturin et al., 1972; Veeh et al., 1973; Manheim et al., 1975; Burnett, 1977; Burnett and Veeh, 1977) and SW Africa (Baturin, 1969, 1971; Senin, 1970; Calvert and Price, 1971; Romankevich and Baturin, 1972; Summerhayes, 1973; Price and Calvert, 1978), indicate that there are three main requirements for the formation of contemporary phosphorites:—

(1). An oxygen-minimum layer impinging on the sea-floor.

(2). a limited supply of terrigenous and carbonate detritus,

(3). strong and persistent upwelling.

The oxygen-minimum layer is usually between 100 and 500 m in the present oceans, but may expand and thereby encroach into shallower water during periods of slowed oceanic circulation (e.g. Fischer and Arthur, 1977). It has been recognized that, off Peru, phosphorite formation appears to be concentrated in bands which coincide with the upper and lower boundaries of the oxygen-minimum layer where it impinges on the sea-floor (Veeh et al., 1973; Burnett, 1977). This distribution may be related to two factors. Firstly, under totally anoxic conditions, phosphate is free to diffuse into oceanic bottom waters (Mortimer, quoted in Manheim et al., 1975) and will not be retained in the sediment pore water. Under oxic conditions, however, it is bound to iron and manganese ions to become insoluble (Bray et al., 1973; Berner, 1973). Thus, an environment of partial, or perhaps intermittent, anoxia is that most favorable to modern phosphorite formation.

The preservation of organic matter, reduced iron and pyrite in unoxidized phosphatic chalks is indicative of anaerobia, while the abundance of infauna, the occurrence of epifauna and other benthic organisms, indicate aerobic conditions on the sea-floor and within the upper portion of the sediment. Consequently, any anoxic phases must have been short lived or restricted (see above).

There is no evidence for expansion of the oxygen-minimum layer during the late Santonian to early Campanian, although oceanic evidence is inconclusive, since the majority of DSDP boreholes reveal hiatuses at this level. Thus, although expansion of the oxygen-minimum layer does not provide a plausible mechanism, the relationship of Recent phosphorites to anoxia (in the present oceans, provided by the layer), appears very similar in these Cretaceous examples.

Little land was available in Europe as a source of detrital sediment during the post-Coniacian portion of the Late Cretaceous (fig. 18), so that terrigenous input was minimal in all facies during this period of time (Hancock, 1975) and not only limited to the phosphatic chalk lithofacies. The supply of carbonate detritus, since the sediment is a calcareous nannoplankton ooze, was slow throughout the period of Chalk deposition, a maximum rate of 15 cm/1000 years being estimated by Håkansson et al. (1974), while the extremely fine grain size of the sediment (75–90% of the rock is between 0.5 and 4 μm [Black, 1953; Håkansson et al., 1974]) means that the carbonate was easily removed by current action. Another fact that may have some bearing on the matter is the suggestion of Cooper (1977) that the input of biogenic detritus is lowest during regressive episodes. Thus, sediment input was low for most of the Upper Cretaceous, and current activity in the cuvettes would have reduced it further, possibly beyond the threshold value necessary for phosphorite formation.

We are left with the concept of strong and persistent upwelling. Upwelling is dependant on current movements, which in turn are controlled by the geometry of the ocean basins and wind systems. This could be the major environmental factor which separates pre- from post-Santonian times.

In the marine environment, above average concentrations of phosphate occur (Cook, 1976) in association with:—

(1). estuarine waters,

(2). cold surface waters,

(3). upwelling currents.

Biological production might be regarded as an additional source of phosphate but this is not so, since phosphate is one of the biolimiting elements (Broecker, 1974). High biological production is therefore the result of a pre-existing abundance of phosphorus (Cayeux, 1950; Charles, 1953; Cook, 1976), and usually the other biolimiting elements, silicon and nitrogen (although normally only one element is actively biolimiting at any one time), and as such is the result of, rather than the cause of, a high phosphorus concentration in sea-water. This dissolved phosphate can then be utilized and thereby concentrated by pelagic and benthic organisms which, on death, transfer it to the bottom water and sediment as organic matter, where, on decay, it is liberated and provides a source of phosphorus for precipitation and replacement. In the deposits being considered, we are dealing with fully marine conditions, on a planet with an equable climate and no icecaps. The first two modes of enrichment can therefore be dismissed, leaving upwelling currents as the source of the biolimiting elements, in particular phosphorus. McKelvey (1959) has demonstrated that such a process is more than adequate to provide the considerable amount of phosphorus in phosphorites.

The conditions conducive to upwelling have been summarized by Freas and Eckstrom (1968; also in Cook, 1976). The Anglo-Paris Basin lies on the west side of a continent within the belt of the westerlies (approximately between 20° and 40°), and is surrounded by, albeit much reduced, landmasses (fig. 18) with arid climates. Consequently, the eastern side of the Basin was a potential area of oceanic upwelling caused by seaward moving surface water (upwelling by divergence) or shelving of a current over a submarine topographic high (dynamic upwelling).

Luyendyk et al. (1972) and Hart (1976) suggest that a primitive 'gyre' developed in the North Atlantic Ocean during the late Cenomanian and that this was an early development of a proto-Gulf Stream. If the Gulf Stream was initiated in the Cenomanian, the continuing opening of the North Atlantic during the Turonian and Coniacian would have led to the development of a strong permanent current by the Santonian. At the present day the Gulf Stream is able to intrude onto the continental shelves (Atkinson, 1977), so the current would have been able to flow into the Chalk sea during the late Cretaceous.

There is no evidence for extensive land during the Campanian in any of the massifs surrounding the area under consideration (fig. 18), and it is possible that Armorica, Cornubia and the Ardennes were transgressed by this time. That these areas provided a sea-floor topography seems more likely. 'Marginal' glauconitic chalks of late Campanian age occur in east Belgium (Calembert, 1956, Schmid, 1959) and similar facies occur in the Santonian-Campanian of Northern Ireland (Hancock, 1961). Thus, the permanent current set up in the proto-Atlantic may have been deflected and caused to upwell along a trend which parallels the London-Brabant Massif and western Ardennes.

CONCLUSIONS

(1). Phosphatic chalks are a distinctive and economically important lithofacies within the late Santonian to early Campanian chalks of the Anglo-Paris Basin.

(2). Phosphatic chalk sedimentation was preceded by the erosion of cuvettes up to 1 km long, 250 m wide and 30 m deep into the underlying white chalk.

(3). The cuvettes are floored by well-lithified and mineralized basal hardgrounds penetrated by numerous *Thalassinoides* burrow systems. The upper portion of these hardgrounds is phosphatized, glauconitized and coated by a thin (<1 mm) phosphate skin of possible algal origin.

(4). Sediment remaining in the cuvettes was winnowed by currents which had also provided the initial erosion. Winnowing led to a coarsened sediment and this resulted in early diagenetic lithification, possibly by a Mg-calcite cement, a few centimetres below the sediment/water interface. Later exposure of these surfaces produced the hardground.

(5). A distinctive fauna developed on the hardground surface, typified by *'Terebella' phosphatica*, *Diblasus arborescens* and *Lopha semiplana*.

(6). The rich biota associated with the cuvettes concentrated phosphorus from sea-water and, on death, produced organic-rich substrates. Subsequent decomposition of organic matter released PO_4 into the pore water and overlying bottom water and resulted in the mineralization of material of an initially high phosphate content and lithified sediment.

(7). Phosphatization was a sea-floor or early post-burial phenomenon which pre-dated both the decomposition of fecal pellets and aragonite dissolution.

(8). Phosphatization was predominantly a replacement process, but precipitation may have occurred within the microenvironments provided by fecal pellets, algal and other organic coatings.

(9). The preservation of organic matter, reduced iron and disseminated pyrite in unoxidised phosphatic chalks is indicative of intermittent and/or subsurface and microenvironmental anoxia. Comparison with Recent analogues suggests that such conditions produce an environment favorable to phosphate precipitation and replacement.

(10). The increased abundance of biota was primarily due to a readily available supply of nutrients, in particular phosphorus. A combination of this prolific biota and a sediment trap led to the infilling of the cuvettes by a phosphatic chalk which was continuously upgraded by winnowing.

(11). Upwelling of nutrient-laden waters occurred along a line parallel to the London-Brabant Massif and western Ardennes. This upwelling was linked to the establishment of a permanent current system, possibly a proto-Gulf Stream, which resulted in local erosion where it flowed onto the continental shelf, producing structures similar to those found on the West African shelf today.

(12). The limited periods of phosphatization may be related to:—

(a). regressive events which provide periods of increased current scour,

(b). the lack of a permanent current flowing on to the shelf prior to Santonian times.

Many of the foregoing conclusions have utilized comparisons with Recent phosphates, which are being precipitated in diatomaceous muds at the present day. These sediments would produce a phosphorite-black shales-chert assemblage in the geologic record, a facies association which contrasts with the phosphatic chalk-hardground-soft white chalk sequences of the Senonian. Nevertheless, these modern deposits provide valuable insights into the mode of formation of Cretaceous phosphatic chalks.

Acknowledgements

I would like to thank the friends who have accompanied me on my fieldwork in France, especially Pete Woodroof and Andy Gale with whom I have had many fruitful discussions on the problems of phosphatic chalk genesis; and Ann Richardson for her continual support. I would like to acknowledge a NERC postgraduate research grant at the University of Oxford, which provided the finance for the research which led to this paper. NERC, Wolfson College and Oxford University provided the funds for attendance of the IAS 1978 Congress in Jerusalem, at which this paper was first presented. R. G. Bromley, H. C. Jenkyns, W. J. Kennedy, A. S. Gale and P. Woodroof kindly read through and greatly improved earlier drafts of the manuscript.

REFERENCES

ATKINSON, L. P., 1977, Modes of gulf stream intrusion onto the South Atlantic Bight shelf waters: Geophys. Res. Letters, v. 4, no. 12, p. 583–86.

BANDY, O. L., AND RODOLFO, K. S., 1964, Distribution of Foraminifera and sediments, Peru-Chile Trench area: Deep-Sea Res., v. 11, p. 817–837.

BATHURST, R. G. C., 1976, Carbonate sediments and their diagenesis. (Second Edition): Developments in Sedimentology, v. 12. Elsevier, Amsterdam, London, New York, 658 p.

BATURIN, G. N., 1969, Authigenic phosphate concretions in Recent sediments of the Southwest African Shelf: Dokl. Earth Sci. Sect. English Transl., v. 189, p. 227–230.

——, 1971, Stages of phosphorite formation on the ocean floor: Nature, (London), 232 no. 29, p. 61–62.

——, MERKULOVA, K. I., AND CHALOV, P. I., 1972, Radiometric evidence for recent formation of phosphatic nodules in marine shelf sediments: Marine Geology, v. 13, p. M37–M41.

BAYER, P. S., GUINNESS, E. A., LYNCH-BLOSSE, M. A., AND STOLZMAN, R. A., 1977, Greensand faecal pellets from New Jersey: Jour. Sed. Pet., v. 47, p. 267–280.

BERNER, R. A., 1969, Migration of iron and sulfur within anaerobic sediments during early diagenesis: Am. Jour. Sci. v. 267, p. 19–42.

——, 1973, Phosphate removal from sea water by absorption on volcanogenic ferric oxides: Earth Planetary Sci. Letters, v. 18, p. 77–86.

BLACK, M., 1953, The constitution of the Chalk: Geol. Soc. Lond Proc., 1499, p. 81–86.

BRAY, J. T., BRICKER, O. P., AND TROUP, B. N., 1973, Phosphate in interstitial waters of anoxic sediments: oxidation effects during sampling procedure: Science, v. 180, p. 1362–1364.

BROECKER, W. S., 1974, Chemical Oceanography. Harcourt Brace Jonavovich, Inc., New York, Chicago, San Francisco, Atlanta, 214 p.

BROMLEY, R. G., 1965, Studies in the lithology and conditions of sedimentation of the Chalk Rock and comparable horizons: Ph.D. thesis. University of London.

——, 1967, Some observations on burrows of thalassinidean crustacea in chalk hardgrounds: Quar. Jour. geol. Soc. Lond., v. 123, p. 157–182.

——, 1970, Borings as trace fossils and *Entobia cretacea* Portlock, as an example, *in* Trace Fossils (Ed. Crimes and Harper). Geol. J. Special Issue, v. 3, p. 49–90.

——, 1975, Trace fossils at omission surfaces, *in* The Study of Trace-fossils (Ed. by R. W. Frey), Springer Verlag, Berlin, p. 399–428.

BROQUET, P., 1973, La craie phosphatée en Picardie, perspectives d'avenir de la prospection: Ann. Sci. Univ. Besançon, v. 3, no. 20, p. 143–152.

BRYDONE, R. M., 1914, The Zone of *Offaster pilula* in the South English Chalk, Parts I–IV: Geol. Mag. v. 6 no. 1, p. 359–69, 405–11, 449–57, 509–13.

BURNETT, W. C., 1977, Geochemistry and origin of phosphorite deposits from off Peru and Chile: Geol. Soc. Am. Bull., v. 88, p. 813–823.

——, AND VEEH, H. H., 1977, Uranium-series disequilibrium studies in phosphate nodules from the west coast of South America: Geochim. et Cosmochim. Acta., v. 41, p. 755–764.

BUTEUX, M., 1849, Esquisse géologique du département de la Somme. Paris, 122 p.

CALEMBERT, L., 1956, Le Crétacé supérieur de la Hesbaye et du Brabant: Excursion du 19 Sept. 1955. Ann. Soc. Géol. Belgique, v. 80, p. B129–B156.

CALVERT, S. E., AND PRICE, N. B., 1971, Recent sediments of the South West African shelf, *in* Geology of the East Atlantic Continental Margin (ed. by F. M. Delany), ICSU/SCOR Working Party 31 Symp. Cambridge 1971, Inst. Geol. Sci. Rep., v. 70/16, p. 171–185.

CAYEUX, L., 1939, Les Phosphates de chaux sédimentaires de France. I. France metropolitaine. Etudes des gîtes mineraux de la France: Impr. Nationale, Paris 349 p.

——, 1941, Les Phosphates de chaux sédimentaires de France. II: Impr. Nationale, Paris. 659 p.

——, 1950, Les Phosphates de chaux sédimentaires de France. III: Impr. Nationale, Paris, 458 p.

CHARLES, G., 1953, Sur l'origine des gisements des phosphates de chaux sédimentaires: 19c Congr. Géol. Intern., Compt. Rend., Algiers, 1952, v. 11, p. 163–184.

CHRISTENSEN, W. K., 1975, Upper Cretaceous belemnites from the Kristianstad area in Scania: Fossils Strata, v. 7, p. 1–69.

COOK, P. J., 1976, Sedimentary Phosphate Deposits, in Handbook of Strata-Bound and Stratiform Ore Deposits (Ed. by K. H. Wolf), Elsevier, Amsterdam, London, New York, p. 505–535.

COOPER, M. R., 1977, Eustacy during the Cretaceous: its implications and importance: Palaeogeogr., Palaeoclimatol., Palaeoecol., v. 22, p. 1–60.

CORNET, F. L., AND BRIART, A., 1878, Sur la craie brune phosphatée de Ciply: Ann. Soc. Géol. Belgique, v. 5, p. 11–22.

CORNET, J., 1905, Sur les facies de la Craie phosphatée de Ciply: Ann. Soc. Géol. Belgique, v. 32, p. M137–M146.

DELATTRE CH, MERIAUX E., AND D'ARCY D., 1974, Carte Géologique de la France à 1/50,000, 34, Doullens, B.R.G.M. France.

DE GROSSOUVRE, A., 1901, Recherches sur la Craie Supérieure: Mem. à la Carte Géol. détailée de la France, 1013 p.

FISCHER, A. G., AND ARTHUR, M. A., 1977, Secular variations in the pelagic Realm, in Deep-Water Carbonate Environments (Ed. by Cook, H. E. and Enos, P.), SEPM Spec. Pub., v. 25, p. 19–50.

FRANKENBERG, D., AND MENZIES, R. J., 1968, Some quantitative analyses of deep-sea benthos off Peru: Deep Sea Res., v. 15, p. 623–626.

FREAS, D. H., AND ECKSTROM, C. L., 1968, Areas of potential upwelling and phosphorite deposition during Tertiary, Mesozoic and late Palaeozoic time, in U.N. Min. Res. Dev. Ser., v. 32, p. 228–238.

GORDON, W. A., 1973, Marine life and ocean surface currents in the Cretaceous: Jour. Geol., v. 81, p. 269–284.

GOSSELET, J., 1893, Note sur les gîtes de Phosphate de Chaux des environs de Fresnoy-le-Grand: Ann. Soc. Géol. Nord, v. 21, p. 149–159.

———, 1896, Note sur les gîtes de Phosphate de Chaux d'Hem-Monacu, d'Etaves, du Ponthieu, etc: Ann. Soc. Géol. Nord, v. 24, p. 109–134.

———, 1897, Limites supérieures et latérales des couches de Craie phosphatée d'Etaves et de Fresnoy: Ann. Soc. Géol. Nord, v. 26, p. 119–129.

———, 1900, Phosphates de chaux de Picardie: Livret Guide 8, Congrès géologique international, Paris.

HÅKANSSON, E., BROMLEY, R. G., AND PERCH-NIELSEN, K., 1974, Maastrichtian chalk of north-west Europe—a pelagic shelf sediment, in Pelagic Sediments: on land and under the sea. (Ed. by K. J. Hsü and H. C. Jenkyns): Spec. Publ. Int. Ass. Sediment., v. 1, p. 211–33.

HANCOCK, J. M., 1961, The Cretaceous System of northern Ireland: Quat. Jour. geol. Soc. Lond., v 117, p. 11–36.

———, 1975, The petrology of the Chalk: Proc. Geol. Ass., v. 86, no. 4, p. 499–535.

HART, M. B., 1976, The mid-Cretaceous successions of Orphan Knoll (North-west Atlantic): micropalaeontology and palaeo-oceanographic implications: Can. J. Earth Sci., v. 13, p. 1411–1421.

HEEZEN, B. C., AND HOLLISTER, C. D., 1971, The Face of the Deep: Oxford University Press, New York, London, Toronto, 659 p.

JEFFERIES, R. P. S., 1962, The palaeoecology of the Actinocamax plenus Subzone (lowest Turonian) in the Anglo-Paris Basin: Palaeontology, v. 4, p. 609–647.

JOHNSON, H. D., 1978, Shallow silicoclastic Environments and Facies, in Sedimentary Facies (Ed. by H. G. Reading). Blackwell Scientific Publications, Oxford., p. 207–258.

KENNEDY, W. J., 1970, Trace-fossils in the Chalk environment: Geol. Jour. Special Issue, v. 3, p. 263–282, 5 pls.

KENNEDY, W. J., AND GARRISON, R. E., 1975, Morphology and genesis of nodular chalks and hardgrounds in the Upper Cretaceous of southern England: Sedimentology, v. 22, p. 311–86.

KIRTLEY, D. W., AND TANNER, W. F., 1968, Sabellariid worms: Builders of a major reef type: Jour. Sed. Pet., v. 38, p. 76–78.

LASNE, H., 1892, Sur les terrains des environs de Doullens (2nd note): Bull. Soc. Géol. France, 3rd (series), v. 20, p. 211–236.

LERICHE, M., 1909, Sur la limite entre le Turonien et le Sénonien dans le Cambrésis et sur quelques fossiles de la Craie grise: Ann. Soc. Géol. Nord, v. 38, p. 53–73.

———, 1935, Sur le Crétacé supérieur du Hainaut et du Brabant: Ann. Soc. Géol. de Belgique, v. 58, p. 118–141.

LUYENDYK, B. P., FORSYTH, D., AND PHILLIPS, J. D., 1972, Experimental approach to the palaeocirculation of the oceanic surface waters: Geol. Soc. Am. Bull., v. 83, p. 2649–2664.

MCKELVEY, V. E., 1959, Relation of upwelling marine waters to phosphorite and oil: Geol. Soc. Am. Bull., v. 70, p. 1783–1784 (Abstract).

MANHEIM, F., ROWE, G. T. AND JIPA, D., 1975, Marine phosphorite formation off Peru: Jour. Sed. Pet., v. 45, p. 243–251.

MENNESSIER, G., AKBAR, R., SKANDARI, A., DURZADA, A., BROQUET, G., MONCIARDINI, G., AND AGACHE, R., 1974, Carte Géologique de la France à 1/50,000, 45-2, Hallencourt: B.R.G.M. France.

NEGRE, G., 1913, Découverte de Craie phosphatée dans l'assise à Belemnitella quadrata a Saint-Martin-du-Tertre près Sens (Yonne): Bull. Soc. Géol. Fr. v. 4, no. 13, p. 212–223.

NEWTON, R. S., SEIBOLD, E., AND WERNER, F., 1973, Facies distribution patterns on the Spanish Sahara continental shelf mapped with side-scan sonar: 'Meteor' Forsch. Ergebnisse, v. 15, p. 55–77.

PRICE, N. B., AND CALVERT, S. E., 1978, The Geochemistry of phosphates from the Namibian Shelf: Chem. Geol., v. 23, p. 151–170.

RAGUIN, E., 1926, Phosphates de France, *in* Les Réserves mondiales en phosphates. 14th. Int. Geol. Congr., Spain, p. 197–214.

ROMANKEVICH, Y. A., AND BATURIN, G. N., 1972, Composition of the organic matter in phosphorites from the continental shelf off southwest Africa: Geokhimiya (English trans.), v. 6, p. 719–726.

SALVAN, H., 1960, Les phosphates de chaux sédimentaires du Maroc, leurs caractéristiques et leurs problèmes (essai de synthèse): Notes Marocaines, v. 14, p. 7–20.

SCHMID, F., 1959, Biostratigraphie du Campanien-Maastrichtien du NE de la Belgique sur la base de Bélemnites: Ann. Soc. Géol. Belgique, v. 82, p. B235–B256.

SCHOLLE, P. A., 1974, Diagenesis of Upper Cretaceous chalks from England, Northern Ireland and the North Sea, *in* Pelagic Sediments: on land and under the sea. (Ed. K. J. Hsü and H. C. Jenkyns): Spec. Publ. Int. Ass. Sediment., v. 1, p. 177–210.

————, 1977, Chalk diagenesis and its relation to petroleum exploration: Oil from Chalks, a Modern Miracle?: Amer. Assoc. Petrol. Geol. Bull., v. 61, no. 7, p. 982–1009.

SCHOLLE, P. A., AND KENNEDY, W. J., 1974, Isotopic and petrophysical data on hardgrounds from Upper Cretaceous chalks from western Europe: Abstr. Progr. Geol. Soc. Amer., v. 6, no. 7, p. 943.

SENIN, Y. M., 1970, Phosphorus in Bottom Sediments of the Southwest African Shelf: Lithology and Mineral Resources, Consultants Bureau, New York, v. 25, p. 8–20.

SHEPARD, F. P., 1973, Submarine Geology (Third Edition): Harper and Row, New York, Evanston, San Francisco, London. 517 p.

SMITH, A. G., AND BRIDEN, J. C., 1977, Mesozoic and Cenozoic Paleocontinental Maps. Cambridge University Press, Cambridge, 63 p.

STRAHAN, A., 1896, On a phosphatic chalk with *Holaster planus* at Lewes, with an appendix on Foraminifera and Ostracoda by F. Chapman: Quart. Jour. Geol. Soc. Lond., v. 52, p. 462–473.

STUMM, W., AND MORGAN, J. J., 1970, Aquatic chemistry, an introduction emphasizing chemical equilibria in natural waters: Wiley-Interscience, New York, 583 p.

SUMMERHAYES, C. P., 1973, Distribution, Origin, and Economic Potential of phosphatic sediments from the Agulhas Bank, South Africa: Trans. Geol. Soc. S. Afr., v. 73, p. 271–277.

TABATABAÏ, C. M., 1977, La sédimentation phosphatée (ses modalités): Pétrographie et sédimentologie des Craies phosphatées du Nord du Bassin de Paris: Thèse, Diplôme de docteur de 3ᵉ cycle, l'Université Pierre et Marie Curie, Paris, 243 p. 34 pl.

VAN HINTE, J. E., 1976, A Cretaceous time scale: Am. Assoc. Pet. Geol. Bull., v. 60, p. 269–287.

VEEH, H. H., BURNETT, W. C., AND SOUTAR, A., 1973, Contemporary phosphorites of the continental margin of Peru: Science, v. 181, p. 844–845.

WILCOX, N. R., 1953, Some coprolites from phosphatic chalks in S.E. England: Ann and Mag. Nat. Hist. Ser. 12, p. 369–375.

WÜRZBURGER, U., 1968, A survey of phosphate deposits in Israel, *in* U.N. Min. Res. Dev. Ser., v. 32, p. 152–165.

ZIEGLER, P. A., 1978, North-Western Europe—Tectonics and Basin development: Geol. en Minj., v. 57, p. 589–626.

SEPM Special Publication No. 29, p. 193–205, November 1980

THE MAASTRICHTIAN PHOSPHATE SEQUENCE OF THE CONGO

PIERRE GIRESSE
Département de Géologie, Université Marien N'Gouabi
Brazzaville, R.P. Congo
present address: CRSM Perpignan, Université, Avenue de Villeneuve,
66025, Perpignan, France

ABSTRACT

The Maastrichtian phosphate series of the Congo is exposed in a narrow belt, about 750 m wide, trending parallel to the NW-SE direction of the Precambrian Massif of Mayombe and was preserved from erosion by down-faulting. The generally lenticular and thin phosphate occurrences can be grouped in two facies types:
— siliceous fossiliferous phosphate facies deposited in an open sea by upwelling, sheltered from coarse influx from the continent;
— a coprolitic-quartzose facies, representing a bioclastic accumulation, probably of deltaic origin.
The rather arid climate facilitated the deposition of feldspar, but also lead to an intense silicification at the top of the horizons. Later, hydrolysis intensified and affected also the top of the deposit, which was entirely decalcified and partly kaolinized, with formation of aluminum-phosphates.
The apatites, which are frequently decarbonized, are of the fluor-apatite type; they are associated with sometimes important quantities of uranium oxides. A provisional estimate indicates the presence of 5 million tons of phosphorites containing 22 to 25% P_2O_5.

INTRODUCTION

In 1928, Lebedeff (1928) reported the presence of a phosphatic sequence in the late Cretaceous section along the southern coast of Gabon. Their lenticular layers, frequently decalcified and silicified, are exposed on the coast and in the lagoons between Iguela and Fernan Vaz. Furon (1932) drew attention to some outcrops in the same area (N'Kéro lagoon), relatively rich in P_2O_5 (11 and 16%).

Somewhat farther south, in the sedimentary Congo basin, reconnaissance surveys for oil found phosphate layers for the first time in the Congo, and Haas (1935) discovered a phosphate horizon in the Sintou-Kola area (valley of the Tchissa). On first evaluation, a modest reserve of several hundred thousand tons was shown to be present here.

After the war, additional deposits were discovered in the Holle area, mainly in the Koubambi and Tchivoula valleys. Several lenses were opened up by numerous trenches, galleries and pits which proved a total reserve of some 5 million tons. After 1955, research slowed down and several discoveries farther south (Djeba, Loufica, Tchioupi, Zonde) in the direction of the already known deposits of the Cabinda raised hopes that proven reserves could be increased. Furthermore, the presence of aluminum-phosphates at the top of several layers interested for some time the Société Pechiney, while the not negligible but irregular uranium contents lead to exploration by the CEA.

After independence, the occurrences were re-evaluated in about 1968 by the Soviet and Bulgarian Technical Assistance which studied mainly the already known lenses and did not furnish much new information.

We note in addition the discovery, on the submarine shelf of the Congo, of Eocene phosphates redeposited in the Miocene and Quaternary (Giresse and Cornen, 1976).

The main results of the exploration mentioned are contained in several reports but have never been subjected to scientific analysis. Cayeux, in his fundamental treatise (1939), could only allude briefly to the Congo deposits which were, and still are, imperfectly known. We have consulted the documents, frequently difficult to use, as they are of a purely technical nature related to mining; we have in addition reexamined the still existing outcrops as well as the drillings of the Bulgarian mission and have undertaken a modern analysis of the petrographic, mineralogic, paleontologic and chemical characteristics of these phosphates with the aim of presenting a general view of the phosphatogenesis in this region at the end of the Mesozoic. Our conclusions can serve for comparison with neighboring occurrences along the Atlantic coast of Africa or with contemporaneous phosphates of other regions.

Geology of the Coastal Basin of Pointe Noire
(fig. 1)

a) The oldest rock units exposed in the basin are of early Cretaceous age. These are fluvio-marine or lagoonal, and sometimes lacustrine, deposits which seem to overlie the Precambrian

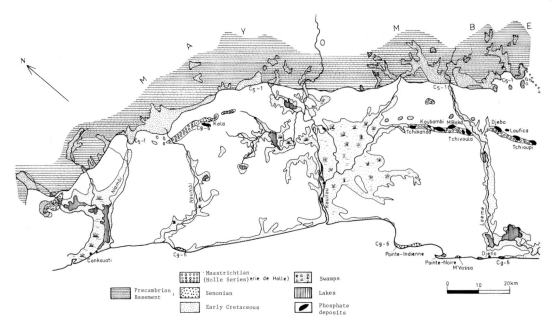

FIG. 1.—Geological Map of the Congo Coastal Basin; position of the phosphatic Holle Series.

Mayombe basement along a normal transgressive contact which, however, is slightly disturbed by compaction or slumping. The map shows that sedimentation penetrated inland along narrow gulfs with rias or lakes on the continental side. The position of these old valleys coincides with that of several present rivers, e.g. Loémé and Noumbi, but not with that of the Kouilou which seems to be more recent. These strata are marked C1 to C5 on the geological map (Dadet, 1966). They contain at their base black, frequently bituminous, platy marls reminiscent of the Cocobeach facies in Gabon and dated as Barremian to early Aptian. They are overlain by conglomerates, sandstones and unfossiliferous marls and limestones. The sandstones and limestones might correspond to the top of the Cocobeach or to part of the Madiela in Gabon (late Aptian and Albian). These strata pass locally into an evaporite sequence (halite, gypsum, potassium-salts), the importance of which increases westward in the subsurface.

This Aptian-Albian sequence might be represented in the outcrops along the valleys of the Holle area by the sandstones and dolomites of the Loufika, which lie at the base of the phosphatic deposits in this area.

b) The late Cretaceous section (C6 to C9 on the map) is generally masked by the thick detrital Plio-Pleistocene sequence of the Terminal Continental (Series of the Cirques); exposures are limited to coastal sections and to several valleys in the interior where they occur because of small local tectonic accidents. The general structure is monoclinal with very gentle dips toward the ocean; several surface undulation would explain the Senonian outcrops of Kola, where slight anticlinal dips were observed by the first miners, as well as the outcrops of Turonian strata at Pointe Noire and of rocks of Maastrichtian age at Holle. A play of faults subparallel to the Mayombian direction could also account for these outcrops, particularly near the basement exposures. A set of compensation faults, perpendicular to the first, might confine these outcrops.

The Senonian transgression reached its maximum during the early Santonian; rocks of this age form the base of the phosphatic formation in the Kola region. The coastal outcrops of M'Vassa are of late Santonian or early Campanian age; those of Pointe Noire and the Loya are of Coniacian age (Cosson, 1955).

The Maastrichtian is represented by the so called Holle Series which contains the phosphate occurrences to be described. The layers, which are frequently eroded, show a marked littoral, even lagoonal, character. They are exposed in very narrow belts, not more than 750 m in width, which continue, however, over considerable distances along the small valleys of the Holle area, those of the Koubambi, the Kandika, Tchivoula, Bakamba, Tchioupi and others; they are also found near Kola and Conkouati toward Gabon. These exposures occur on subsided blocks, shel-

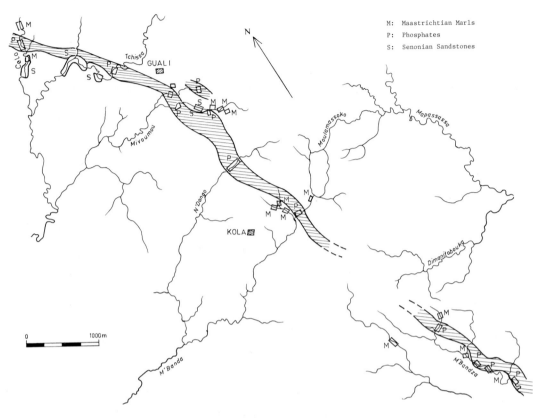

M: Maastrichtian Marls

P: Phosphates

S: Senonian Sandstones

FIG. 2.—Position of phosphate outcrops in the Kola area (after Bergé, 1939).

tered from mechanical erosion and represent, therefore, only a small part of the Maastrichtian littoral sedimentation. The top of the Holle Series, which is frequently altered, is probably already of Paleogene age and thus reminiscent of the Ypresian phosphate mineralization in neighboring Cabinda.

The Eocene transgression left but few traces above present sea level and some of them are doubtful. Pointe-Indienne (Peschuel-Loesche, 1876), others at Futa represent small blocks (Schneegans and Lombard, 1932). Numerous larger remains, however, have been preserved in the Cabinda, where marine, sometimes phosphatic, strata of Miocene age are found. The system of orthogonal faults in the Mayombian direction seems to have caused an uplift of the Tertiary deposits increasing in scale from north to south: the Miocene shoreline is at −80 m off the Gabon-Congo border, but is on land along the coast of the Cabinda (Giresse and Tchikaya, 1975). These movements are part of tensional tectonics consequent to the opening of the South Atlantic; local phases of moderate compression, however, also seem to have occurred, such as those of the

Bénoué (Burke et al., 1972), if the various observations of small dips in opposite directions are confirmed.

The Phosphate Facies

Kola section (figs. 2 and 3).—Outcrops are restricted to the bottom of valleys: Celo, Tchissa, M'Bandza and Missiéssi. According to the early miners (Bergé, 1939), they are related to an anticlinal ridge, 12 to 15 km long and 2 km wide trending NE-SW; the ridge is terminated to the north by a fault trending NW-SE and toward the south by the, possibly not faulted, plunge of the anticlinal axis toward the swamps of the Kouilou. All measured dips are less than 10°.

The underlying Santonian sequence consists of sandstones and dolomites with an estimated thickness of 25 m; the rocks are very rich in fish remains, lingula and bivalves (*Cytherea, Inoceramus*). Two units can be distinguished:

— the sandy and sometimes calcareous Migoumo layers at the base,

— the sandy and calcareous-dolomitic layers of the Tchissa at the top.

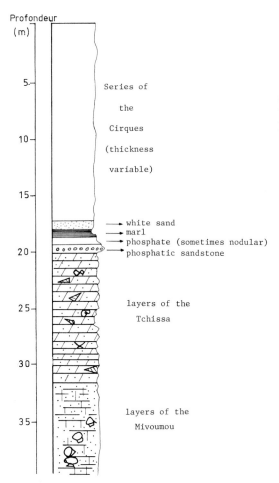

Fig. 3.—Schematic section along river valleys in the
Kola area.

These strata are overlain by the following schematic section:

— very lenticular mineralized layers of soft,
  phosphatic sandstones and marls in an
  average thickness of 2 m; they contain 21
  percent P_2O_5 on the average, but the tonnage
  does not exceed 300,000 tons. Some rocks
  contain phosphate grains and fish remains
  (teeth, scales, vertebra) and many organic
  remains point to open although littoral
  conditions: corals, gastropods, lingulas are
  very abundant as more or less silicified
  molds. Sometimes, very hard nodules of pure
  phosphate are enclosed in silicified or argillaceous rocks;

— variegated marls (gray, green, blue, rusty
  brown) in layers 1–2 m thick with some
  recurrent very thin phosphatic layers (e.g.
  N'Dongo River);

— white sands or gravels (aquifer), argillaceous
  at top;

— red surface cover of variable thickness, part
  of the Series of the Cirques.

The phosphatic horizons continue toward the
NW into Gabon near Conkouaty where they are
no longer of economic interest. Erosion seems
to increase in this direction and the facies disappears: the Series of the Cirques overlies directly
Senonian strata.

Holle section (figs. 4, 5, 6).—Toward the south

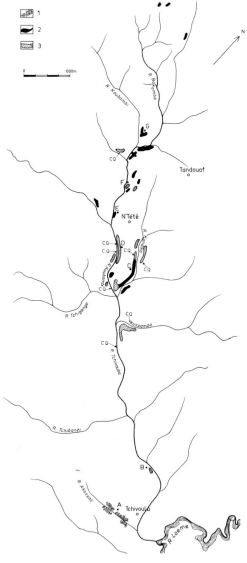

Fig. 4.—Location of outcrops of the coprolitic-quartzose (1), phosphato-siliceous (2) and both (3) facies in
the valleys of the Tchivoula and Koubambi.

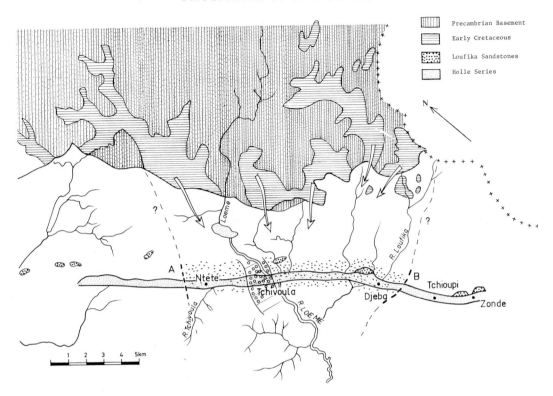

Precambrian Basement
Early Cretaceous
Loufika Sandstones
Holle Series

FIG. 5.—Position of the detrital facies of the phosphatic Holle Series in relation to the early Cretaceous rias; schematic position of the coprolitic-quartzose facies.

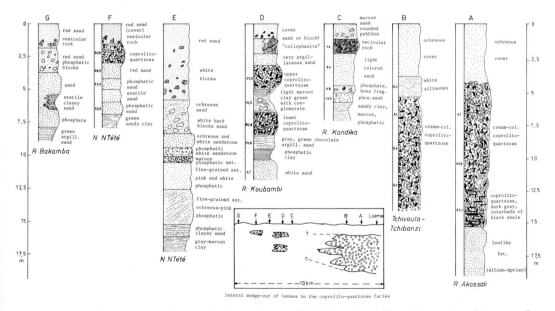

FIG. 6.—Succession of schematic sections through Holle Series north of the Loémé (for positions see fig. 4); sections based on mining reports (drillings, pits, galleries) and on personal observations.

the amount of erosion seems to diminish and the assumption that thicker and more continuous phosphate sections are here preserved is confirmed by observation.

Schematically, the Maastrichtian Holle sequence, which is transgressive on the doubtlessly Albian sandstones of the Loufika, is composed of pebble, sand, clay and sandy clay lenses, all more or less phosphatized. The thickness is variable but does not exceed 10 meters.

a) The **lateral** paleogeographical changes can be reconstructed by the distribution of facies types. A very coarse facies, a conglomerate of quartz pebbles, shark teeth, coprolites and fishbones—the **coprolitic-quartzose facies**—contrasts with a finer grained detrital facies, with a phosphatic or quartzose cement—the **phosphato-siliceous facies**—which is sometimes reminiscent of the Kola facies.

The coprolitic-quartzose facies is probably the result of leaching of a formation originally rich in organic matter and is, without doubt, of deltaic origin. It was reached by drilling at the base of the sequence. This facies attains its greatest thickness in the lower Tchivoula valley and particularly in the Akoussali valley which is near the present course of the Loémé, e.g. on the line of the mouth of the early Cretaceous rias which drained the erosion products of the Mayombe. Tchivoula with its 10 m of coprolitic-quartzose sediments and Loufika farther south might correspond to the main channels of a deltaic system. This facies thins to the north and to the south of the Loémé. In the north, it is represented by several recurrent layers (zone of Koubambi, Kandika), interstratified with argilo-sandy layers; in the south it is widespread near Djeba and Djenguessé (near the Loufika), but disappears at Tchioupi and Zonde (argillaceous-sandy facies) to reappear near the border of the Cabinda (Kintanzi).

The most important phosphatic lenses known at present are, therefore, in the area of the Loémé; they are 1500 m long, 200 m wide and 15 to 20 m thick and contain a phosphate reserve of nearly 1,850,000 tons. Farther north and south, the drill holes penetrated irregular lenticular phosphato-siliceous layers (maximum thickness 2–3 m). A particular feature of these deposits is the fact that the highest phosphate contents are found in the most detrital layers. This coprolitic-quartzose facies might correspond to zones of high energy from which the finer components were winnowed toward a nearby marine environment.

b) The influence of deltaic sedimentation seems to be dominant in several stratigraphic sections. The channelling at the top of the formation was highly variable. Thus, a 60 m thick sequence with phosphatic interlayers was encountered in some drillings. Some faults with small throws juxtapose mineralized layers with sterile ones.

Point G—is situated 10 km north of the Loémé, near M'Boma in the valley of the Bakamba. Here, the phosphatic layer is very irregular and only up to 2–3 m thick. Green sandy shales, poor in phosphate, are overlain by sands which enclose blocks of gravels or of phosphatic vesicular sandstone. Aluminum-phosphate (wavellite) has repeatedly been noted at the top of this sequence.

Point F—slightly north of N'Tété, the phosphates are thicker, but always markedly lenticular and thus of minor economic interest (small pockets with 50 to 150,000 tons of phosphate). A narrow-spaced network of pits disclosed very strong lateral variations. Here, the coprolitic-quartzose facies is observed for the first time, but is only 1.5 m thick. In some reports, this layer was interpreted as a "base conglomerate" of the Eocene transgression. It rests here on a sequence of sands, which are sometimes pseudo-oolitic and then resemble Kola, and shales which are alternately phosphatic or sterile. At the base, the green clays of point G reappear. The top is formed by an ochreous-red surface carapace which encloses vesicular rocks and small silico-phosphatic nodules with wavellite.

Point E—Although this point is situated farther south, the coprolitic-quartzose facies is absent; instead, one finds here an alternation of thin sandy-argillaceous layers, silicified in their upper parts and phosphatic near the base overlying a gray-brown clay which resembles the neighboring green clay.

Point D—(valley of the Koubambi). The outcrops are silicified (chalcedony) and contain very hard phosphate nodules which were qualified as collophane in the first reports and are exceptionally high in phosphate—up to 38% P_2O_5—and therefore raised high hopes they could be mined. Under this roof, numerous pits and galleries revealed a succession of phosphatic layers, both clayey-sandy (phosphato-siliceous) and pebble (coprolitic-quartzose) with some sterile intercalations. The presence of two thin (1.5 m average) coprolitic-quartzose beds, as well as of the gray, green, maroon argillaceous facies at the base are noteworthy. Too frequently, however, they appear as isolated or altered patches with contents of $CaCO_3$ and P_2O_5, which on the whole change simultaneously and in the same sense, decreasing upward. Several interruptions of the layers, independent of the facies variations, are attributed to faulting.

Point C—(River Kandika). The coprolitic-quartzose facies disappears again in favor of the phosphato-siliceous facies. The sandy beds contain fish bone debris and are relatively rich in P_2O_5. At the decalcified roof, the alteration into gray vesicular rocks is found again, but the large nodules are absent. Drilling showed the mineralized beds to disappear toward the east and west.

Points A and B—In the area of the Tchivoula and Akossali Rivers the richest lenses—four lenses estimated to contain 3,200,000 tons—are found. The Holle Series occurs here almost entirely in the coprolitic-quartzose facies and is up to 10 m thick. The gray rock, rich in organic carbon and slightly argillaceous at the base, is creamy-white and unconsolidated near the roof or over the whole thickness of the section.

At Point B, the roof is formed by a white sterile siltstone layer.

In the direction of the Cabinda several factors appear to be favorable: the cover is preserved, mechanical erosion and alteration are limited, the deposits are homogeneous. Phosphate layers have been observed at Djeba, Djenguessé, Kintanzi (coprolitic-quartzose) and at Tchioupi and Zonde (phosphato-siliceous), but as yet these occurrences cannot be evaluated quantitatively. Obviously, future exploration should be directed to this area.

PETROGRAPHY OF THE PHOSPHATE SEQUENCE

Microfacies

Kola Area—This area was protected from coarse continental detritus and sustained a variety of life: fish remains (scales and teeth), small nodular corals, various molluscs. The rocks contain mostly fine grained detrital quartz, but the environment could also be turbulent as shown by the occurrence of ooze flakes associated with silts in a variable synsedimentary cement. The abundance of feldspars points to moderate hydrolysis on the neighboring continent, which was subject to a rather sub-tropical climate.

Micro- or cryptocrystalline phosphate occurs in the cement and is either isotropic or anisotropic in polarized light. Locally, particularly in the Celo River area, phosphatic grains can be observed; they are pseudo-oolites very rich in carbonaceous inclusions (probably of planktonic origin) and anisotropic apatite forms an external aureole; the form of these grains varies from sub-spherical to oblong. They resulted either from mechanical abrasion or represent small coprolites; some of them are armoured by a peripheral ring of small quartz grains acquired during transport by traction before induration. This is the only zone in the basin where granular phosphate occurs. The contribution of a planktonic biomass to sedimentation is confirmed by the presence of radiolaria.

This area was, therefore, the site of a sedimentation in which both mechanical and chemical (or biochemical) factors intervened. The character of phosphatization seems to be comparable with that in most other basins of that time, but the mineralized layers are of rather modest thickness.

The economic prospects are further diminished by several important diagenetic features:

Secondary dolomitization: rhombohedrons are observed in the micro-quartzic cement from which apatite and calcite have completely disappeared; dolomitization also affected the organic remains (corals and molluscs), but their calcite is only partly replaced, rarely by phosphate, more frequently by silica.

Secondary silicification: An intense and frequent silicification of the cement leads to the formation of micro-quartz associated with isotropic apatite or of spathic quartz filling pores and fissures. Silicification affects also mollusc and coral tests where it invades phosphate (apatite with associated silica) or carbonate (dolomite with associated silica); none of the original calcite is preserved. The tests of the large gastropods show spectacular radial fibers of chalcedony which have preserved the coprolitic phosphate filling the voids.

In several cases (Celo River), silicification formed concentric envelopes which isolate phosphatic islands, centimeters to decimeters across. These islands might correspond to very advanced centers of phosphatization in which only the more porous and altered periphery was silicified. These islands are reminiscent of the "phosphatization cells" described by Lamboy (1976) from the north Iberian shelf. Phosphate nodules (very rich in P_2O_5) are either preserved or totally silicified. The stages of silicification are indicated by the successive envelopes or by septa of chalcedony.

Thus, the microfacies reveals three processes:
— Directly silicified calcite;
— Calcite first phosphatized and then silicified;
— Calcite first dolomitized and then silicified.
Each one of the three processes enumerated took longer than the preceding one.

Holle Area—A facies characterized by fine grained detrital quartz, comparable to that of Kola, occurs in the valleys of Bakamba, Koubambi and Kandika. Phosphatization affects either the cement or the bioclasts (coprolites, teeth, bones, scales); the latter become increasingly prominent farther south.

The roof of the formation is frequently entirely silicified. Some of these sandstones show problematical organic ghost structures, in which discontinuities are crowded with isolated chalcedony needles.

At N'Tété, large nodules of pure isotropic apatite occur at the top of the phosphatic beds. Their extreme induration recalls again the "phosphatization cells" refractory to either silicification or alteration.

The coprolitic-quartzose type occurs as a conglomerate of quartz pebbles or bioclastics in a very irregular phosphatic or quartzic cement, locally impregnated by bitumen.

The oblong coprolites of Selacians seem to have quickly undergone strong induration and were entirely rigid before final deposition; imprints of constrictions or spiral valves are well preserved. Some individuals are abraded or were broken after mechanical abrasion postdating induration. The small non-phosphatic pebbles, in contrast, are deformed or armoured by small quartz grains (compaction, impressions, fissures). A very rapid phosphatization of these coprolites must therefore

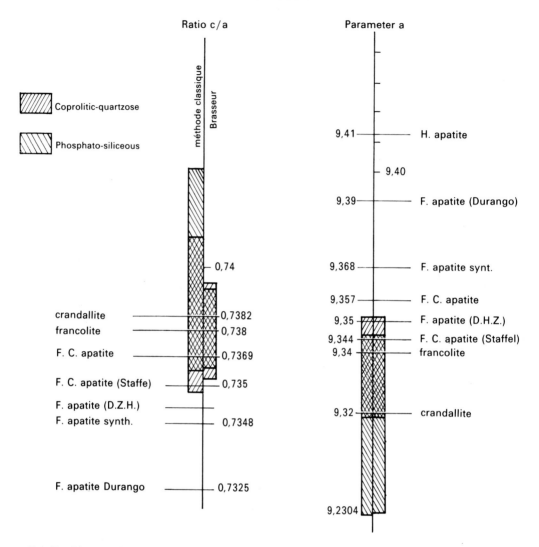

Fig. 7.—Diagram of a and c parameters of apatite; comparison between the coprolitic-quartzose and phosphato-siliceous facies.

be envisaged leading to immediate induration in which fluorine might have played a role. Some coprolites are rich in carbonaceous matter derived from the planktonic biomass. One radiolarian fossil, *Spumellaria*, could be determined (Ancelle et al., 1955). Similar to the phosphate grains at Kola, pure apatite frequently forms a peripheral aureole, but this mineralization is generally isotropic, although some fibrous alignments and undulating extinction can be observed.

Some large platy coprolites may be derived from other organisms, unless they represent boudins deformed before induration.

Skeletal remains are mainly Selacian teeth (*Lamna, Odontaspis*) which, because of their fluorine content, were better indurated and protected from alteration than the bones (some vertebra are preserved). The orthodentine might have isolated small phosphatization cells. Cryptogams or perforating algae as well as bacterial infections penetrated the teeth by their roots and are common in the porous bone tissues. They are best seen along the Haversian canals which are thus emphasized, or in the medullary canals of the vertebra.

The lithoclasts are mainly quartz in various grain sizes with two modes, one in the silt range, smaller than 80 μm, the other in the millimeter to centimeter range. Some show structures typical of the metamorphic rocks of the neighboring massif. They are in part strongly abraded, generally more than the coprolites which have undergone no fluvial transport. The complex fluvio-marine delta environment is thus emphasized and reveals different periods of reworking according to origin; thus, some coprolites could be transported from the outer to the inner shelf.

In this very peculiar deposit silicification is limited and affects only part of the cement and some rare bones.

Diffractometer Analysis

Total Rock Powder—The analysis of non-oriented mineral preparations shows a relatively simple composition in which a small number of minerals participate: apatite, quartz, feldspars and dolomite; very small amounts of calcite also show up. The diffractograms can be divided into three groups:

— Purely siliceous layers;
— Layers of dolomite and silica. In the Holle area, where mechanical sedimentation is dominant, dolomite is very rare;
— Layers of apatite and silica. In one case, a trace of calcite was found. The dark layers at the base of the coprolitic-quartzose strata represent another particular case: here, the association quartz, apatite, dolomite is found.

Almost all phosphates of the Congo contain a siliceous cement except the nodules at the top of the Koubambi section which consist of pure, remarkably well crystallized, apatite.

Finally, the detrital fraction of the rock in all three groups can contain feldspars, mainly alkaline ones.

Clay Minerals—Most of the Maastrichtian phosphatic deposits in both the Holle and the Kola area contain only small quantities of clay minerals recognizable in the X-ray diagrams. Montmorillonite and traces of illite are commonly found in the phosphato-siliceous rocks of the Holle area and in the beds of dark clay at the base of the coprolitic-quartzose sequences; an undetermined 10°.2 to 10°.5 2Θ-mineral is also associated.

In all the altered and rubefied levels of the roof, the kaolinite of the carapace makes its appearance; it might be attributed to neoformation at the expense of montmorillonite.

Palygorskite is the main mineral of the interstratified clays in the Paleocene and Eocene phosphatic horizons in the outcrops along the present shore line.

Mineralogy of the Apatites—Precise measurements of the main peak positions in the diffractograms (Cu-radiation) were made in an effort to distinguish between the various apatite species or, at least, to measure the crystallographic a and c values. The parameter a is, in principle,

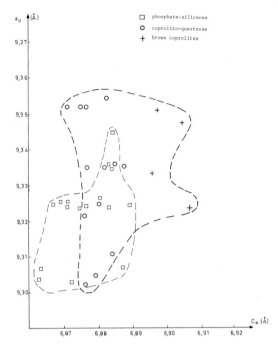

Fig. 8.—Comparison of c/a-ratios of different apatites from the literature and from the Congo.

inversely proportional to the CO_3-content.

Classical Method (figs. 7, 8)—The parameters a and c are calculated from the (h k l)-reflections, using the equation

$$d_{(hkl)} = \cfrac{1}{\sqrt{\cfrac{4(h^2 + k^2 + hk)}{3a^2} + \cfrac{l^2}{c^2}}}$$

For purposes of comparison, the reflections used for this calculation were the same as for a recent analysis of apatites from Ouled Abdoun in Morocco (El Mountassir, 1977), i.e. (002), (004), (321) and (210). Measurements based on (310) and (410) gave slightly higher values which might possibly be attributed to a mediocre hexagonal crystallization, already near to monoclinic symmetry. It seems, further, that the determination of a and c is more precise when based on high-angle and not on low-angle reflections (Vigne, personal communication).

The c-values found are essentially in the range of 6.87 to 6.88 Å and thus relatively constant. Some slightly higher values (6.90 Å) were found in Selacian coprolites. These values are exact to 0.01 Å.

The a-values are more significant in the distinction of apatite species: they vary from 9.30 to

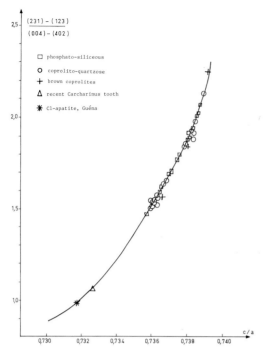

FIG. 9.—Determination of the c/a-ratio by the Brasseur method.

9.35 Å. References in the literature are sometimes contradictory:

— Altschuler et al. (1953) give 9.413 Å for hydroxi-apatite, 9.386 Å for fluor-apatite and 9.344 Å for carbonate-fluor-apatite.

— For other authors (in: Deer, Howie, Zussman, 1963) the average values are 9.41 Å for hydroxi-apatite, 9.34 Å for carbonate-fluor-apatite and only 9.35 Å for fluor-apatite.

— The francolite of McConnel (1938) has 9.34 Å, the carbonate-fluor-apatite of Montel 9.36 Å and synthetic fluor-apatite, 9.37 Å.

Relatively low values of a should probably be attributed to the presence of CO_3^{-2}-ions substituting for PO_4^{-3}. This conclusion is corroborated by the infrared diagrams, which indicate replacement of PO_4^{-3}, as well as by measurements after calcination, which give an average value of 9.37 Å.

It follows that on the basis of the a and c parameters, our apatites could equally well be classified as fluor-apatite as as carbonate-fluor-apatite, a conclusion confirmed by the c/a-ratio.

In the Congo apatites, contrary to those of Ouled Abdoun, it is impossible to distinguish different groups of apatites. An effort was made to differentiate between the apatites of the coprolitic-quartzose facies, which are frequently biogenic, and those of the phosphato-siliceous

facies which frequently grew freely on a substratum. The first belong to a detrital formation, which was redeposited and sometimes oxidized and contains debris which consisted originally of hydroxi-apatites; these could have had higher than average values. In fact, however, there is barely an indication for this in the data and the projection points corresponding to apatites of both groups are largely superimposed (figs. 7 and 8).

All these apatites correspond to the fresh facies of Ouled Abdoun. The c/a-ratios, however, of some of the apatites of the phosphato-siliceous facies of N'Tété are greater than 0.74.

Method of Brasseur (fig. 9)—Brasseur (1950) has constructed a graph which permits the determination of the c/a value by a calculation of the ratio between the angular distance of two pairs of neighboring peaks such as [(321)–(123)/(004)–(402)]. The c/a values obtained by this method compare well with those of the classical method. The diagram (fig. 9) shows that some of the highest values are those of apatites

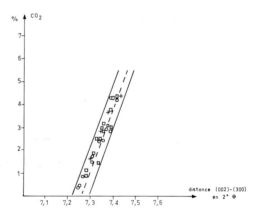

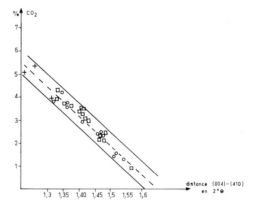

FIG. 10.—Estimation of CO_2-content of apatites from the Congo by the Gulbrandsen method (symbols as in fig. 9).

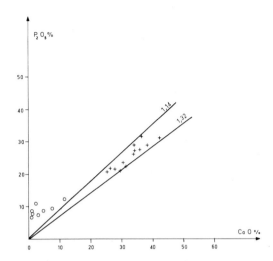

FIG. 11.—Correlation diagram CaO/P_2O_5 for apatites without carbonate gangue.

of the phosphato-siliceous facies ($c/a = 0.739$). It is, however, even more difficult to differentiate between apatites of the two facies types by this than by the classical method. Moreover, some reflections, e.g. (123) and (402) are not sharp and consequently some apatites of the Kola facies could not be analyzed at all.

CO_2-Contents (fig. 10)—CO_2-contents were estimated indirectly by the method of MacLellan and Lehr (1969) in which $x = \Delta 2° \theta$ of (002) and (300) is measured and the CO_2-percent y is calculated by the equation $y = 185.0 + 25.27x$. In a similar method by Gulbrandsen (1970) $x = (004) - (410)°2\theta$ and $y = 23.341 - 14.7361x$.

Just as for the c/a values, calculations show the apatites of the different deposits to be rather homogeneous. Statistically, the apatites of the coprolitic-quartzose facies are slightly poorer in CO_2 but the two spectra show a very large overlap, particularly for (004)–(410). The highest CO_2-contents (4–5%) are found in brown or white shark coprolites and teeth, as if the apatite in them was protected from the influence of the environment.

The broad range of CO_2-contents (0.5 to 5.5%), however, seems too large for a single mineral species. Gulbrandsen (1970) found an average value of 1.8 percent and a maximum value of 3.3 percent for the carbonate-apatite of the Phosphoria Formation. It appears to be increasingly admitted that calculated CO_2-contents are generally larger than those obtained by chemical analysis. This has been verified for the fluor-apa-

tites of Taïba in Senegal (Menor, 1975) in which the difference seems to increase with increasing CO_2-contents (1.21% analyzed values; 2.27% calculated).

The presence of small amounts of poorly crystallized calcite in the matrix, which does not show up in the X-ray diffractogram, could explain these results although the rather large variations of the CO_2-content are not fully understood.

All direct chemical analyses made sofar on the apatites of the Congo show less than 2 percent CO_2 for P_2O_5-contents of 30 percent. These determinations, as well as the crystallographical parameters a and c, point to a composition close to fluor-apatite.

Chemical Analyses—A detailed chemical study is still underway and its results cannot be included in this paper. We are limiting ourselves here to a short review of data from earlier reports.

Most analyses made during mining prospection concerned only contents of phosphate, silica, alumina and iron.

The most common P_2O_5-contents fall in the range 11.5 to 25 percent with the exception of the indurated nodules of N'Tété which carry 32–37 percent. This ore is, therefore, not commercial in its natural state. Moreover, the contents of iron oxides (0.5–3%) and of alumina (1.5–4.5%) exceed frequently the limits imposed by the fertilizer industry.

As already mentioned, aluminum-phosphates are observed toward the top of the formation. These parts contain an average of 14 percent Al_2O_3 for 16.3 percent of P_2O_5 and 46.8 percent SiO_2.

The reserve estimate of 5 million tons is based on a reconnaissance of layers containing at least 22 percent P_2O_5 which are mainly found in the Tchivoula area. Here, several of these layers occur with a thickness of 2 to 7 m. Fluorine contents are high throughout: 3.75–4.18 percent.

An important radioactivity was measured by the CEA on outcrops of the phosphato-siliceous facies, particularly on those containing indurated nodules at N'Tété. The laboratory at Mulhouse made 10 measurements of UO_3 and found important (up to 5600 ppm), but very irregular contents, which do not seem to correlate with P_2O_5-concentrations. A priori, the phosphato-siliceous facies appears to be more favorable than the coprolitic-quartzose facies.

Only one correlation diagram (fig. 11), that of P_2O_5 against CaO, could be drawn on apatites in a carbonate-free matrix. The CaO/P_2O_5-ratio varies from 1.14 to 1.32 and also points, on the average, to rather strong decarbonation characteristic of fluor-apatite (Young, 1969; McConnel, 1938), thus confirming the inference from the crystallographical analysis.

CONCLUSIONS

As far as can be said at present, phosphatogenesis in the Congo is mainly of Maastrichtian age continuing, without doubt, into the Eocene. This series is thus chronologically similar to that of the large phosphorite deposits of North Africa, although the latter are slightly younger. No mineralization was found so far in formations of Senonian age.

In connection with the planned project of chemical analyses of the different occurrences it should be pointed out that the phosphates of the Congo, just as many other deposits formed at about the same time on the Atlantic side of Africa (Togo, Senegal, Morocco) have undergone, since deposition, a succession of diagenetic modifications, some of them causing enrichment, others of an unfavorable nature. A study of these mechanisms should, in our view, form an integral part of future research work.

Deposits of a chemical nature, protected from the open ocean, grouped as the phosphato-siliceous facies, were originally calcareous and rich in remains of corals, lamellibranchs and gastropods. Phosphatogenesis lead to a progressive elimination of the carbonate and to replacement of fluor-carbonate-apatite by fluor-apatite; the calcareous matrix diminished except in the case of the more resistant dolomite, which is common at Kola.

The fluvio-marine detrital deposits of the co-prolitic-quartzose facies are direct bio-clastic deposits from which carbonates have disappeared leaving only some dolomite in the basal layers. The cement was phosphatized and fluor-apatite probably again substituted for fluor-carbonate-apatite.

The always moderate CO_2-contents of the apatites, the rare preservation of carbonates and, particularly, the absence of preserved tests show that rocks of both facies types underwent a similar chemical evolution.

Later, processes of a rather epigenetic nature came into play depleting the deposits:

— Formation of aluminum-phosphate in the roof of the formations by a reaction of clays with phosphatic matter; simultaneously, kaolinite replaced montmorillonite.

— Silicification, also at the top of the formations, seems to have avoided the layers or bodies highest in phosphate.

A geochemical study should aim to establish:

— the rules of paleogeographical distribution of the elements,

— the rules of the diagenetic modification of this distribution.

REFERENCES

ALTSCHULER, Z. S., CISNEY, E. A., AND BARLOW, I. H., 1953, X-ray evidence of the nature of carbonate-apatite: Amer. Min., v. 38, p. 328.

ANCELLE, H., VISSE, L. D., AND RICHARD, R. S., 1955, Etude du permis de Holle, Moyen-Congo: Gouvernement Général de l'AEF, Service des Mines, Rapport R. 39, p. 6–9.

BERGE, G., 1939, Etude préliminaire du gisement des phosphates de Sintou-Kola-district de Maringou-Kayes au M.C: Gouvernement Général de l'AEF, Service des Mines, Rapport R. 39, p. 2–6.

BRASSEUR, H., 1950, Méthode permettant d'obtenir avec rapidité et précision le rapport c/a d'une apatite: Acad. Roy. Belgique, Bull. Class. Sci., 5 ser., v. 36, 521 p.

BURKE, K. C., DESSAUVAGIE, T. F. J., AND WHITEMAN, A. J., 1972, Geological history of the Benue Valley and adjacent areas: African Geology, Ibadan Congr., 1970, p. 187–205.

CAYEUX, L., 1939, Les phosphates de chaux sédimentaires de France—Etude des gîtes minéraux de la France, t. I, II, III.

COSSON, J., 1955, Notice explicative sur les feuilles Pointe-Noire et Brazzaville. Carte géologique de reconnaissance au 1/500,000e: Dir. Min. Géol. AEF, 56 p.

DADET, P., 1969, Notice explicative de la carte géologique de la Rép. du Congo-Brazzaville au 1/500,000e (zone comprise entre les parallèles 2° et 5° S): Paris, BRGM 21/27, 103 p.

DEER, W. A., HOWIE, R. A., AND ZUSSMANN, M. A., 1963, Rock forming minerals—Non silicates, vol. 5: Longmans, edit. London, 363 p.

ELLIOT, J. C., 1964, The Crystallographic Structure of dental Enamel related apatites: Doctoral Thesis, London.

EL MOUNTASSIR, M., 1977, La zone rubéfiée de Sidi Daoui; altération météorique du phosphate de chaux des Ouled Abdoun (Maroc): Doct. Spéc. 3e cycle, Strasbourg, 126 p. 3 pl.

FURON R., 1932, Les roches phosphatées de la côte du Gabon: C. R. Acad. Sc. 1959, 1960.

GIRESSE, P., AND CORNEN, G., 1976, Distribution, nature et origine des phosphates miocènes et éocènes sous-marins des plate-formes du Congo et du Gabon: Bull. BRGM, s. IV, no. 1, p. 5–15.

———, AND TCHIKAYA, J. B., 1975, Contribution à la carte géologique de la plate-forme sous-marine congolaise (mission N. O. Nizery de janvier 1974): Ann. Univ. Brazzaville, t. XI.

GULBRANDSEN, R. A., 1970, Relation of carbon dioxide content of apatite of the Phosphoria Formation to regional facies: U.S. Geol. Survey Prof. Pap. 700B, p. 9–13.

HAAS, J. O., 1935, Rapport du Gouverneur général relatif au gisement de phosphate de Sintou—Kola et aux travaux et recherches qu'impliquent sa mise en exploitation: Rapport R 39, P6-1, 43 p.

LAMBOY, M., 1976, Géologie marine et sous-marine du plateau continental au Nord-Ouest de l'Espagne-Genèse des glauconies et des phosphorites: Th. Doct. ès Sc. Nat., Rouen, 255 p.

LEBEDEFF, V., 1928, Les recherches de pétrole en Afrique Equatoriale Francaise: Gouvernement Général de l'AEF, Service des Mines, Imprimerie du Chateau d'Eau, Paris, 112 p.

LUCAS, J., 1977, Les phosphorites de la marge nord de l'Espagne, étude pétrographique, minéralogique et géochimique: Rapp. final sur la Convention de Recherche, CNRS-CNEXO, no. 74/1053, 75 p.

McCONNEL, D. C., 1938, A structural investigation of the isomorphism of the apatite group: Amer. Min., v. 23, p. 1.

MacLELLAN, G. H., AND LEHR, J. R., 1969, Crystal chemical investigation of natural apatite: Amer. Min., v. 54, p. 1374–1391.

MENOR, E., 1975, La sédimentation phosphatée. Pétrographie, Minéralogie et Géochimie des gisements de Taïba (Sénégal) et d'Olinda (Brésil): Thèse Doct. Ing., Strasbourg, 153 p.

MONTEL, G., 1956, Contribution à l'étude des mécanismes de synthèse de la fluor-apatite: Thèse ès Sc. Ann. Chim., v. 13, no. 3, p. 313–368.

PESCHUEL-LOESCHE, 1876, Loango und die Loango Küste: Mitt. Ver. Erdkunde Dtsch.

SCHNEEGANS, D., AND LOMBARD, J., 1932, Sur la présence de l'Eocène marin à Fouta (A.E.F.): C.R. Acad. Sci. Paris, v. CXCV, p. 163–165.

TANKARD, A. O., 1974, Chemical composition of the phosphorites from the Langebaanweg—Saldanha area, Cape Province: Trans. Geol. Soc. South Afr., v. 77, p. 185–190.

VISSE, L. D., 1950, Rapport de la Mission d'Afrique Equatoriale Française pour le compte de la Société Minerais et Engrais Rapport R 39, p. 6–10.

YOUNG, E. J., MYERS, A. T., MUNSON, E. L., AND CONKLIN, N. M., 1969, Mineralogy and geochemistry of fluor apatite from Cerro de Mercado, Durango, Mexico: U.S. Geol. Survey Prof. Paper 660D, p. D84–D93.

SEPM Special Publication No. 29, p. 207–213, November 1980

THE EARLY EOCENE OF THE LAKE OF GUIERS (WESTERN SENEGAL)—REFLECTIONS ON SOME CHARACTERISTICS OF PHOSPHATE SEDIMENTATION IN SENEGAL

A. BOUJO,[1] B. FAYE,[2] D. GIOT,[1] J. LUCAS,[3] H. MANIVIT,[4] C. MONCIARDINI,[1] AND L. PRÉVÔT[3]

[1]Bureau de Recherches Géologiques et Minières—Service Géologique National; B. P. 6009—45018 ORLEANS CEDEX, FRANCE
[2]Direction des Mines et de la Géologie-DAKAR-SENEGAL
[3]Université de Strasbourg—Centre de Sédimentologie et Géochimie de la Surface; 1, rue Blessig—67084 STRASBOURG CEDEX
[4]C.N.R.S.—Détachée au B.R.G.M.

ABSTRACT

A study of cores from drillings on the anticlinal structure of the Lake of Guiers shows a transition from a Paleocene sequence deposited in an open environment (organogenic limestones) to an early Eocene sequence deposited in a strongly confined environment which becomes open again only at the top of the sequence. Simultaneously, montmorillonite, the only clay mineral present in the Paleocene section, is replaced higher up by palygorskite (attapulgite), an evolution common in phosphatic deposits.

Mineralization of a marked lenticular character is initiated under confined conditions which change in the Lutetian to an open paleo-environment in which the various deposits of the Taïba-Thiès region farther south were deposited.

INTRODUCTION

The anticlinal structure of the Lake of Guiers is an important feature in the geology of Senegal. It has been studied many times, more recently by Sainton (1957) who examined all the outcrops along the shores of the lake and those in the Ferlo Valley; other authors (Degallier, 1962; Debuisson, 1970) studied the area in the frame of water research surveys or phosphate investigations (Chino, 1962; Heetveld, 1965; Boujo, 1975). More basic studies (Monciardini, 1968, 1970a, 1970b) have been of help in these economic surveys, whereas the preparation of the geological map on the 1:200,000 scale (Pascal, 1967) and research conducted at the universities (Trenous, 1968, 1970a, 1970b) have led from time to time to a synthesis mainly in terms of a stratigraphic sequence of the area or its structure.

This anticlinal structure forms in the northern part of the country a high plateau extending practically parallel to the Senegal coast between Dakar and Saint-Louis, while farther south, this plateau, which is here even more elevated, is represented by the dome of N'Diass (fig. 1).

The paleogeographical reconstructions of Monciardini (1966) show that the uplift of the N'Diass Dome started during the Maastrichtian at a time when no anticlinal structure had as yet formed in the Lake of Guiers area. The individualization of these two elements occurred in the Lutetian and Late Eocene and was fully developed in the Miocene.

In its present state, these two units are characterized by the absence of an Early Eocene section on the western flank of the N'Diass Dome, while this stage, although strongly affected by erosion, is still present on the east flank of the dome and over the entire region of the Lake of Guiers.

The uplift of this belt also lead to a strong condensation of the Tertiary series in a zone outlined by the villages of Kotiedia, M'boss and Kaffrine.

A final element of this structural unit is the strong fracturation which affected the Cap Vert Peninsula. On both sides of this uplifted zone, the basinal structure is well indicated by the trace of the isopachs on the Lutetian level. Two important zones of subsidence were formed, the one in the northwest in the region of Mekhe-Louga-Leona, the other in the south around the Casamance and Gambia.

We have also shown on fig. 1 the remarkable position of the deposits exploited at Taïba and Thiès on the margin of the high plateau of N'Diass and the position of known indications of phosphorite occurrences according to locality and age.

The present work is based on the information obtained from a recent prospection survey by continuously cored drillings emplaced in the eastern part of the Lake of Guiers[1] (Boujo, 1975);

[1]This work consisted of 16 cored bore-holes made by a syndicate comprising the Government of Senegal, the Société Sénégalaise des Phosphates de Thiès (S.S.P.T.), U.S. Steel and the Bureau de Recherches Géologiques et Minières, which served as operator.

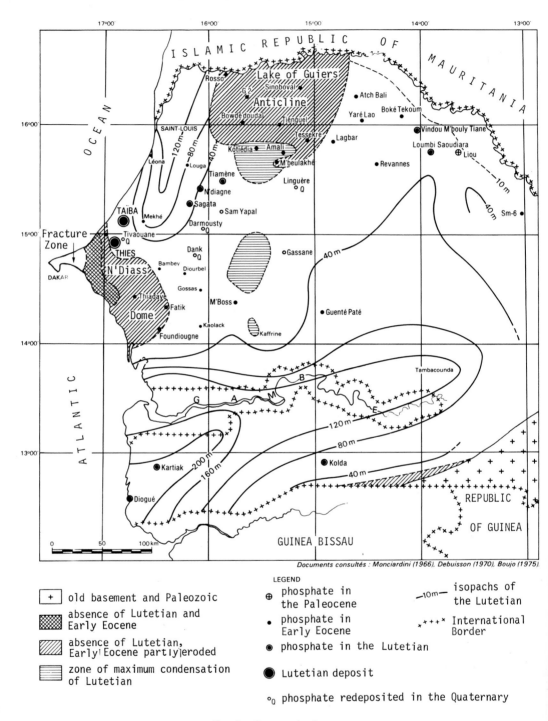

Documents consultés : Monciardini (1966), Debuisson (1970), Boujo (1975).

LEGEND

⊞ old basement and Paleozoic	⊕ phosphate in the Paleocene
▨ absence of Lutetian and Early Eocene	• phosphate in Early Eocene
▨ absence of Lutetian, Early Eocene partly eroded	◉ phosphate in the Lutetian
▤ zone of maximum condensation of Lutetian	● Lutetian deposit

—10m— isopachs of the Lutetian

×+++× International Border

°Q phosphate redeposited in the Quaternary

FIG. 1.—Structural scheme.

the localities are indicated in fig. 2. This paper consists of two main parts:
— A review of the present knowledge concerning the stratigraphy and structure of the area.

It is based on earlier data supplemented by new faunistic determinations by Monciardini and Manivit;
— A sedimentological and mineralogical study

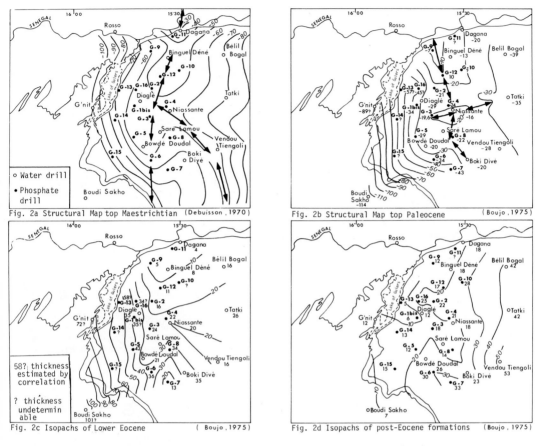

Fig. 2a Structural Map top Maestrichtian (Debuisson, 1970)

Fig. 2b Structural Map top Paleocene (Boujo, 1975)

Fig. 2c Isopachs of Lower Eocene (Boujo, 1975)

Fig. 2d Isopachs of post-Eocene formations (Boujo, 1975)

FIG. 2.—Structural maps and isopachs of the Lake of Guiers area.

made possible by the quality of the sections established by the continuous cores. The observations of Giot reveal the characteristics of the environments of deposition, their energy, the mode of direct precipitation or redeposition of the phosphate, whereas those of Lucas and Prévôt concern the association of the main constituent minerals and the variations within the clay fraction.

Stratigraphy

The drilled section—Since the 16 recent drillings were done for phosphate prospects, no efforts were made to reach Maastrichtian strata, known to be non-phosphatic or even to penetrate the full Paleocene section which is poor in phosphate. The aim was to reach the top of the Paleocene section; this, however, was not always possible because of technical drilling problems encountered several meters above the Paleocene coquina (e.g. Drillholes G-6, G-1 bis—fig. 1).

Our observations concern, therefore, mainly the early Eocene section, as the overlying post-Eocene strata (continental terminal Ogolian) were not cored.

Facies and Fauna (fig. 1)

Maastrichtian—We note that the Maastrichtian facies are frequently entirely sandy, yellowish-gray to brown-red and practically azoic. An argillaceous-sandy or argillaceous dark-gray to black facies, rich in organic matter, also occurs; it contains rare foraminifera and small ostracodes. Rocks of this type were frequently penetrated in drillings for water, such as those at Boudi Sakho, Diagle, Bowde Doudal, Binguel Dene, Niassante and Tatki.

Paleocene—Although the Paleocene throughout Senegal is characterized by a large spectrum of lithofacies types (Monciardini, 1966), the major rock types in the area here under study are pure organogenic, *lumachellic limestones* with abundant debris of lamellibranchs, gastropods and also echinoderms, as well as foraminifera: braided nummulites and Discocyclinas. The rock is white to light yellow, corroded and fragmented, with dissolved molds and very fine lamellae or irregular, frequently amygdule-like phosphatic inclusions. Thicker, yellow or gray interlayers of carbonatic clay occur also within or adjacent to the limestone layers.

Early Eocene—Within the area under study, the early Eocene section is largely eroded. It is conserved almost in its totality only near the eastern shore of the Lake of Guiers (drill-holes G-12, G-15) and in the Boudi Sakho drill-hole.

Sedimentation is generally dominated by massive carbonatic clays or argillaceous dolomites; in the lower part of the section occur decimeter thick, more rarely meter-thick, layers of granular phosphate which sometimes exhibit a very characteristic brecchoid structure (plate 1, fig. 1). Very irregular lenticular phosphatic inclusions also occur and certainly represent levels of redeposition. The carbonatic clays are frequently fractured, the fractures being outlined by black organic matter; siliceous or cherty streaks are rare. Finally, a horizon of dolomitized echinoid spines occurs 3 to 10 m above the top of the Paleocene limestone, a marker horizon in the Eocene section of Senegal (plate 1, fig. 2).

Although Monciardini stressed the rarity of microfauna in this sequence, some forms, indicative of an early Eocene age, have been found in these cores, particularly:

> *Leguminocythereis senegalensis*
> *Globigerina esnaensis*
> *Eviceratocythea glabella*
> *Daviesina khatiyahi.*

The abundance of dolomite is unfavorable for the preservation of nannofossils. Drill-hole G-14, however, encountered at a depth of 21 to 25 m, *Princius bisulcus* and *Discoaster gemmcus,* both characteristic of the early Eocene.

Lutetian—As already pointed out, Lutetian strata are preserved only near the eastern shore of the Lake of Guiers. They have been recognized in the water drills of G'nit and Boudi Sakho and are assumed to exist farther east within the transition layers with ostracodes and *Discorbids* encountered in the upper part of some drill-holes, such as G-6.

Post-Eocene strata—Post-Eocene sediments are mainly represented by the Terminal Continental: these are fine to medium grained sands and red and yellow argillaceous sandstones with ferruginous spots or nodules. The youngest sediments are dune belts (red Ogolian sands) and a Quaternary ferruginous surface crust (Pascal, 1967).

Structure

The marked asymmetry of the Lake of Guiers Anticline is well shown in fig 2: a strong dip

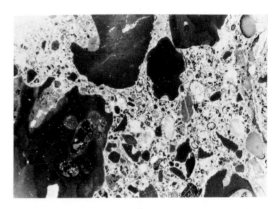

1

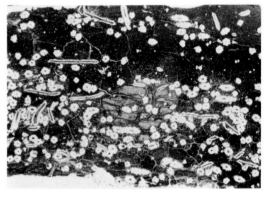

2

PLATE 1
FIGURE 1.—Phosphatic breccia Drill-hole G-2, sample 3 bis, 23 m (A 92310) polarized light, X6.
FIGURE 2.—Marker horizon: Dolomitized echinid spines, Drill-hole G-2, sample 6, 29.5 m (A 92312) natural light, X6.

to the west, a much more moderate one to the east. Contour lines on the top of the Paleocene sequence (fig. 2b) also reveal this asymmetry and show an anticlinal axis trending essentially NNW-SSE as well as a second direction perpendicular to the first which follows approximately the line of drill-holes G-3 Niassante-Tatki.

The area underwent some deformation during the deposition of the rock sequence discussed here. A comparison of the structural map of the Paleocene (fig. 2b) with that established by Debuisson (1970) for the top of the Maastrichtian sequence (fig. 2a) reveals that, while the main axis was not greatly affected, movements are indicated by a lateral displacement of the top of the growing structure.

This fact explains the differential erosion of the early Eocene sequence, which is strongly eroded in the east, where only 5–20 m of the lower part of the section have been preserved, while in the west, thicknesses increase and attain 100 m in the drill-hole of Boudi Sakho. This feature is well illustrated in the isopach maps (fig. 2b) and the cross-section of fig. 3b.

During the emergence of the anticlinal ridge in the Lutetian, marls and limestones were deposited on the flanks of the structure, while post-Eocene deposits filled the lows in the topographic late Lutetian surface.

As figs. 2b and 2d show, this infill was accompanied by an important subsidence of the eastern part; in fact the post-Eocene formations thicken strongly toward the east in the area of minimum erosion during the early Eocene. These observations confirm and extend the conclusions to be drawn from the work of Monciardini (1966)

and from the block-diagrams accompanying the more recent publication of Trenous (1970b).

The Lake of Guiers Anticline obtained its final shape by the orthogonal system of faults as established by the work of the oil geologists. These faults control the positions of the Lake of Guiers and of the Ferlo Valley.

Mineralogy

This study concerns drill-holes G-14, G-8 and G-2; the first penetrated the upper part of the early Eocene succession, the two latter the top of the Paleocene and the lower part of the Eocene section (fig. 3). Together with the facies variations described above, a mineralogical study of the penetrated section leads to useful observations (fig. 4).

Non-Clay Minerals—The Paleocene section which exhibits lumachellic facies consists of biocalcarenites in which the components generally support each other: locally, they float in a micritic cement while spathic cement is less common. The

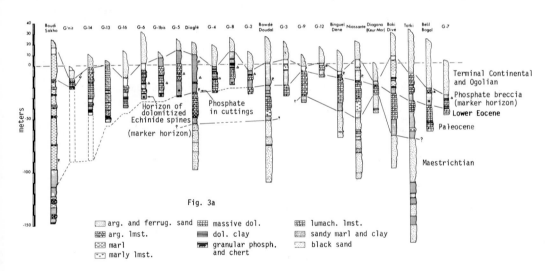

Fig. 3a

arg. and ferrug. sand   massive dol.   lumach. lmst.
arg. lmst.   dol. clay   sandy marl and clay
marl   granular phosph.   black sand
marly lmst.   and chert

FIG. 3a.—Correlation of water and prospection drills in the area of Lake of Guiers.

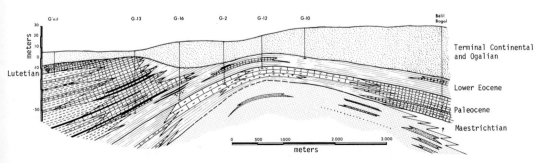

FIG. 3b.—Tentative lithostratigraphic and structural interpretation.

components are exclusively organogenic: echinoderms, lamellibranchs, gastropods, annelids are abundant; foraminifera are rare. Calcite is largely predominant, quartz and glauconite are present only in traces.

At the beginning of early Eocene, i.e. essentially in the section comprised between the marker horizon of echinoid spines and the phosphatic breccia, the carbonate fraction, practically the only one present, shows a clear lateral variation from almost exclusively dolomitic (area of G-2) to predominantly calcitic.

The higher levels of the early Eocene sequence correspond to the time of phosphate deposition. The latter comprises the characteristic phosphate breccia at the base and several short episodes in which thin layers and lenses of phosphate were deposited. The phosphate is associated with dolomite and quartz; calcite reappears only rarely and during short intervals.

In the still higher levels of the early Eocene (penetrated in G-14), the classical sequence of phosphate deposition is completed by the appearance of carbonates among which calcite clearly predominates over dolomite to become finally the only carbonate mineral present.

Clay Minerals—The common rule of a phosphate series is here fulfilled: In the lower levels montmorillonite predominates over palygorskite (attapulgite); higher up the amount of the latter increases progressively although not regularly until it is almost the only clay mineral present in the younger layers.

Environment of Sedimentation

All the observations point to a rather high variability of the sedimentary environment (fig. 4). It was largely open during the formation of the Paleocene calcareous *lumachelle*, but became increasingly confined during the deposition of the phosphatic and dolomitic rock sequence. It turned open again only rather late with the deposition of the pure organogenic limestones, as can be seen in G-14.

The phosphate itself shows all the characteristics of an abortive mineralization as indicated by the small thickness of the deposits, their frequent redeposition and their pronounced lenticular form. This is another case of a frequently described phenomenon: The inhibition of phosphate deposition in a too confined environment, too rich in magnesium (Martens and Harris, 1970). The same sedimentary sequence produces in the open environment of the Lutetian the important phosphate deposits of the Taïba-Thiès region.

CONCLUSIONS

The conclusions to be drawn from all the observations are that the region of the Lake of Guiers shows many of the general and remarkable features characteristic of phosphate basins: a stratigraphic succession in which fine grained clastic rocks are overlain by chemical sediments, facies types which vary rapidly in space and time, a marked mineralogical polarity within the basin, a morphology of high plateau, tectonic mobility, all these features have frequently been described

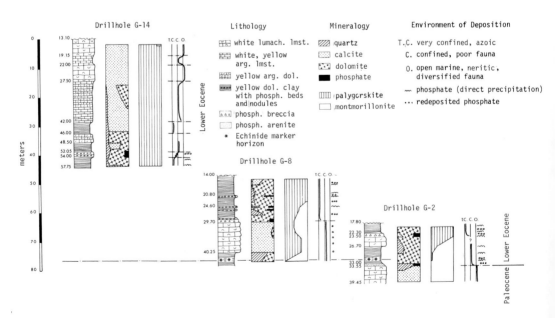

FIG. 4.—Mineralogy and environment of deposition.

(Bentor, 1953; Sheldon, 1964; Slansky, 1964; Boujo, 1968, 1972, 1975; Sassi, 1974; Lucas and Prévôt, 1975).

Within the general framework of the Eocene phosphate sequence in Senegal, the region of the Lake of Guiers represents a precocious phase of early Eocene age; here phosphatogenesis starts to reach its full development during the Lutetian with the important deposits of Taïba-Thiès.

The detailed study of some phosphate series and/or of some phosphate deposits has enabled us to follow the modalities in the evolution of such a series in space and time. This, however, does not apply to Senegal, where, because of the paucity of research, there still remains in the study an important gap between the beginning of this phenomenon in the early Eocene and its full development in the Lutetian. It would be valuable to fill this gap, not only as an aid to the general concept of phosphatogenesis in Senegal, but also because of its potential economic implications.

REFERENCES

AUDIBERT, M., 1967, Hypothèse de travail pour l'étude du quaternaire du delta du Sénégal: VIe Congrès panafricain de prehistoire et du quaternaire (Dakar) 10 p., 1 pl. h.t. ronéo.

BENTOR, Y. K., 1953, Relations entre la tectonique et les dépôts de phosphate dans le Neguev israélien: C. R.. 19th Intern. Geol. Congr. ALGER, sect. XI, v. 11, p. 93–101.

BOUJO, A., 1968, Nouvelles données sur le Crétacé et l'Eocene phosphaté du gisement des Ganntour: Notes Serv. géol, MAROC, v. 26, (211), p. 7–15.

———, 1972, Contribution à l'étude géologique du gisement crétacé-éocène des Ganntour (Maroc Occidental): Thèse Doct. Etat Université Louis Pasteur (Strasbourg), ronéo, 387 p., 1972. Notes serv. géol. MAROC, v. 262, 227 p., 1976; Sciences géologiques Strasbourg, Mem. 43, 227 p., 1976.

———, 1975, Le gisement de phosphate crétacé-éocène des Ganntour (Maroc Occidental). Morphologie et mobilité du fond. Polarités faciologiques et géochimiques. Conséquences économiques: 9e congrès intern. sediment. Nice 1975, thème 9, p. 15–21.

CHINO, A., 1962, Sédimentation phosphatée au Sénégal. Le phosphate de chaux de la vallée du fleuve Sénégal et de la partie nord orientale de l'anticlinal de Dahra: Rapport inédit B.R.G.M. DAK v. 62 AL9.

DEBUISSON, J., 1970, Compte rendu de surveillance des travaux de recherche et d'exploitation d'eaux souterraines (1966–1968). Programme de 9 forages d'exploitation et 15 forages-puits: Rapport inédit B.R.G.M. v. 70 DAK 6.

DEGALLIER, R., 1962, Hydrogéologie du Ferlo septentrional (Sénégal): Mem. B.R.G.M. 19, 1962.

HEETVELD, H., 1965, Syndicat du lac de Guiers. Rapport final. Campagne 1964–1965: Rapport B.R.B.M. no no.

LUCAS, J., AND PRÉVÔT, L., 1975, Les marges continentales pièges géochimiques; l'exemple de la marge atlantique de l'Afrique à la limite Crétacé-Tertiaire: B.S.G.F. v. XVII, no. 4, 1975.

MARTENS, C. S., AND HARRIS, R. C., 1970, Inhibition of apatite precipitation in the marine environment by magnesium ions: Geoch. Cosmochim. Acta, v. 34, p. 621–625.

MONCIARDINI, C., 1964, Sédimentation éocène au Sénégal; le phosphate de chaux de la région LOUGA-LINGUERE: Rapport B.R.G.M. DAK 64 A4.

———, 1968, La sédimentation éocène au Sénégal: Mem. BRGM no. 43.

———, 1970a, Etude de 25 sondages hydrauliques du Sénégal: Etude 68/6 B.R.G.M., D.S.G.N., Orléans.

———, 1970b, Etude des sondages éocènes de BOUDI SAKHO, KEUR BASSINE et COKI, région du lac de Guiers, Sénégal: Etude 68/11 B.R.G.M., D.S.G.N., Orléans.

PASCAL, M., 1967, Notice explicative de la carte géologique au 1/200 000 "DAGANA": Rep. du Sénégal, Minist. du Commerce, de l'Industrie et de l'Artisanat, Direction des Mines de la géologie.

SALVAN, H., 1957, Les rapports entre les facteurs tectoniques et la sédimentation phosphatée dans les gisements Marocains: 2ème Congr. géol. Intern. MEXICO, section V. p. 347–354.

SASSI, S., 1974, La sédimentation phosphatée au Paléocène dans le Sud et le Centre Ouest de la Tunisie: Thèse Doct. Etat, Université Paris Sud, 292 p.

SHELDON, R., 1964, Exploration for phosphorite in Turkey—A case history: Econ. Geol. v. 59, p. 1159–1175.

SLANSKY, M., 1964, Sédimentologie et recherche des gisements sédimentaires marins de phosphate, in Sedimentology and Ore Genesis, v. 2, Elsevier, p. 137–142.

SLANSKY, M., AND FAUCONNIER, D., 1973, Influence possible de certains facteurs biologiques sur la géochimie des sédiments. Bull. B.R.G.M., 2ème série, Section IV, no. 4, p. 209–228.

TRENOUS, J. Y., 1968, Rapport de mission dans la région du lac de Guiers, la vallé du Ferlo, la zone LINGUERE, DAHRA, COKI, LOUGA: Université de Dakar, Labor, de géologie, rapport n° 28, octobre 1968, 13 p.

———, 1968, Nouveaux forages dans le Sénégal Nord-Occidental. Echelle stratigraphique de la vallée du Ferlo: Université de Dakar, Labor. de géologie, in rapport annuel 1967–68, p. 41–43.

———, 1970a, Echelle stratigraphique de la basse vallée du Ferlo (Sénégal Nord-Occidental): Université d'Aix-Marseille, Annales Fac. des sciences, v. XLIIIB, p. 237–242.

———, 1970b, Etude géologique dans le Sénégal Nord-Occidental et le Ferlo: Trav. Labor. sciences terre St. Jérôme—Marseille (1), no. 4, sept. 1970, 28 p.

SEPM Special Publication No. 29, p. 215–225, November 1980

PHOSPHATE GEOCHEMISTY IN NEARSHORE CARBONATE SEDIMENTS: A SUGGESTION OF APATITE FORMATION

HENRI E. GAUDETTE and W. BERRY LYONS
Department of Earth Sciences
University of New Hampshire
Durham, New Hampshire 03824 USA

ABSTRACT

Carbonate sediment cores from nearshore shallow water environments in Bermuda were collected in June, 1977. Pore waters were removed and processed in a nitrogen atmosphere at *in situ* temperatures to prevent any sample processing artifacts and Ca^{2+}, Mg^{2+}, pH, SO_4^{2-}, titration alkalinity, salinity, PO_4^{3-}, NH_4^+ and F^- were determined.

Stoichiometric nutrient regeneration models suggest that observed PO_4^{3-} concentrations are considerably lower than calculated values. The ion activity product (IAP) of fluorapatite in the pore fluids is substantially greater than the K_{sp} indicating a supersaturation with respect to the fluorapatite mineral phase. Inorganic and organic phosphate analyses of the sediments show large concentrations of both, with C/P ratios lower than the normally observed ones for biogenic calcium carbonate minerals.

These data strongly suggest phosphate removal from the pore water during diagenetic transformation of the organic matter (i.e. during microbial metabolism) and incorporation in fluorapatite mineral phases associated with calcium carbonate in the sediments. Such processes may be the most important factor in apatite formation in organic-rich shallow water carbonate regimes.

INTRODUCTION

The study of pore water chemistry has proven useful in the understanding of early diagenetic processes (Berner et al., 1970; Sholkovitz, 1973; Murray et al., 1978; Martens and Goldhaber, 1978). Microbial sulfate reduction, the most important diagenetic process in nearshore marine environments (Goldhaber and Kaplan, 1974), produces reactive by-products, which influence subsequent diagenetic processes. The general equation for the oxidation of organic matter via sulfate reduction is:

$$(CH_2O)_{106}(NH_3)_{16}(H_3PO_4) + 53\ SO_4^{2-}$$
$$= 106\ HCO_3^- + 53\ HS^- + 16\ NH_4^+$$
$$+ HPO_4^{2-} + 39\ H^+ \qquad (1)$$

The pore water data that are available for nearshore carbonate sediments (Berner, 1974) indicate that reactive phosphate concentrations are much lower than those of nearshore clastic sediments. Berner (1974) has shown that pore fluids of anoxic carbonate sediments are in equilibrium with fluorapatite and that the reactive phosphate concentrations in these pore waters are controlled by the formation of authigenic apatite. Recent work in hemipelagic sediments (Manheim et al., 1975; Burnett, 1977) has suggested that the interaction of pore water phosphate and calcium carbonate foram tests may be extremely important diagenetically.

The purpose of this paper is to show that the dissolved reactive phosphate produced during organic matter decomposition is rapidly removed from the pore waters in nearshore carbonate rich sediments as an apatitic coating on the carbonate mineral grains. This coating may be extremely important in controlling later diagenetic processes and may inhibit $CaCO_3$ recrystallization and/or dissolution as suggested by Morse (1974).

Methods

Study Area—Seven sediment cores were taken from water depths of less than 2 m at mean low water in June, 1977 from coastal Bermudian waters (fig. 1). Because samples SG-1 and CH-1 are similar in character and composition to FR-2, only five of seven sets of data will be presented in this paper. Samples CB-1, FR-2, and GS-1 were taken within 10 m of extensive mangrove growth, sample FR-1 within a turtle grass (*Thalassia testudinum*) bed and sample GS-2 through a *Cladophora prolifera* mat.

Sample Collection—The cores were obtained manually by pushing precleaned (washed with 1N HCl and rinsed with distilled-deionized water) 8 cm ID polycarbonate core liners into the sediment. The cores were immediately capped, placed into N_2 filled polyvinyl chloride (PVC) core carriers (Lyons and Fitzgerald, 1978), sealed with PVC caps and returned to the laboratory at the Bermuda Biological Station for Research for immediate processing.

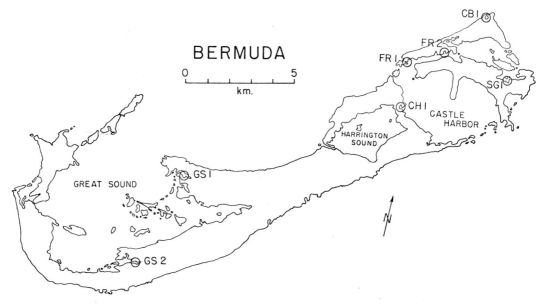

Fɪɢ. 1.—Location map of sample sites, nearshore waters of Bermuda, 1977.

Pore Water Removal and Analysis

The cores were extruded and sectioned in a N_2 filled glove bag, placed into 500 ml conventional polyethylene (CPE) bottles and centrifuged at 10,600 g's for 1 hr at *in-situ* temperatures under N_2. The bottles were placed back into the glove bag and the supernatent water was filtered through acid-precleaned 0.4μ Nucleopore[T.M.] membrane filters held by acid-precleaned Millepore[T.M.] filter holders. The filters and filter holders as well as the centrifuge bottles were cleaned according to Patterson and Settle (1976). While in the glove bag, ten milliliter samples were micropipetted into 60 ml CPE bottles. These samples were analyzed for pH and titration alkalinity (Strickland and Parsons, 1972) within 2 hrs of pore water separation. One ml samples were analyzed for salinity using a Goldberg refractometer within 2 hrs of collection.

Upon return to our laboratory in New Hampshire, 4 ml samples from the original 10 ml aliquot were analyzed for sulfate gravimetrically using the method of Presley (1971). Ammonia and phosphate were analyzed on 1 ml acidified samples using the techniques outlined in Strickland and Parsons (1972) after appropriate dilutions. Calcium and magnesium were measured on diluted samples by flame atomic absorption using diluted Copenhagen Standard Seawater as standards (Kaltenback, 1976). Fluoride was measured on 1–3 ml samples using the colorimetric method of Greenhalgh and Riley (1961) modified by us for small volume pore water samples.

While in the glove bag, 1 ml pore water samples were placed into Pyrex[T.M.] test tubes containing 0.5N Zn acetate to "fix" any dissolved sulfide present as ZnS (Goldhaber, 1974). These samples were later analyzed colorimetrically for Σ H_2S (Cline, 1969). All the above analyses were completed within 60 days of sample collection. The precision of each method is given in table 1.

The inert atmosphere (N_2) was maintained during complete sediment-pore water processing to avoid the possible oxidation of reduced chemical species present in the pore waters. In clastic sediments, reactive phosphate concentrations are affected by oxidation artifacts (Bray et al., 1973; Loder et al., 1978). At the time these samples were collected it was not known whether or not artifacts due to oxidation would occur, if anoxic carbonate sediments and pore waters were exposed to a laboratory atmosphere. To insure reliable data, the samples were, therefore, handled entirely under an inert atmosphere.

Recently, we have returned to Bermuda and conducted an experiment similar to that of Loder et al. (1978) to ascertain whether laboratory exposure of anoxic carbonate sediments does affect pore water nutrient and trace metal concentrations (Lyons et al., 1979). Table 2 shows the two sets of dissolved iron and reactive phosphate data from sampling site CB-1 collected in June, 1978. One set of data was processed entirely under N_2, the other exposed to the laboratory atmosphere for a maximum of 75 minutes. It is evident that at pore water iron concentrations greater than 2

TABLE 1.—ANALYTICAL TECHNIQUES AND ANALYTICAL PRECISION

Chemical Species	Analytical Techniques	Precision
salinity	Refractometer	±0.4‰
pH	—	±0.2 pH
titration alkalinity	Strickland & Parsons (1972)	less than 0.1 meql^{-1}
calcium	Kaltenback (1976)	±2%
magnesium	Kaltenback (1976)	±1%
ammonium	Strickland & Parsons (1972)*	±5%
phosphate	Strickland & Parsons (1972)*	±2%
sulfate	Presley (1971)	±0.5 mMl^{-1}
sulfide	Cline (1969)	±12%
fluoride	Greenhalgh & Riley (1961)	±5%

*Technicon II Auto-Analyzer was utilized

μMl^{-1} ($\sim$100 μgl^{-1}), not unlike clastic sediments, iron and reactive phosphate are lost from the pore fluids during atmospheric exposure. These data suggest that pore water samples from anoxic carbonate-rich sediments must be processed under an inert atmosphere if reliable PO_4^{3-} data are to be obtained.

In addition to the pore water analyses, the air-dried sediment samples were analyzed for: 1) organic carbon using the technique of Gaudette et al. (1974) after removal of the $CaCO_3$ by 20 percent trichloracetic acid, and 2) inorganic and organic phosphorus using the extraction scheme of Aspila et al. (1976) and the colorimetric analysis of Murphy and Riley (1962) modified for higher PO_4^{3-} concentrations by Bray et al. (1973). Duplicate organic carbon analyses were always less than 10 percent. The precision of the sedimentary phosphorus method presented as a coefficient of variation was ±4 percent at the 10 $\mu M/g$ level.

Results

Sediment Chemistry—The organic carbon and total, inorganic and organic phosphorus data from

TABLE 2.—PORE WATER Fe^{2+} AND PO_4^{3-} DATA FROM COOT BAY, BERMUDA, PROCESSED UNDER LABORATORY ATMOSPHERE AND UNDER INERT ATMOSPHERE

	Atmosphere Exposed		N_2 Processed	
Depth cm	Fe^{2+} μgl^{-1}	PO_4^{3-} μMl^{-1}	Fe^{2+} μgl^{-1}	PO_4^{3-} μMl^{-1}
5	105	3.5	445	7.4
25	66	4.2	462	6.5
35	50	1.5	95	1.8
55	49	2.2	46	2.2
65	—	4.6	49	4.3
75	77	3.6	80	5.1
overlying water values	22*	0.4		

*Unfiltered sample taken $\sim$5 cm from sediment-water interface

the five sampling sites are presented in table 3. It is evident that sample GS-1 has a much higher concentration of organic carbon than the other areas. This is also the area where sulfate reduction processes are the most evident (table 4).

In general, the sedimentary phosphorus concentrations are high, in fact, much higher than those reported from nearshore clastic sediments (Sholkovitz, 1973; Lyons et al., 1977; Lyons et al., in review) and the continental shelf and deep ocean sediments (Morse and Cook, 1978). The concentrations of total P at Station GS-2 in the *Cladophora* bed are among the highest reported in the literature. The role of the recycling of phosphorus by *Cladophora* in nutrient-poor tropical regions is of major importance to the overall ecology of the region (Bach and Josselyn, 1977; Morris et al., 1977), but its discussion is beyond the scope of this paper. it does appear, however, that sediments underlying *Cladophora* mats contain usually high concentrations of phosphorus.

Pore Water Chemistry—Pore water sulfate, sulfide, titration alkalinity and salinity data are tabulated in table 4. Fluoride, ammonium and reactive phosphate data are shown in table 5. Based on the sulfate data alone, it appears that only in core GS-1 is sulfate depletion occurring. However in core CB-1, the large titration alkalinities and high concentrations of ammonium suggest sulfate reduction has taken place. The dissolved ΣH_2S data indicate that SO_4^{2-} reduction has occurred in all the sampling locations to some extent. With the exception of FR-2, the F^-/Cl^- ratio decreases below normal sea-water values across the sediment water interface (fig. 2) indicating F^- removal with depth. Calcium and magnesium concentrations are close to sea-water values and are similar to other pore water values reported for nearshore Bermuda (Berner, 1966; Thorstenson and Mackenzie, 1974). It does appear however that the Mg/Cl ratio does decrease with depth in core GS-2 indicating possible Mg removal.

TABLE 3.—ORGANIC CARBON, TOTAL PHOSPHORUS, INORGANIC PHOSPHORUS AND ORGANIC PHOSPHORUS IN BERMUDA
SEDIMENTS

Sample	Depth cm	Organic Carbon % dry wt	Total P µM/g	Inorganic P µM/g	Organic P µM/g
FR-1					
	5.5	0.9	27.2	12.7	14.5
	16.5	1.4	15.0	8.9	6.1
	27.5	0.8	15.4	6.1	9.3
	38.5	0.8	17.4	7.8	9.6
	49.5	0.9	20.6	8.5	12.1
	60.5	0.9	22.6	9.6	13.0
FR-2					
	5.5	1.4	45.9	20.6	25.3
	16.5	1.3	57.0	28.5	28.5
	27.5	1.4	30.5	13.4	17.1
	38.5	1.4	26.9	10.2	16.7
	54.5	1.9	31.7	9.5	22.2
	69.5	1.7	23.0	8.3	14.7
CB-1					
	5.5	1.7	38.1	20.1	18.0
	16.5	1.2	27.6	19.9	7.7
	27.5	1.2	25.5	15.0	10.5
	38.5	1.2	24.5	12.6	11.9
	49.5	1.2	29.4	17.9	11.5
	58.5	1.3	49.9	18.1	31.8
GS-1					
	5.5	12.3	20.3	7.7	12.6
	16.5	20.0	16.9	7.8	9.1
	27.5	11.5	24.4	10.4	14.0
	38.5	16.0	27.4	9.3	18.1
	49.5	17.6	23.0	7.0	16.0
	68.5	14.2	22.8	6.5	16.3
GS-2					
	5.5	5.9	84.8	39.6	45.2
	16.5	5.2	99.1	39.7	59.4
	27.5	4.5	83.3	37.7	45.6
	38.5	5.9	109.4	41.7	67.7
	49.5	5.6	114.0	37.5	76.5

DISCUSSION

Concentration of Reactive Phosphate in the Pore Waters

The concentrations of reactive phosphate in the pore waters of these sediments are low. This is particularly true when they are compared to pore water reactive phosphate values obtained from nearshore anoxic pore waters from clastic sediments (table 6). Although the NH_4^+ data are similar at comparable depths, the phosphate concentrations in the carbonate nearshore sediments are an order of magnitude lower than those from the clastic environment. Although a portion of the excess PO_4^{3-} in the clastic sediments may be explained either by the decomposition of phosphorus rich organic matter (Martens et al., 1978) or the solubilization of unstable Fe^{3+} minerals containing large amounts of PO_4^{3-} as the Eh of the sediment decreases (Lyons et al., 1977; Lyons

et al., in review), the dearth of reactive phosphate on the Bermudan pore waters strongly suggests the diagenetic removal of PO_4^{3-} onto calcium carbonate mineral grains. This can be substantiated by three lines of independent evidence.

Sedimentary Phosphorus

First, as we have already indicated, the concentrations of sedimentary phosphorus are very high. Unlike nearshore clastic sediments in which the organic P is generally much less than 50% (Sholkovitz, 1973; Thornton et al., 1977; Lyons et al., 1977) of the total phosphorus, the Bermuda sediments mean OP/TP ratio is 55%. Therefore, a large amount of the phosphorus found in these carbonate sediments is organic in character. Suess (1973) has observed that calcium carbonate sediments from Fanning Island contain organic-rich surface coatings with abnormally low C:P ratios. The average C:P ratio of the sedimentary organic

TABLE 4.—SALINITY, SULFATE, $\Sigma H_2 S$ AND TITRATION ALKALINITY DATA FROM BERMUDA PORE WATERS

Sample	Depth cm	Salinity ‰	Sulfate mMl^{-1}	Sulfide μMl^{-1}	Titration Alkalinity meql^{-1}
FR-1					
	5.5	34.9	27.8	122	—
	16.5	34.9	27.6	228	2.5
	27.5	35.0	27.1	304	2.5
	38.5	34.4	27.7	366	2.5
	49.5	34.3	27.0	304	2.4
	60.5	34.5	27.4	304	2.4
FR-2					
	5.5	36.0	24.9	214	4.2
	16.5	35.6	26.7	290	4.1
	27.5	36.0	27.4	380	2.6
	38.5	35.3	25.2	260	2.3
	54.5	35.4	27.2	304	—
	69.5	35.0	26.8	624	2.3
CB-1					
	5.5	35.5	27.7	—	5.9
	16.5	35.3	26.0	—	7.4
	27.5	35.3	26.2	—	6.3
	38.5	35.3	26.0	—	7.0
	49.5	35.3	25.9	—	7.4
	58.5	35.3	25.8	—	7.4
GS-1					
	5.5	34.6	23.0	1371	8.8
	16.5	33.8	16.4	1265	11.6
	27.5	32.6	13.2	1028	10.4
	38.5	33.7	14.3	1013	11.0
	49.5	32.4	13.6	1067	10.6
	68.5	32.8	17.6	1105	11.9
GS-2					
	5.5	32.0	24.3	229	2.4
	16.5	32.8	23.6	215	—
	27.5	33.4	24.9	229	—
	38.5	34.0	24.4	190	—
	49.5	33.0	24.0	458	2.4

matter for each of the Bermuda sites is tabulated in table 7 along with the average C:P ratio for marine plankton and the data from Suess (1973).

Except at site GS-1 and FR-1 where the organic carbon concentrations of the sediment are greater than 10.0 percent, the C:P values are all less than the Redfield ratio (i.e. 106:1) and closer to the values obtained by Suess (1973) for the surface coatings of coarse grained carbonate sediments (i.e. 56:1). Suess (1973) has argued that this increase of P relative to C is due to the sorption of organic phosphorus and possibly phosphate onto the mineral surfaces. The low C:P ratios of the Bermuda sediments suggest that organic phosphorus is preferably absorbed onto $CaCO_3$ sediments at higher phosphorus values than that of marine plankton.

Stoichiometric Models

Secondly, simple pore water stoichiometric nutrient regeneration models can be utilized to indicate that the pore waters from these sediments are depleted in PO_4^{3-} relative to NH_4^+. Two different models can be used: 1) a sulfate reduction model based on sulfate depletion with depth and the average C:P ratio of the sedimentary organic matter (Sholkovitz, 1973) and 2) a model that predicts the PO_4^{3-} concentration from the pore water NH_4^+ concentration and the N:P ratio of the decaying organic matter. The first model can be utilized on cores GS-1 and perhaps CB-1 where sulfate reduction has occurred; the second on cores FR-1, FR-2, and GS-2 where no significant sulfate depletion is observed.

The results from GS-1 and CB-1 are shown in table 8. In core GS-1, the predicted PO_4^{3-} values calculated from the model are similar to those observed indicating little or no PO_4^{3-} pore water removal. On the other hand, the phosphate values predicted by the model for CB-1, with the exception of the 5.5 cm sample are all higher than those observed. At the depths of 49.5 cm and

TABLE 5.—F^-, NH_4^+ AND PO_4^{3-} PORE WATER DATA FROM BERMUDA

Sample	Depth cm	F^- μMl^{-1}	NH_4^+ μMl^{-1}	PO_4^{3-} μMl^{-1}
FR-1				
	5.5	66	—	6
	16.5	63	101	less than 1
	27.5	62	24	1
	38.5	61	11	1
	49.5	63	14	2
	60.5	62	34	3
FR-2				
	5.5	55	262	2
	16.5	73	69	1
	27.5	74	69	1
	38.5	76	44	2
	54.5	65	13	2
	69.5	—	18	1
CB-1				
	5.5	54	—	18
	16.5	48	887	17
	27.5	49	827	15
	38.5	49	735	11
	49.5	45	851	8
	58.5	39	896	8
GS-1				
	5.5	58	617	6
	16.5	53	1102	17
	27.5	46	1219	21
	38.5	55	1658	34
	49.5	52	1684	40
	68.5	47	1469	30
GS-2				
	5.5	55	97	8
	16.5	49	72	5
	27.5	41	—	4
	38.5	44	21	6
	49.5	37	285	7

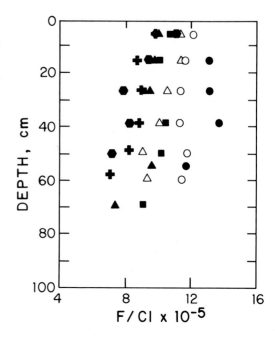

FIG. 2.—F/Cl vs depth from Bermuda pore water samples; Collected June 1977 $\bigcirc$ – FR1; $\bullet$ = FR2 + = CB1, $\triangle$ = SG1, $\blacktriangle$ = CH1, $\blacksquare$ = GS1, $\bullet$ = GS2.

58.5 cm, the observed values are close to an order of magnitude less than the model predictions (table 8).

Table 9 demonstrates the actual PO_4^{3-} values and predicted PO_4^{3-} concentrations using the NH_4^+ values for cores FR-1, FR-2 and GS-1 and assuming that the decomposing organic matter present in the sediments has a N:P ratio close to that of marine plankton, i.e. 7:1 (Redfield et al., 1965). Unfortunately sediment N:P ratios are not available. The ammonium present in these pore waters indicates that anaerobic decomposition is occurring but little SO_4^{2-} reduction has occurred, as measured by SO_4^{2-} depletion with depth. Except for the bottom two sections of FR-1 and FR-2, the predicted values are higher than the observed phosphate pore water concentrations. Therefore, with the exception of core GS-1, the phosphate regeneration models indicate

that there has been a loss of PO_4^{3-} from the pore waters of these sediments.

Thermodynamic Considerations

The third line of evidence that suggests phosphorus-$CaCO_3$ interactions and PO_4^{3-} removal are taking place in these pore fluids is a thermodynamic one. Berner (1974) has shown through thermodynamic calculations that nearshore carbonate sediment pore waters are saturated with respect to a fluorapatite mineral phase. This removal of PO_4^{3-} through apatite precipitation cal also be inferred by the decrease in the F^-/Cl^- ratio with depth in our cores (fig. 2). We have calculated the ion activity product (IAP) for calcium fluorapatite $Ca_5(PO_4)_3F$ as well as for calcium carbonate-fluorapatite, $Ca_{10}(PO_4)_5 CO_3 F_2(OH)$. Kitano et al. (1978) have recently shown that carbonate fluorapatite is more likely to form surface coatings on $CaCO_3$ than is fluorapatite. A summary of the physicochemical parameters used to make the calculations is shown in table 10.

The IAP's calculated from the pore water data for fluorapatite, $Ca_5(PO_4)_3 F$, ranged between 1.5×10^{-47} and 1.6×10^{-55} and those for $1/2 Ca_{10}(PO_4)_5 CO_3 F_2(OH)$ between 5.0×10^{-48}

TABLE 6.—COMPARISON OF NEARSHORE CARBONATE AND NEARSHORE CLASTIC PO_4^{3-} AND NH_4^+ PORE WATER DATA

GS-1-Bermuda			Footman Is.-Great Bay, N.H.		
Depth cm	PO_4^{3-} μMl^{-1}	NH_4^+ μMl^{-1}	Depth cm	PO_4^{3-} μMl^{-1}	NH_4^+ μMl^{-1}
5.5	6	617	5	138	428
16.5	17	1102	12	174	600
27.5	21	1219	21	230	1002
38.5	34	1658	29	288	1160
49.5	40	1684	42	328	1562
60.5	30	1469			

CB-1-Bermuda			Inner Bay-Great Bay, N.H.		
Depth cm	PO_4^{3-} μMl^{-1}	NH_4^+ μMl^{-1}	Depth cm	PO_4^{3-} μMl^{-1}	NH_4^+ μMl^{-1}
5.5	18	—	5	108	110
16.5	17	887	12.5	120	302
27.5	15	827	21	104	551
38.5	11	735	29	120	985
49.5	8	851	42	152	1450
58.5	8	896			

TABLE 7.—AVERAGE ORGANIC CARBON TO ORGANIC PHOSPHORUS RATIOS OF THE BERMUDA SEDIMENTS

Sample	C:P	
FR-1	96:1	
FR-2	66:1	
CB-1	73:1	
GS-1	985:1	this work
GS-2	80:1	
marine plankton	106:1	Redfield et al. (1963)
surface coatings of CaCO$_3$ grains	17–56:1 (average 28:1)	Suess (1973)

TABLE 8.—PHOSPHATE MODEL CALCULATIONS USING THE MODEL OF SHOLKOVITZ (1973)

$$\Delta PO_4^{3-} = \frac{2\Delta SO_4^{2-}}{C:P}; \quad PO_4^{3-} = \text{initial } PO_4^{3-} + \Delta PO_4^{3-}$$

Core GS-1 C:P = 985:1			Core CB-1 C:P = 73:1		
Depth cm	Observed PO_4^{3-} μM	Predicted PO_4^{3-} μM	Depth	Observed PO_4^{3-}	Predicted PO_4^{3-}
5.5	6	9	5.5	18	8
16.5	17	22	16.5	17	55
27.5	21	29	27.5	15	55
38.5	34	29	38.5	11	55
49.5	40	29	49.5	8	58
58.5	30	29	58.5	8	60

GAUDETTE AND LYONS

TABLE 9.—PHOSPHATE PREDICTION MODEL BASED ON THE MEASURED AMMONIUM PORE WATER CONCENTRATIONS

$$\Delta PO_4^{3-} = \frac{\Delta NH_4^+}{N:P}; \quad N:P \sim 7:1 \text{ (Redfield et al., 1963)}$$

	FR-1			FR-2			GS-2	
Depth cm	Observed PO$_4^{3-}$ μMl^{-1}	Predicted PO$_4^{3-}$ μMl^{-1}	Depth cm	Observed PO$_4^{3-}$ μMl^{-1}	Predicted PO$_4^{3-}$ μMl^{-1}	Depth cm	Observed PO$_4^{3-}$ μMl^{-1}	Predicted PO$_4^{3-}$ μMl^{-1}
5.5	6	—	5.5	2	37	5.5	8	14
16.5	less than 1	15	16.5	1	10	16.5	5	10
27.5	1	3	27.5	2	10	27.5	4	—
38.5	1	2	38.5	2	6	38.5	6	3
49.5	2	2	54.5	1	2	49.5	7	41
60.5	3	5	69.5		2			

TABLE 10.—THERMODYNAMIC DATA USED FOR PORE WATER ION ACTIVITY PRODUCT (IAP) CALCULATIONS

Ca^{2+}		
	% free = 91 $\gamma = 0.26$	Garrels & Thompson (1962)
PO$_4^{3-}$		
	% free = 0.1 $\gamma = 0.033$	Atlas (1976)
F$^-$		
	% free = 50 $\gamma = .57$	Brewer et al. (1970) Whitfield (1975)
CO$_3^{2-}$		
	% free = 10.5 $\gamma = 0.20$	Garrels & Thompson (1962)

k_1', k_2', k_3' for Σ H$_3$ PO$_4$ from Atlas et al. (1976)

k_2' for Σ H$_2$CO$_3$ from Mehrback et al. (1973)

ksp	Ca$_5$ (PO$_4$)$_3$ F	
	1 × 10^{-59}	Nriagu (1976)
	1 × 10^{-63}	Robertson (1966)
ksp	1/2 Ca$_{10}$ (PO$_4$)$_5$ CO$_3$ F$_2$ OH	
	3.2 × 10^{-61}	Nriagu (1976)

$- 1.4 \times 10^{-55}$. If Robertson's (1966) or Nriagu's (1976) thermodynamic data are utilized, the pore fluids of these sediments are supersaturated by as much as 12 orders of magnitude. The discrepancy in ksp values obviously has a profound effect on the interpretation of the calculated pore water ion activity products. Nriagu (1976) has discussed the scatter in the reported constants for apatite minerals and considers it not surprising because of: 1) the differences in experimental procedure and methods of data interpretation used by different investigators and 2) differences in the nature of the starting materials used in the experiments. For instance, the degree of crystallinity and minor chemical compositional changes both have great influence on ksp determinations. Therefore, the variance in the fluorapatite ksp values does not enable us to discuss our IAP calculations with any rigor.

However, the carbonate-fluorapatite IAP's in the pore water are much higher than the ksp of this mineral phase (table 10) again suggesting that the pore fluids are supersaturated and that authigenic carbonate-fluorapatite coatings may be forming. Stumm and Leckie (1970) have shown that the precipitation of apatite is enhanced by $CaCO_3$ surfaces which act as nucleating sites for crystallization, Kitano et al. (1978) observed the same phenomenon and stated that carbonate-fluorapatite is the more likely apatite to be precipitating. Our data certainly suggest that this is the case in nearshore Bermuda sediments. In addition, mineralogical evidence indicates that phosphorite deposits are composed only of carbonate-fluorapatite (McConnell, 1973).

CONCLUSIONS

A review of the literature indicates that there are at least four possible modes of phosphate–$CaCO_3$ interactions in the sediment—pore water system of recent anoxic sediments. They are:

1) The **direct precipitation** of **authigenic apatite** on surfaces of biogenic silica and/or inorganic phases as outlined by Burnett (1977). This happens only after large amounts (10's of μMs) of PO_4^{3-} have been generated in the pore waters by SO_4^{2-} reduction and the removal of interfering Mg^{2+} ions from the pore waters by some other diagenetic processes.

2) The **direct precipitation** of **amorphous calcium phosphate** (Ca/P molar ratio of ~1.4) in supersaturated solutions of sea-water with normal Mg/Ca ratios (Martens and Harriss, 1970; Nathan and Lucas, 1976). (Mg^{2+} appears to inhibit apatite precipitation.)

3) **Apatite replacement of $CaCO_3$** as first studied by Ames (1959) in the laboratory and described by D'Anglejan (1968) and Manheim et al. (1975) in the field. The reaction would be:

$$100\ CaCO_3 + 53\ HPO_4^{2-} + 14F^- + 66\ (OH)$$
$$\rightarrow 10\ [Ca_{10}(PO_4)_{5.3}(CO_3)_{0.7}(OH)_{1.3}(F)_{1.4}]$$
$$+ 93\ CO_3^- + 53\ H_2O$$

Because the rate of replacement is inversely proportional to the amount of CO_3^- or carbonate alkalinity present (Ames, 1959; D'Anglejan, 1968; Stumm and Leckie, 1970) as well as pH, this reaction could only proceed if sulfate reduction was slight (i.e., little carbonate alkalinity present) or if the carbonate alkalinity was removed by some other reaction.

4) The **absorption** of **reactive phosphate** by cal-

cium carbonate in the presence of Mg^{2+}. This adsorption may (Kitano et al., 1978) or may not (deKanel and Morse, in review) be enhanced by the presence of F^-. The absorption of phosphate on to organic coatings covering the $CaCO_3$ minerals also appears to be important (Suess, 1973).

Which one, or several, of these reactions is actually taking place in the Bermuda sediments is unknown. Because the Mg^{2+} concentration of the pore fluids that we have analyzed only varied with salinity and in general did not decrease with depth independent of salinity, mode #1 seems improbable in these sediments. Since the F^- concentration in the majority of samples decreases with depth (fig. 2) and because the thermodynamic calculations show supersaturation with respect to apatite, mode #3 seems a real possibility. Cook (1976) points out that diagenetic phosphatization takes place mainly through replacement reactions regardless of sediment type.

It is apparent, however, that no matter what the mechanism, PO_4^{3-} is being removed from the pore waters on to $CaCO_3$ mineral grains in nearshore Bermuda sediments. At this time we are exploring this problem in more detail using scanning electron microscopy and microprobe techniques.

Acknowledgements

We thank A. D. Hewitt for his invaluable help in obtaining and analyzing the samples. We appreciate the help of A. D. Hewitt, C. McLean, P. Rosenberg and G. Smith in analyzing the pore water and sediment samples. We thank K. Wilson for reviewing the manuscript. We appreciate the discussion with W. Burnett regarding apatite ksp values. This work was supported in part by the following grants; NSF-CHE 7503474, NSF-OCE-77-20484, Vollmer Fellowship Foundation of the Bermuda Biological Station and U.N.H. Hubbard Marine Fund. One of us (WBL) acknowledges the travel support of the U.N.H. Marine Program, National Science Foundation—American Geological Institute and the U.N.H. Research Foundation in order that he could present this paper at the 10th International Congress on Sedimentology in Jerusalem. This is Contribution No. 795 from the Bermuda Biol. Station for Research and Contribution No. 15 from U.N.H. CREAM.

REFERENCES

AMES, L. L., 1959, The gensis of carbonate apatites: Econ. Geol., v. 54, p. 829–841.

ASPILA, K. I., AGEMIAN, H., AND CHAN, A. S. Y., 1976, A semi-automated method for the determination of inorganic, organic and total phosphate in sediments: Analyst, v. 101, p. 187–197.

ATLAS, E., 1976, Phosphate equilibria in seawater and interstitial waters: Ph.D. Thesis, Oregon State University, p. 1–154.

———, CULBERSON, C., AND PYTKOWICZ, R. M., 1976, Phosphate association with Na$^+$, Ca^{2+} and Mg^{2+} in seawater: Mar. Chem., v. 4, p. 243–254.

————, AND PYTKOWICZ, R. M., 1977, Solubility behavior of apatites in seawater: Limnol. Oceanogr., v. 22, p. 290–300.

BACH, S. D., AND JOSSELYN, M. N., 1978, Mass blooms of the alga *Cladophora* in Bermuda: Mar. Pollut. Bull., v. 9, p. 34–37.

BERNER, R. A., 1966, Chemical diagenesis of some modern carbonate sediments: Am. Jour. Sci., v. 264, p. 1–36.

————, 1974, Kinetic models for anoxic marine sediments, *in* The Sea, volume 5, John Wiley and Sons, New York, p. 427–450.

————, SCOTT, M. R., AND THOMLINSON, C., 1970, Carbonate alkalinity in the pore waters of anoxic marine sediments: Limnol. Oceanogr., v. 15, p. 544–549.

BRAY, J. T., BRICKER, O. P., AND TROUP, B. N., 1973, Phosphate in interstitial waters of anoxic sediments: Oxidation effects during sampling procedure: Science, v. 180, p. 1362–1364.

BREWER, P. G., SPENCER, D. W., AND WILKNISS, P. E., 1970, Anomalous fluoride concentrations in the North Atlantic: Deep-Sea Res., v. 17, p. 1–7.

BURNETT, W. C., 1977, Geochemistry and origin of phosphorite deposits from off Peru and Chile: Geol. Soc. Am. Bull., v. 88, p. 813–823.

CLINE, J. D., 1969, Spectrophotometric determination of hydrogen sulfide in natural waters: Limnol. Oceanogr., v. 14, p. 454–458.

COOK, P. J., 1976, Sedimentary phosphate deposits, *in* Handbook of strata-bound and stratiform ore deposits, vol. 7, Elsevier Scientific, New York, p. 505–535.

D'ANGLEJAN, B. F., 1968, Phosphate diagenesis of carbonate sediments as a mode of *in-situ* formation of marine phosphorites: observations in a core from the eastern Pacific: Can. Jour. Earth Sci., v. 5, p. 81–87.

DEKANEL, J., AND MORSE, J. W., 1978, The chemistry of orthophosphate uptake from seawater onto calcite and aragonite: in press, Geochim et Cosmochim. Acta.

GARRELS, R. M., AND THOMPSON, M. E., 1962, A chemical model for seawater at 25° C and one atmosphere total pressure: Am. Jour. Sci., v. 260, p. 57–66.

GAUDETTE, H. E., FLIGHT, W. R., TONER, L., AND FOLGER, D. W., 1974, An unexpensive titration method for the determination of organic carbon in recent sediments: Jour. Sed. Pet., v. 44, p. 249–253.

GOLDHABER, M. B., 1974, Equilibrium and dynamic aspects of the marine geochemistry of sulfur: Ph.D. Thesis, University of California at Los Angeles, 399 p.

————, AND KAPLAN, I. R., 1974, The sulfur cycle, *in* The Sea, volume 5, John Wiley and Sons, New York, p. 569–656.

GREENHALGH, R., AND RILEY, J. P., 1961, The determination of fluorides in natural waters with particular reference to seawater: Anal. Chim. Acta, v. 25, p. 179–188.

KALTENBACK, A. J., 1976, Major cations in interstitial waters of Long Island Sound: M. Sc. Thesis, University of Connecticut, 76 p.

KITANO, Y., OKUMURA, M., AND IDOGAK, M., 1978, Uptake of phosphate ions by calcium carbonate: Geochem. Jour., v. 12, p. 29–37.

LODER, T. C., LYONS, W. B., MURRAY, S., AND MCGUINNESS, H., 1978, Silicate in anoxic pore waters and oxidation effects during sampling: Nature, v. 273, p. 373–374.

LYONS, W. B., AND FITZGERALD, W. F., 1978, Nutrient production in nearshore tidal flat pore waters: A kinetic study, *in* Environmental Biogeochemistry and Geomicrobiology, Vol. 1, Ann Arbor Press, p. 237–244.

————, FOGG, T. R., AND GAUDETTE, H. E., 1977, Importance of inorganic processes on the production of phosphate in pore waters of estuarine anoxic sediments: Abstr. Geol. Soc. Am. Meeting, p. 1079.

————, HEWITT, A. D., AND GAUDETTE, H. E., in review, Marine sedimentary phosphorus fractionation studies: Comparison and evaluation.

————, GAUDETTE, H. F., AND SMITH, G. M., 1979, Pore water sampling in anoxic carbonate sediments: Oxidation artifacts: Nature, v. 277, p. 48–49.

MANHEIM, F., ROWE, G. T., AND JIPA, A., 1975, Marine phosphorite formation off Peru: Jour. Sed. Pet., v. 45, p. 243–251.

MARTENS, C. S., AND HARRISS, R. C., 1970, Inhibition of apatite precipitation in the marine environment by magnesium ions: Geochim. Cosmochim. Acta, v. 34, p. 621–625.

————, AND GOLDHABER, M. B., 1978, Early diagenesis in transitional sedimentary environments of the White Oak River Estuary, N. C.: Limnol. Oceanogr., v. 23, p. 428–441.

————, BERNER, R. A., AND ROSENFELD, J. K., 1978, Interstitial water chemistry of anoxic Long Island Sound sediments. 2. Nutrient regeneration and phosphate removal: Limnol. Oceanogr., v. 23, p. 605–617.

MCCONNELL, D., 1973, Apatite, Springer, New York, 111 p.

MEHRBACK, C., CULBERSON, C. H., HAWLEY, J. E., AND PYTKOWICZ, R. M., 1973, Measurements of the apparent dissociation constants of carbonic acid in seawater at atmospheric pressure: Limnol. Oceanogr., v. 18, p. 897–907.

MORRIS, B., BARNES, J., BROWN, F., AND MARKHAM, J., 1977, The Bermuda Marine Environment, Bermuda Biol. Station Special Publ. no. 15, p. 1–120.

MORSE, J. W., 1974, Dissolution kinetics of calcium carbonate in seawater. V. Effects of natural inhibitors and the position of the chemical lysocline: Am. Jour. Sci., v. 274, p. 638–647.

————, AND COOK, N., 1978, The distribution and form of phosphorus in North Atlantic Ocean deep-sea and continental slope sediments: Limnol. Oceanogr., v. 23, p. 825–831.

MURPHY, J., AND RILEY, J. P., 1962, A modified single solution method for the determination of phosphate in natural waters: Anal. Chim. Acta, v. 27, p. 31–36.

MURRAY, J. W., GRUNDMANIS, V., AND SMETHIE, W. M. JR., 1978, Interstitial water chemistry in the sediments of Saanich Inlet: Geochim. Cosmochim. Acta, v. 42, p. 1011–1026.

NATHAN, Y., AND LUCAS, J., 1976, Expériences sur la précipitation directe de l'apatite dans l'eau de mer: Implication dans la genèse des phosphorites: Chem. Geol., v. 18, p. 181–186.

NRIAGU, J., 1976, Thermodynamic data for phosphate minerals: Canada Centre for Inland Waters Internal Report, 32 p.

PATTERSON, C. C., AND SETTLE, D., 1976, The reduction of orders of magnitude errors in lead analysis of biological materials and natural waters by evaluating and controlling the extent and sources of industrial lead contamination introduced during sample collecting and analysis, *in* Accuracy in Trace Analysis, Proceed. 7th Materials Res. Symp., Nat. Bureau Standards Spec. Publ., p. 321–352.

PRESLEY, B. J., 1971, Techniques for analyzing interstitial water samples, *in* Initial Rpts. of D.S.D.P., vol. 7, U.S. Government Print Office, p. 1749–1755.

REDFIELD, A. C., KETCHUM, B. H., AND RICHARDS, F. A., 1963, The influence of organisms on the composition of sea water, *in* The Sea, vol. 2, Wiley Interscience, New York, p. 26–77.

ROBERTSON, C. E., 1966, Solubility implications of apatite in seawater: U.S. Geol. Survey Prof. Paper 550-D, p. D178–D185.

SHOLKOVITZ, E. R., 1973, Interstitial water chemistry of The Santa Barbara Basin sediments: Geochim. Cosmochim. Acta, v. 37, p. 2043–2073.

STRICKLAND, J. D. H., AND PARSONS, T. R., 1972, A Manual of Seawater Analysis: Bull. Fish. Res. Bd. Can. 167, 2nd edition, 310 p.

STUMM, W., AND LECKIE, J. O., 1970, Phosphate exchange with sediments; its role in the productivity of surface waters: Water Poll. Res. Conf., III, 26, p. 1–16.

SUESS, E., 1973, Interaction of organic compounds with calcium carbonate—II Organo-carbonate associations in recent sediments: Geochim. Cosmochim. Acta, v. 37, p. 2435–2447.

THORNTON, S. E., HAMMOND, D. E., BLOOM, L., KOROSEC, M., MALOUTA, D., SHEPARD, J., SIEGAL, J., SMITH, D., AND WALLIN, S., 1977, Interstitial Water Chemistry in an Estuary, Newport Bay, California: Abstracts with Programs, Annual Meeting, G.S.A., p. 1199–1200.

THORSTENSON, D. C., AND MACKENZIE, F. T., 1974, Time variability of pore water chemistry in recent carbonate sediments, Devil's Hole, Harrington Sound, Bermuda: Geochim. Cosmochim. Acta, v. 38, p. 1–19.

WHITFIELD, M., 1975, The extension of chemical models for seawater to include trace components at 25° C and 1 atm. pressure: Geochim. Cosmochim. Acta, v. 39, p. 1545–1557.

TABLE 1.—THE COMPONENTS OF THE GREEN PELLETS (PELLETAL GLAUCONITIC FACIES).

Deposited initial framework	Authigenesis
inherited components	authigenic components
quartz ; feldspars ; micas, aragonite ; calcite ; dolomite; illite, smectites ; kaolinite ; volcanic glass shards or ashes, consolidated mud ; phosphates, silex ; volcanic, plutonic debris	glauconitic smectite to glauconitic mica (the glauconite-mineral)
minerals thermodynamically unstable	minerals in equilibrium on the sea bottom
ALTERATION	CRYSTAL GROWTH

Most of the time, glauconitization affects deposited initial frameworks of pelletal habit the possible composition of which is summarized in the left column. The table shows that there is no systematic chemical affinity between the initial composition of such pellets and the authigenic glauconitic mineral which grows inside them (right column). The elements of the components of the left column are altered and leave the framework, whereas elements of the authigenic clays must enter the framework from the external water.

Glauconitization occurs **far from zones of active sedimentation** at relatively low temperature (7 to 15° C after the few *in situ* measurements). Climatic conditions do not appear to be specific: today, green pellets occur from latitude 50° S to 65° N

(Collet, 1908; Odin, 1973). In continental hot-temperate and intertropical zones, however, more iron is carried to the sea and here, the frequency of glauconitization is clearly higher. No recent glauconies are observed in the highest latitudes.

Glauconitization generally occurs today at a water depth between 60 m and 350 m. Too warm and too oxidizing water destroys glauconitic minerals at a depth of less than 30 m. Green pellets may occur at more than 350 m.

As to the time factor, glauconitization appears in some place during practically all of geological times, over more than 1 billion years. There is evidence that some periods are more favorable: e.g. Middle Cretaceous or Early Miocene, while others are poorer: e.g. Permian or Early Jurassic.

As an example, glauconies occur on the Atlantic margin of Africa at different times in various marginal basins: Early and Late Paleocene of Senegal; Paleocene, Middle and Late Eocene of the Ivory Coast; Eocene of Nigeria; Early Miocene of Morocco, Gabon, Cabinda, Congo (Reyre, 1966; Giresse and Cornen, 1976). The margin off South Africa also shows green pellets reworked from Cretaceous and Tertiary strata (Birch et al., 1976). Plio-Quaternary glauconies are present on the shelf off northern Spain (Lamboy, 1976). Recent glauconitization or resembling facies (less than 100,000 years old) are recognized on the shelves off Portugal, Morocco, Senegal, Ivory

TABLE 2.—SOME MARINE OCCURRENCES OF GLAUCONIES AND PHOSPHATES FROM THE AFRICAN ATLANTIC MARGIN.

	North Spain	Portugal	Morocco	Senegal	Guinea	Ivory Coast	Nigeria	Gabon Congo	South Africa
Holocene	:		:	:		:	:		: |
Plioquaternary	: |	|	:	|					|
Miocene			|					: |	|
Eocene			|			:	: ||	:	:
Palaeocene				:			:	|	
Maastrichtian			|	:				|	
"Cretaceous"			|				:		:

points: glaucony; lines: phosphorite

Thin symbols indicate either poorly correlated occurrences or those represented by few concentrated outcrops only. Points are for glauconies, lines for phosphates. Data are from Baturin et al. (1972), Birch et al. (1976), Cornen et al. (1973), Giresse (1978), Giresse and Cornen (1976), McArthur (1978), Odin (1975), Tooms et al. (1970).

It is clear that the correlation between both facies is far from being systematic. Where green pellets and phosphate elements occur together in a sediment, there are often evident marks of redeposition (i.e. Paleocene from Senegal, Holocene of South Africa). We conclude that conditions of genesis were different although similar.

Coast, Nigeria, Gabon, Congo (Odin, 1975; p. 79); see table 2.

The inherited pelletal framework evolves with time to a glauconitic pellet. It is a classical view now to **relate the mineralogical components of these glauconitic pellets to the duration of their formation,** hence to the lack of deposition during which they have evolved, though knowledge of the time interval involved would be precious to the sedimentologist. From the data available at present (Robert and Odin, 1975; Giresse, 1975; Odin, 1975) one may state precisely, although schematically, that a glauconitic smectite may be formed from a previously altered framework in a few thousand years (fig. 3, step 1); at this time the pellets are yellow-green to olive-green; this can be exemplified by buried glauconies of the Mediterranean Sea. After some 10^4 years, the inherited framework is altered, the pellets are cracked, green and the authigenic minerals contain approximately 6% K_2O, but 10 Å micaceous sheets are still absent (see, for example, glauconies from the Gabon and Congo shelves, California borderland) From here on evolution seems to be less rapid because these minerals become successively more stable on the sea bottom. Real glauconitic mica needs clearly more time—probably 10^5 to 10^6 years (see, for example, outcrops from the NW Spain or E. New Zealand shelves). Such pellets are generally well rounded and dark-green (fig. 3, step 4 further on). K_2O-content is higher than 8%. This evolution may occur entirely on the sea bottom in close contact with the open sea water without any burial.

The classical normal evolutionary sequence of Goldschmidt is a convenient frame to define the place of glauconies in a general geochemical scheme. As revised by Millot (1964), this sequence is composed of five members deposited successively: the coarse residues, the fine residues (or hydrolyzates), the oxidates, the carbonates, the saline deposits. This typical sequence of the sediments permits to relate marine deposits with the degree of abrasion of the near continent (see fig. 1, left column). As glauconies are essentially dependant on a sufficient influx of iron into the ocean, it is not surprising to find glauconitic sedimentation to correlate with the oxidate member of the sequence, classically the major time of input of iron into the sea. Many glauconies are part of this member (the thickest part of the dotted figure, column glauconies, fig. 1) following clayey and preceding carbonate deposition. They may, however, be encountered at the beginning of Goldschmidt's normal evolutionary sequence mixed with coarse and fine insoluble residues as well as with the carbonate member at the end. They are never present in the last member, the saline deposits.

Such "green minerals" are described only in normal open sea water and not in confined seas. We may note that glauconies may exist in deposits made of coarse and fine insoluble residues often with a carbonate phase, or in carbonates, but they are formed later: the glauconitic minerals replace these components.

In parallel with this series, we may try to relate the time of formation of glauconitic minerals to the deposition of other marine clay minerals. The glauconitic minerals appear after the inherited clay minerals (the first member), after the berthierines (the first newly formed marine mineral under fluvial influence) but clearly before the magnesian clay minerals (palygorskite and sepiolite) which indicate an increasing confinement of the sea. Glauconitization, therefore, occurs after the deposition of the fine residues and before the beginning of confinement of a sedimentary basin.

This is illustrated by the fact that in fossil sequences the clay fraction accompanying glaucony is almost always smectitic and illitic; there is often an inverse relationship between the presence of kaolinite, an indicator of detrital deposition in this case, and that of glaucony. On recent shelves, kaolinitic coprolites are often the framework for glauconitization. Magnesium clays are practically absent from glauconitic beds.

The last general factor to be examined are the eustatic changes. A general glauconitization occurs sometimes at the base of a transgressive series. This is an example of a favorable location due to the abundant presence, on the transgressed sea bottom, of the necessary initial framework for glauconies, sometimes accompanied by an absence of deposition. As sea level rises, continental abrasion slows down and the detrital deposits may be limited to a zone nearer the shore or stopped all together. Under these conditions, glauconies develop on a large scale. We must add that there is not a necessary bond between transgression and the green facies.

Local Environment

The importance of the presence of carbonates in sediments where glauconies are forming has been stressed. Glauconitic sands and clays are more or less rich in carbonates at least during sedimentogenesis. The pH of the overlying sea water itself is clearly basic. On the continent, the genesis of smectites is specific of basic soils (Paquet, 1970). This character seems decisive also for glauconitization.

Relations with organic compounds are complex. For the pelletal facies there are numerous possible initial frameworks (Cayeux, 1916), but four main types are recognized: (1) mud coprolites (50 to 500 μm); (2) micro-organisms tests; (3) organic carbonates debris (50 to 5000 μm); and (4) mineral

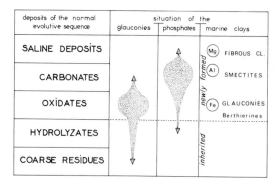

FIG. 1.—Position of glauconies and phosphates in relation to deposits of the normal evolutionary sequence. The left column lists the classical members of Gold-schmidt's sequence as revised by Millot (1964). They are deposited from the base to the top as indicated by the figure for a normal sequence. In this sequence, glauconitization is essentially related to the oxidate stage, whereas phosphatization occurs in the carbonate stage. This indicates that phosphate deposition is related to a period in the evolution of sedimentary basin characterized by a higher confinement; the nearby continent is more eroded and only the most soluble ions are transported by the rivers. The right column shows the position of glauconitic minerals in the theoretical sequence of deposition of the clay minerals.

debris of various nature as indicated in table 1. The three first types are related to the biosphere but not the fourth. Another relation has been shown: the alteration of the initial framework and the creation of porosity is considerably helped by living organisms. If debris of organic origin are favorable for glauconitization, one must not confuse the action of the biosphere in the formation of the initial framework with a necessary presence of organic compounds during the marine mineral formation. At the present time the direct interference of organic compounds in glauconitic mineral genesis **remains to be demonstrated.** Their role is probably of the same order as in the genesis of smectites in soils.

The second facies analyzed by Odin (1975) is named here film facies.

Glauconitization incrusts gravels, pebbles or hard-ground of various mineralogic composition including pure calcitic or siliceous frameworks. The green minerals do not form on the surface but inside the framework: in holes, cracks and pores, often created by biological activity.

The last local factor to be considered is the redox potential. The best way to comment on this factor would be to say that the conditions for the formation of glauconitic minerals are those of the sea bottom, 60 m to 350 m deep, within the uppermost few centimeters (sometimes meters) of the sediment inside a pellet, but this

pelletal micromilieu has not yet been investigated precisely (Bromley, 1967).

Such an environment is not very reducing: iron would occur as sulfide and octahedral iron of the authigenic pelites would be Fe^{++} instead of dominant Fe^{+++}. The environment is not very oxidizing: not all octahedral iron is Fe^{+++}.

Some authors assumed an oxidizing environment because brown-red pellets are sometimes present in the glauconitic facies; such an argument contradicts our interpretation: if green pellets are rusted they have been **altered** in an oxidizing environment and are not in equilibrium with it but with a more reducing water. Slightly reducing conditions seem on the contrary a necessary requisite for iron mobility.

It is also commonly assumed that glauconitic pellets form in agitated waters because they are often rounded and glazed. In fact, the pellets are rounded because they are eroded in an environment which *ipso facto* stops crystal growth; rounding is an effect of alteration. Glauconitization does not occur in an agitated or oxidizing environment.

This later type of environment may, however, be met when a regression occurs on glauconitic levels. A good example is the African Atlantic coast where a thin belt of red pellets is found from Morocco to the Congo at a depth of 100–120 m. This is the vestige of the last Holocene regression, 20,000 years ago, which lead to a typical marine alteration of previously unburied glauconitized pellets.

Microenvironment

The "film facies," just as the pelletal facies, of the glauconitization is generated in a **semi-confined microenvironment** (Odin and Giresse, 1972), which is very common. We have defined this semi-confined environment, at the millimeter scale, as the result of a thermodynamic equilibrium between the water contained in the framework and the external water. It is slightly confined, permitting crystal growth in a protected milieu but slow exchanges remain active. Proofs of the relative confinement of this original microenvironment, intermediate between the open sea-water and the buried sediment, are multiple.

The glauconitic minerals do not grow by direct precipitation on the framework as oolites or stromatolites do, but inside micropores, cracks and other protected environments. Authigenesis occurs under shelter from the diluting action of open ocean water.

If we analyse the powder diffractograms of various granulometric fractions of green pellets, a common observation is that the small pellets (less than 100 μm) are less evolved, i.e. less glauconitized (glauconitic minerals less closed,

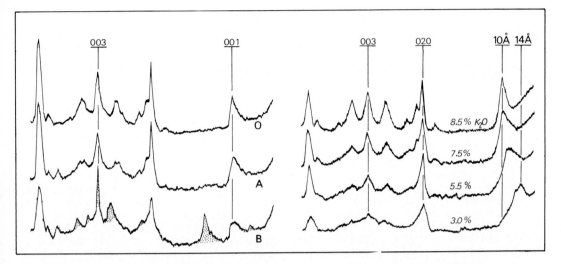

FIG. 2.—Powder diffractograms of glauconitic pellets. Right side: Four glauconies from the Cenomanian, Lutetian, Recent and Recent with respectively 8.5- 7.5- 5.5 and 3.0% K_2O. The aspect of the diffractogram and the potassium content are related to the evolution of the pellets. The evolution may be read on the (001) diffraction which changes from a broad peak at 14 Å to a sharp peak at 10 Å. An interesting evolution may also be followed on the two peaks on both sides of the (003) diffraction. Left side: Glaucony of the Middle Miocene of Aquitania separated from various granulometric fractions: 1000 μm < 0 < 500 μm; 500 μm < A < 160 μm; 160 μm < B < 100 μm. The mineralogical nature of authigenic minerals is related to the size of the pellets. In the small pellets traces of the initial support are still visible, but not in the large ones. The peaks on both sides of (003) are higher in fraction 0 than in fraction B. We conclude that the evolution is more pronounced in the larger pellets than in the smaller ones because of better confinement.

less ordered, traces of inherited framework more visible) than the bigger ones (150–500 μm). This indicates that, for small pellets, the environment is too open and not sufficiently confined with respect to open sea-water (fig. 2).

During glauconitization of a pelletal support, the glauconitic minerals grow faster inside the pellet (a more confined environment) than in peripheric zones. The result is that cracks appear on the surface of the pellets like in the crust of a bread which raises during cooking. This fact explains the generally cracked aspect of the glauconitic pellets. Simultaneously, the mineral sheets appear under the scanning electron-microscope to be more developed inside than outside the pellet (Odin and Lamboy, 1975; Lamboy, 1976, pl. 17-28-36). These cracks are themselves a new confined microenvironment for a second generation of glauconitization: (Lamboy, 1976; pl. 37-38 and fig. 3, step 4 further on).

A second aspect of this milieu is that **minimum exchanges** with sea-water occur and are necessary in spite of this relative confinement.

A proof of these exchanges is given by various cases of mineral authigenesis in coprolites: (Giresse and Odin, 1973) and micas (Odin, 1975; p. 130-137). For these initial frameworks, the mineral development depends on the general en-

vironment: in a sub-deltaic environment, 7Å sheets grow in the coprolites or between the mica sheets (berthierinization); in an open marine milieu, T O T sheets grow. In the Guinean Gulf, Bezrukov and Senin (1970) observed that the same type of pellets have evolved to goethite at less than 30 m depth, to berthierine between 50 and 70 m depth, and to glauconitic minerals between 200 and 300 m depth. The general environment controls the authigenesis inside the intimacy of the framework.

This is also true for a carbonate framework, where an exchange is clearly necessary because no one ion of the glauconitic minerals is initially present in the framework. This consideration is valid for most cases of glauconitization: exchange of ions is a primary condition for the growth of the authigenic minerals and the elimination of the initial framework. An initial framework for glauconitization with a chemical and mineralogical composition related to glauconitic minerals (ferric smectites or micas) seems to be very exceptional and not particularly favorable. This new observation contradicts the often accepted general theory (Burst, 1958) of the glauconitization of **inherited phyllites** during which crystal architecture is preserved. In the general case, glauconitic minerals are really marine authigenic in origin and not inherited minerals only modified in the sea. In this authigenesis most of the ions, including major elements such as Si, Fe, Al come from the external water and are assembled in the pores of the framework (Odin, 1969, 1972, 1975; Giresse and Odin, 1973; Lamboy, 1976, Birch et al. 1976). If the useful ions are present in the framework itself, they may be used, but what we insist on is that their presence there is not an important factor.

Finally, the fact that grains of more than three mm in diameter are not completely glauconitized may be interpreted as due to a too confined environment in the center of the framework, which prevents sufficient exchanges for the subsequent growth of glauconitic minerals. This factor determines the boundary between the pelletal and the film facies depending on the possibilities of exchange with open sea-water.

In summary, glauconitization occurs in a semi-confined micro-environment, sufficiently confined to allow concentration of ions and crystal growth not possible in open sea-water. Slow exchanges, however, must be possible to feed the crystallizations of glauconitic smectites and the elimination of ions of the altered framework. After this initial phase, the development of more evolved minerals requires admission of additional ions. In this process, the framework acts as an ion-pump catching ions from the sea,especially iron, which is consumed by the growing crystal.

This environment applies to glauconitization and certainly also to other authigenics as berthierine or barite deposited at the bottom of the sea. The process must be distinct from the chemical precipitation of calcite or goethite. The contact with open sea water being a primordial and sufficient factor during the whole evolution, glauconitization may be separated from post-burial diagenesis. We are at the boundary between calcite precipitation (oolites for example) and zeolite formation. With some authors (Dunoyer de Segonzac, 1969), we may include all these phenomena in the sedimentogenesis (preburial diagenesis *sensu anglico*) preliminary to the restricted diagenesis (*sensu gallico*).

The most important property of the framework which defines the specific quality of the environment is its internal milieu which might be the result of cleavage (mica, feldspars), initial structure of the tests (calcitic network of echinoderms, foraminiferal lodges), texture of the mud of coprolites, pores due to biochemical or chemical alteration of calcitic or siliceous pellets, pebbles, or hard grounds, a confined micromilieu, and a large surface of reaction favorable for crystal growth and permitting the necessary exchange with sea-water.

The genesis of the pelletal glauconitic facies is summarized in fig. 3. Glauconitization can be arrested at any stage of the evolution described on fig. 3 by the burial of the pellets under detrital or biological sediments. What should be noted in this evolution is that initially one has a physical framework and at the end one has a clay mineral of pelletal appearance. The final pelletal appearance, although very modified in many cases, is due to the initial framework itself being

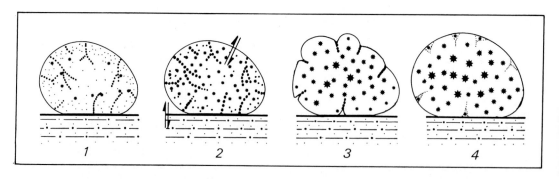

Fig. 3.—Evolutionary scheme of pelletal glaucony. Step 1—An initial framework of variable mineralogical nature is altered on the bottom of the ocean (· — · — ·). Porosity is created and a semi-confined microenvironment results; Step 2—The initial framework rejects inherited ions to the sea while ions from the bottom water are trapped and feed the crystal growth of glauconitic smectites (***); Step 3—Glauconitic smectites are rearranged by recrystallizations into more closed minerals. Surficial cracks appear as the result of faster crystal growth in the center than on the periphery of the framework; Step 4—A new generation of less evolved glauconitic minerals appears and surrounds the glauconitic pellet where glauconitic micas are born through new recrystallization (**). The pelletal nature of this glaucony is the result of the pelletal nature of the initial framework and of the selectivity of the process here described: pellets of 100 to 500 μm are especially favorable. This evolution may stop at any moment either through burial or through alteration.

pelletal; but the specific nature of the clay mineral is not due to the chemical nature of this framework.

ENVIRONMENT OF PHOSPHATIZATION

We will limit the comparison here to marine phosphates, in which most authors have found the dominant component to be a fluorine rich carbonate-fluorapatite, the accepted name of which is francolite.

General Environment

The climatic distribution of marine phosphates seems to indicate that their formation is influenced by temperature. Birch (1977) explains the deposition of shallow phosphorites (at a depth of 50 m and less) by the action of the sun. The classical view of Kasakov (1937) explains the deposition of phosphate by upwelling which leads to an increase in water temperature and, in consequence, waters of deep sea origin become phosphate supersaturated. In the same way Recent phosphorites form in low latitudes, while glacial periods interrupted phosphorite formation off Peru (Burnett and Veeh, 1977). Thus, warm temperatures clearly act on phosphorite deposition.

Concerning the often noted coincidental occurrence of glauconitic and phosphoritic sediments, we show on table 2 the example of the east Atlantic African margin. In summary, glaucony is sometimes formed before phosphorite, sometimes after phosphorite and sometimes both form synchronously.

In North Spain phosphatization is posterior to glauconitization (Lamboy, 1976). An alteration of the glauconitized level by later phosphatization occurs also on the shelf off South-west Africa (Emelyanov, 1973, Parker, 1975) and on Cretaceous hard ground (Kennedy and Garrison, 1975). Bromley (1967) notes a succession of steps in hard-ground from the European Cretaceous: 1) stop in deposition and formation of a classical hard-ground on chalks (Juignet, 1974); 2) glauconitization of the altered hard-ground; 3) phosphatization of the glauconitized hard-ground and last; 4) precipitation of a thin film of phosphates. Bromley notes that the change from glauconitization to phosphatization seems related to a shallowing of the sea. One hundred meters is proposed as the minimum depth while excessive shallowing stops the process of phosphatization. Baturin et al. (1970) indicate 70 meters off Namibia (South-west African margin) as the upper boundary of phosphate genesis.

However, phosphoritic, as glauconitic, sediments are poor bathymetric indicators: Giresse (this volume); Parker (1975) and Birch (1977) indicate possible estuarine, lagoonal or very shallow sea-water phosphatizations.

In other cases, glauconitization postdates the phosphorite. Plio-Quaternary glauconies alter Miocene phosphates of New Zealand (Cullen, 1978). In Early Albian, Early Cenomanian and Early Lutetian of the Paris Basin phosphatic pellets or nodules are often altered by glauconitization. In sea floor samples from Chile, Chatham Rise and Straits of Florida phosphates are also turned green (Bentor, personal communication). There are many examples of phosphatized and glauconitized sediments; there is thus a correlation we will analyze later. These examples also show that both facies are not in thermodynamic equilibrium with sea-water at the same time (therefore under the same conditions). There is an alternation of one facies with the other and not a concomitant development.

Considering the time required for phosphatization various observations must be made. In fossil series, phosphate nodules are often associated with unconformities. The case is well illustrated in the Paris Basin where Early and Middle Albian may be phosphatic or not; where it is not, the formation is much more developed. But phosphatic sediments occur in non-condensed series too. Giresse (1978, and this volume), has shown that initial concentration of phosphorus may be very rapid, but at the same time a high concentration is stopped by too high a rate of deposition.

Just as for glauconies whose presence in a sediment may be interpreted as a weak insignificant break or as an important unconformity depending on their nature, it would be interesting to know, if a constant relation may be obtained between the composition of the phosphorite (the P_2O_5-content or the mineralogical nature or the facies of the marine phosphate for example) and the duration of an eventual depositional break.

Let us examine now the probable position of phosphorites in Goldschmidt's pedagogic model mentioned previously. In considering the sediments off Africa, it should be pointed out that phosphates are often associated with, sometimes dolomitic, limestones: Cretaceous and Paleogene of Tunisia, Senegal, Congo. They may occur with mudstones: Millot (1964) in Mauritania, Giresse (1978) in the Congo and we also, in the Paleogene of Senegal, have observed that phosphates are sometimes associated with palygorskites, a clay mineral typical of the early confinement of a basin. We will see later that the calcium of carbonates often feeds the growth of phosphates. Thus, we propose to put phosphatogenesis in the carbonate member, one step later than glauconization (right column of fig. 1). This is, however, not a reason to suppose that phosphates always form after glaucony: inverse sequences are common in the sedimentary series.

Finally, we note that marine phosphates, in

contrast to glauconies, occur on the open sea bottom as well as near estuaries.

Local Environment

The most frequently discussed factors in the local environment are the conditions under which phosphorus accumulates on the sea bottom. There are some differences with glauconitization in the fact that phosphates are essentially part of the biogeochemical cycle, whereas glauconitic minerals use essentially lithophile elements (Si, Fe, Al). Organic compounds are certainly involved in phosphate accumulation process. A reducing environment is thus generated on the sea bottom and the pH is lowered while organic matter is regenerated. This process is certainly favorable for the mobilization of phosphorus as phosphate solubility is higher at low pH.

It is, however, a different question, if these are exactly the conditions necessary for phosphate crystal growth. Lucas and Prévôt (1975) note that a reducing environment is useful for mobilization of phosphorus, but a more oxidizing one is necessary for phosphate genesis. In this connection, Bentor (personal communication) remarks that a low Eh is favorable for phosphorus accumulation in organic matter but causes immobilization of the phosphorus, liberated by organic matter regeneration, on metal oxide particles. Later it is mobilized from them by an Eh increase. It is clear that the formation of phosphates is the result of a variety of successive conditions in space and time. Iron, the main metal oxide particle immobilizing phosphorus, has an interesting connection with glauconitic facies genesis.

An important classical discussion concerns the relationship between phosphate genesis and upwelling. This relation was first set forth by Kasakov (1937) and by Dietz et al. (1942). Numerous authors have observed a connection between recent upwellings and phosphate deposits on the continental margins. On the other hand, the main outcrops correlate with cold streams: California current, Humboldt current, Labrador current extension, Falkland current, Canarias current, Benguela current, SW monsoon current and occidental Australian current are specially concerned. Tooms et al. (1971, fig. 8) observed a nearly perfect correlation. Kolodny (1969) and Kolodny and Kaplan (1970), however, note that there is a noticeable difference of age between the present upwellings and the age of the phosphorites which probably formed during Pleistocene or Miocene time.

Parker (1975) insists on the fact that this relation remains more speculative than demonstrated. The same question has been asked for glauconitization, but the correlation between Recent glauconies and Recent upwelling appears poor. Phosphatization is, in a more or less indirect way, much more closely related to upwelling and concomitant biological development than is glauconitization.

A less classical observation concerns the episodic correlation between phosphatization and silicification in recent and old formations: Baturin et al. (1972); Birch (1977) and Giresse (1978) have recently observed this relation. The fact that cold waters (local upwellings and regional currents) favor the development of silicoflagellates and diatoms which, after their death, sink to the sea floor, is the probable bond. Once more, one sees here the duality between various apparently opposite factors in such marine genesis: silica is a product of low temperature plankton which concentrates phosphorus, whereas phosphatization itself is favored by higher temperatures.

Microenvironment

Various processes of phosphatization have been observed by different authors. Baturin et al. (1972) and Birch (1977, 1978) suggest that direct chemical precipitation from open sea water is not actually observed but is possible in shallow embayments, with an accumulation due to phosphate enriched waters in interstitial pores. A strictly biological deposition exists and is the result of accumulation on the sea floor of bones, teeth or coprolites more or less rich in phosphorus, where no other deposits occur. This case is often observed in old series. Coprolites are a case intermediate to the next process, the biochemical accumulation, because, if they contain phosphorus, actual phosphatization (enrichment in phosphorus and mineral growth) occurs later in such an initial framework.

Phosphatization of carbonate debris or nodules has recently been studied by many authors: Parker (1975), Kennedy and Garrison (1975). As in the genesis of glauconies, several authors, especially Kennedy and Garrison, often use the notion of **initial framework.** The porosity of this framework which leads to a large internal surface and a confined milieu seems also an important factor. Giresse (1978) notes that fecal pellets of the same nature as those prone to glauconitization may serve for the concentration of phosphorus. In old levels, e.g. Cretaceous from Portugal or Paleogene from Senegal, such pellets of comparable aspect do occur.

Parker (1975) stresses the finely divided nature of the carbonate mud where phosphates are forming during diagenesis as a catalytic factor linked to porosity.

Thus, in the frequently observed case of replacement of carbonate by phosphate, the pelletal facies and confinement may be features shared with glauconitization. The size of the phosphatized framework is much more variable than for glauconitization and is generally bigger: a **stronger confinement,** it seems, can be used for phosphates. This argument fits the preceding observation concerning the place of phosphorites in the normal evolutionary series: nearest to the saline deposits when the basin is more confined. The nature of the initial framework of phosphatization is often calcitic but other initial mineralogies seem possible: shark or fish coprolites are frequent; Lamboy (1976) notes the peripheral and fissural phosphatization of plutonic rocks. This phosphatization follows the previous porosity while in carbonatic components the whole rock is phosphatized. There is here frequently a bond between the chemical nature of the framework and the final mineral. (The common element calcium facilitates the reaction in calcic deposits). Lamboy (1976) insists on the semi-confinement of phosphatization cells. The glauconitic pellets themselves may be a favorable support of phosphatization, the remaining pores defining a protected environment, as do the cracks of plutonic rocks. The author finally notes that the source of phosphorus is multiple and non-decisive, only the microenvironment is important.

DISCUSSION AND CONCLUSION ON POSSIBLE RELATIONS
BETWEEN GLAUCONIZATION AND MARINE
PHOSPHATIZATION

From the elements gathered above it is possible to explain the presence of both phosphatic and glauconitic elements in the same rock although conditions of genesis are slightly different.

Difficulty of Establishing Favorable Factors

A common inference from the reconstitution of the glauconitization and phosphatization processes is the apparent contradiction between various **successive environments** required for the full development of both facies; let us recall that:

— agitated beach water or very shallow waters (less than 50 m) are propitious for the formation of the initial framework of glauconitization, whereas authigenesis itself does not occur in such an oxidizing agitated environment but in a deeper one;

— biological interventions, i.e. organic material creating reducing and acid conditions, is efficient for the formation of the initial framework of glauconitization while glauconitic mineral crystal growth occurs in a slightly reducing and basic micromilieu;

— some glauconitic pellets may be formed quickly while others are the result of a very long evolution associated with a geologically significant break of sedimentation. This difference has been explained above;

— the preliminary biological concentration of phosphorus is favored by rather cool sea-water while phosphate genesis occurs generally at low latitude and phosphate precipitation is facilitated by an increase of temperature;

— phosphorus concentration can be a very rapid phenomenon as shown by some Recent occurrences, whereas fossil phosphoritic levels are sometimes located in condensed levels. The concentration of such a phosphate series is mechanically and chemically favored by a break of deposition through alteration of previously deposited rocks under condition in which phosphates are more stable than other compounds;

— some phosphates appear to have formed on the near-shore continental shelf whereas others are clearly associated with deposition at a depth of 200 meters or more probably after a sea level change.

Some Common Points

A calcium carbonate component favors both facies inspite of the lack of contribution of the chemical elements for glauconitization while calcium is used by phosphatization. The bond seems to be the easy alteration of such a calcitic rock which creates a favorable milieu for geochemical reactions: large internal surfaces because of pores, cracks, holes, confinement towards the open sea.

Pellets, gravels or pebbles seem to be an initial framework useful for the development of both authigeneses under equivalent facies: various pellets in the case of glauconitization; more or less big coprolites, boulders or macrofossils for phosphatization. Once more, the major factors involved are probably surface area and local confinement on the sea floor, but phosphatization is much more independent of these factors than glauconitization. A warm climate facilitates both phosphatization and glauconitization; the former principally because temperature is an important factor in phosphate deposition, the latter especially because the continent liberates larger amounts of iron.

Some Differences

Although formed in a locally semi-confined environment, the glauconitic minerals are specific of the general open sea-water whereas phosphate (francolite) concentrations are described far from the coast or in estuarine sediments.

Phosphatizations seems more dependent on low latitude and the presence of organic compounds than glauconitization. Phosphates use essentially elements of the biosphere (Ca, P, F) while Si, Al, Fe, elements of glauconitic minerals, are essentially lithophile.

In Goldschmidt's sequence, phosphates together with other calcium compounds, are related to a later phase than glauconitic minerals which are more related to silicates.

Evaluating these differences one might conclude that the conditions required for glauconitization and phosphatization are different though similar.

Why Glauconitization and Phosphatization Are Related

We feel the answer to this question has been given by each of the preceding points.

Glauconitization and phosphatization occur in neighboring stages in the evolution of a sedimentary basin. During climatic or eustatic changes the general conditions of sedimentation change but slightly; phosphatization, therefore, may succeed glauconitization in a normal evolution of an epicontinental basin but precede it in an inversed sequence. This is facilitated by the fact that both processes frequently seem to occur at a depth of 100 to 150 m on the continental shelf in low latitudes.

Let us remember also that a protracted absence of detrital deposition makes both authigeneses easier and increases the chances they might overlap in time.

Finally, the present continental shelf to which many sedimentologists refer is a remarkable, but special, example which illustrates our point. At many places of the shelf both glauconitization and phosphatization have occurred. We explain this by the fact that the Quaternary is a period during which many and important changes of sea level and climate have occurred. Therefore, different authigeneses could occur successively. Moreover, the rate of deposition is rarely important and sometimes negative: erosion takes place. Thus, the deposited and buried phosphates or glauconitic pellets were reworked. The relative geochemical stability of these components in sea-water leads to a concentration of glauconitic and phosphatic elements relative to other components such as detrital clays, detrital or biological carbonates which were scattered or altered. As an illustration, different authors described glauconitic or phosphoritic elements of Miocene or even Cretaceous age on the surface of the present continental shelf together with Quaternary and Recent ones. Different authigeneses which have taken place at different times occur thus mixed on a same epicontinental surface.

In summary, the bond between glauconitization and phosphatization is not fortuitous. The probability of connection is high in the condensed series; but this is far from necessary.

ACKNOWLEDGEMENTS

The authors are greatly indebted to Y. K. Bentor for his many remarks and new information on the subject of this paper. The comments of our colleagues P. Giresse (Brazzaville) and of M. Lamboy (Sfax) and the data they offered were very useful in the drafting of this manuscript. To all of them our thanks are due.

REFERENCES

BATURIN, G. N., 1972, Phosphorus in interstitial waters of sediments of S.E. Atlantic: Oceanology, v. 12, p. 849–855.

———, MERKULOVA, K. T., AND CHALOV, P. I., 1972, Radiometric evidence for Recent formation of phosphatic nodules in marine shelf sediments: Mar. Geol., v. 13, p. M37–M40.

———, KOCHENOV, A. V., AND PETELIN, V. P., 1970, Phosphorite formation on the shelf of Southwest Africa: Lithol. and Min. Res., v. 3, p. 266–276.

BEZRUKOV, P.L., AND SENIN, M., 1970, Sedimentation of the West African Shelf: in The Geology of the East Atlantic Continental Margin—A Symposium, Cambridge, 1970, p. 1–8.

BIRCH, G. F., 1977, Phosphates from the Saldanha Bay Region: Trans. Roy. Soc. S. Afr., v. 42, p. 223–240.

———, 1978, Penecontemporaneous phosphatization by replacement and precipitation mechanisms on the western margin of Southern Africa: Xth Intern. Congr. Sedimentology, Abstracts, p. 71–72.

———, WILLIS, J. P., AND RICHARD, R. S., 1976, An electron microprobe study of glauconites from the continental margin off the West Coast of S. Africa: Mar. Geol., v. 22, p. 271–284.

BROMLEY, R. G., 1967, Marine phosphates as depth indicators: Mar. Geol., v. 5, p. 503–509.

BURNETT, W. C., AND VEEH, H. H., 1977, Uranium series disequilibrium studies in phosphorite nodules from the West Coast of South America: Geochim. Cosmochim. Acta, v. 41, p. 755–764.

BURST, J. F., 1958, Mineral heterogeneity in glauconite pellets: Am. Min., v. 43, p. 481–497.

CAYEUX, L., 1916, Introduction à l'étude pétrographique des roches sédimentaires: Glauconie: Imprimerie Nationale, Paris, p. 241–252.

———, 1932, Les manières d'être de la glauconie en milieu calcaire: C. R. Acad. Sc., Paris, v. 195, p. 1050–1052.

COLLET, L. W., 1908, Les Dépôts Marins. Doin Éditeur, Paris, 325 p.

CORNEN, G., GIRESSE, P., AND ODIN, G. S., 1973, Découverte de dépôts phosphatés néogènes sous-marins dans les plateaux continentaux du Sud du Gabon et du Nord du Congo: C. R. Somm. S. G. F., v. 1, p. 9–11.

CULLEN, D. J., 1978, Distribution, composition and age of submarine phosphorites on Chatham Rise: Xth Intern. Congr. Sedimentology, Abstracts, p. 148.

DIETZ, R. S., EMERY, K. O., AND SHEPARD, F. P., 1942, Phosphorite deposits on the sea floor off southern California: Bull. Geol. Soc. Amer., v. 53, p. 815–848.

DUNOYER DE SEGONZAC, G., 1969, Les minéraux argileux dans la diagenèse: Mém. Serv. Carte Géol. Als. Lorr., v. 29, 320 p.

EMELYANOV, E. M., 1973, Composition of low-phosphatic and phosphatic sediments of the West African Shelf: Dokl. Akad. Nauk. USSR, v. 95, p. 239–261.

GIRESSE, P., 1978, Sur les conditions actuelles et récentes du début de concentration des phosphates dans les sédiments marins consolidés de la plate-forme tropicale atlantique de l'Afrique: Xth Intern. Congr. Sedimentology, Résumés, p. 253 and preprint offset.

———, AND CORNEN, G., 1976, Les phosphates miocènes et éocènes des plate-formes du Congo et du Gabon: Bull. Bur. Rech. Géol. Min., v. 1, p. 5–15.

———, AND ODIN, G. S., 1973, Nature minéralogique et origine des glauconies du plateau continental du Gabon et du Congo: Sedimentology, v. 20, no. 4, p. 457–488.

JUIGNET, P., 1974, La transgression crétacée sur la bordure orientale du Massif Armoricain (Aptien-Albien-Cénomanien de Normandie et du Maine; le stratotype du Cénomanien). Thèse d'Etat, Caen, 806 p. offset.

KASAKOV, A. V., 1937, The phosphorite facies and the genesis of phosphorites: Trans. Sci. Inst. Fertil. Fungic., v. 142, p. 95–116.

KENNEDY, W. J., AND GARRISON, R. E., 1975, Morphology and genesis of nodular phosphates in the Cenomanian glauconitic marl of South-East England: Lethaia, v. 8, p. 339–360.

KOLODNY, Y., 1969, Are marine phosphorites forming today? Nature, v. 224, p. 1017–1019.

———, AND KAPLAN, I.R., 1970, Uranium isotopes in sea floor phosphorites: Geoch. Cosmoch. Acta, v. 34, p. 3–24.

LAMBOY, M., 1968, Sur un processus de formation de la glauconie en grains à partir des débris coquilliers. Rôle des organismes perforants: C. R. Acad. Sc., Paris, v. 266, p. 1937–1940.

———, 1976, Géologie marine du plateau continental au N.O. de l'Espagne: Thèse d'Etat, Rouen, 283 p.

———, AND ODIN, G. S., 1975, Nouveaux aspects concernant les glauconies du plateau continental N. O. espagnol: Rev. Géogr. Phys. Géol. Dyn., v. XVII, 2, p. 99–120.

LUCAS, J., AND PREVOT, L., 1975, Les marges continentales, pièges géochimiques: Bull. Soc. Geol. Fr., XVII, 4, p. 496–501.

MCARTHUR, J. M., 1978, The trace element geochemistry of phosphorite rocks: Xth Intern. Congr. Sedimentology, Abstracts, p. 430.

MILLOT, G., 1964, Géologie des Argiles. Masson Éditeur, Paris, 499 p.

MURRAY, J., AND RENARD, A. F., 1891, Voyage of H.M.S. "Challenger" during the years 1873–1876. Report on Deep Sea Deposits, Chapt. VI, Part III, p. 378–391.

ODIN, G. S., 1969, Méthode de séparation des grains de glauconie, intérêt de leur étude morphologique et structurale: Rev. Géogr. Phys. Géol. Dyn., v. XI, p. 171–184.

———, 1972, Observations nouvelles sur la structure de la glauconie en accordéon; description du processus de genèse par néoformation: Sedimentology, v. 19, p. 285–294.

———, 1973, Répartition, nature minéralogique et genèse des granules verts recueillis dans les sédiments marins actuels: Sciences de la Terre, Nancy, v. XVIII, p. 79–94.

———, 1975, De glauconiarum, constitutione, origine, aetateque. Recherches sédimentologiques et géochimiques sur la genèse des glauconies actuelles et anciennes; application à la révision de l'échelle chronostratigraphique: Thèse d'Etat, Paris, 280 p.

———, AND GIRESSE, P., 1972, Formation de minéraux phylliteux (berthiérine, smectites ferrifères, glauconite ouverte) dans les sédiments du Golfe du Guinée: C. R. Acad. Sc. Paris, v. 275, p. 177–180.

———, AND LAMBOY, M., 1975, Sur la glauconitisation d'un support carbonaté d'origine organique: les débris d'Echinodermes du plateau continental nord-espagnol: Bull. Soc. Géol. Fr., v. 17, 1, p. 108–115.

———, AND LETOLLE, R., 1978, Les glauconies et aspects voisins ou confondus; signification sédimentologique: Bull. Soc. Géol. Fr., v. XX, no. 4, p. 553–558.

PAQUET, H., 1970, Evolution géochimique des minéraux argileux dans les altérations et les sols: Mém. Serv. Carte Géol. Als. Lorr., v. 30, 212 p.

PARKER, R. J., 1975, The petrology and origin of some glauconitic phosphorites from the South African Continental Margin: Jour. Sed. Pet., v. 45, no. 1, p. 230–242.

REYRE, D., 1966, Bassins sédimentaires du littoral africain: Symp. Ass. Serv. Géol. Afric. U.I.S.G., 300 p.

ROBERT, C., AND ODIN, G. S., 1975, Glauconie des sédiments de Mer Egée: Bull. Gr. Fr. Arg. v. 27, p. 1–11.

TOOMS, J. S., SUMMERHAYES, C. P., AND CRONAN, D. S., 1969, Geochemistry of marine phosphates and manganese deposits: Oceanogr. Mar. Biol. Ann. Rep., v. 7, p. 49–100.

———, SUMMERHAYES, C. P., AND MCMASTER, R. L., 1970, Marine geological studies on the North West African margin: Rabat-Dakar, in Geology of the East Atlantic Continental Margin—A Symposium (Cambridge), pp. 9–25.

VELDE, B., AND ODIN, G. S., 1975, Further information related to the origin of glauconies: Clays Clay Min., v. 23, p. 376–381.

SEPM Special Publication No. 29, p. 239–247, November 1980

EPISODICITY OF PHOSPHATE DEPOSITION AND DEEP OCEAN CIRCULATION-A HYPOTHESIS

RICHARD P. SHELDON
U.S. Geological Survey
National Center
Reston, Virginia 22092

ABSTRACT

The geochemical cycle of phosphorus includes a cold, deep-ocean-water, phosphorus sink that recycles into the shallow-water biosphere by vertical mixing. At the present time, water of this deep-ocean sink is apparently undersaturated with respect to apatite, even at shallow-water temperatures and pressures. In the present ocean in shallow-water areas of upwelling ocean currents, apatite probably is being precipitated diagenetically within the marine sediments from interstitial waters, but not at the sediment-water interface. In ancient oceans in shallow areas washed by upwelling ocean currents, it probably at times was precipitated primarily at the sediment water interface. This difference between the present and past oceans conforms with the empirically derived hypotheses of episodicity of phosphate deposition of earlier workers.

A general hypothesis of the episodicity of marine phosphate deposition caused by variations of deep-ocean circulation is summarized as follows: 1) episodes of phosphogenesis occur at the onset of episodes of oceanic vertical mixing after episodes of stability, during which the phosphorus content of the deep-ocean has built up to high levels, 2) the major phosphogenic episodes of the Cretaceous to early Tertiary are due to phosphorus withdrawal from the deep-ocean phosphorus sink primarily by equatorial upwelling at the time of high-level, warm seas, and 3) the major phosphogenic episodes of the Cambrian, Ordovician and Permian Periods and the Miocene Epoch are due to phosphorus withdrawals from the deep-ocean phosphorus sink primarily by trade-wind-belt upwelling at the time of transition from the high-level, warm oceans to low-level, cold oceans; the transition relates to glacial episodes. This general process of phosphogenesis began after the transition from the environment that existed 2,200 m.y. ago—with an acidic ocean and oxygen-free atmosphere—to an environment of an alkaline ocean and an oxygen-rich atmosphere.

INTRODUCTION

Hypotheses on the origin of marine phosphorite have been proliferating since the beginning of the century and now can be grouped into three general categories: 1) special events, such as catastrophic destruction of life (Murray and Renard, 1891) or volcanic addition of fluorine to the sea (Mansfield, 1940), 2) direct interaction of land and sea processes, such as introduction of phosphate to the sea from rivers (Pevear, 1966; Bushinski, 1964) and sea bottom flow of brines from shoreline salt pans to the continental shelves (Hite, 1976), and 3) processes of marine upwelling (Kazakov, 1937; McKelvey and others, 1953) leading to deposition of apatite either at the sediment-water interface or diagenetically within the sediments from interstitial water (Baturin, 1971). Most of these hypotheses are still seriously advocated, and no widely accepted general theory of phosphate sedimentation in the marine environment has been put forward.

The marine geologic studies of sea-bottom phosphorite on the continental shelves of North America, South America and Africa have not shown a simple process of genesis that can be easily applied to ancient deposits, but have introduced new complexities (Burnett and Sheldon,

1979). In areas of modern upwelling, no Holocene primary phosphatic sediment can be found in bottom sediments, although apatite has been discovered to be forming diagenetically within fine-grained sediments from interstitially trapped marine water. These diagenetic sediments, however, bear no great similarities to large ancient phosphorite deposits that are found in comparable paleogeographic environments and that bear petrographic evidence (equivocal to some investigators) of being deposited at the sediment-water interface. Despite this problem, a growing number of investigators are willing to accept an important relationship between upwelling oceanic currents and marine phosphate sedimentation. These investigators do not apply this hypothesis to all sedimentary phosphorites because many phosphorites show evidence of entirely different origins, including deposition in other environments, such as estuaries, lagoons, lakes, swamps, caves, and insular environments, deposition by other processes, such as residual enrichment by weathering, beach and fluvial placering, and diagenetic and sea-floor replacement, and deposition from other sources for phosphorus, such as rivers and bird and bat excrement or bone accumulation. However, a real concensus has not been reached.

239

In this paper, I present a general hypothesis that seems to explain much of the conflicting evidence regarding the processes of formation of marine phosphorites. This hypothesis draws heavily on the Fischer and Arthur (1977) hypothesis of secular variations in the pelagic realm, which advances an explanation for the empirically derived episodicity of many phenomena in the ocean.

GEOCHEMICAL CYCLE OF PHOSPHORUS

The main phases of the geochemical cycle of phosphorus have been identified by a number of workers (e.g. Burnett and Oas, 1979; H. H. Veeh, oral communication reported in Burnett and Sheldon, 1979; Froelich, 1979). Phosphorus is weathered from rocks exposed on the land surface and some of it enters actively into the biological cycle. It is transported eventually to the ocean where it is carried into deep water by sinking organisms, building up the phosphorus concentration of the deep ocean waters. The deep ocean is a large geochemical phosphorus sink or reservoir that is relatively stable, but phosphorus in it recycles into the biologic cycle in shallow water by vertical mixing. Other phosphorus sinks in the marine realm include apatitic fish debris, metalliferous sediments, carbonaceous matter, biogenic carbonate sediments, manganese nodules, and guano. Although these sediment sinks might be thought to remove phosphorus from the ocean permanently for the tectonic cycle involved, preliminary data indicate that 15×10^{12} grams of phosphorus are being returned each year presently to the ocean as a flux from ocean-floor sediments; only 0.41–1.9×10^{12} grams of phosphorus are added to the ocean from rivers each year (J. R. Morse, oral communication reported in Burnett and Sheldon, 1979). The details of the marine phases of the geochemical cycle of phosphorus are not clear.

Many lines of investigation show that apatite present on the modern sea floor is not being precipitated now on the sea floor (Baturin, 1971, 1978; Atlas, 1976; Atlas, oral communication reported in Burnett and Sheldon, 1979). Surprisingly, the phosphatic sediments on continental shelves are, in large part, of Miocene age, according to either radiometric or paleontologic data. For example, Miocene ages have been determined for phosphatic sediments off Florida and on the Blake Plateau (Riggs, 1979; Manheim, oral communication reported in Burnett and Sheldon, 1979), off northwest Africa (Summerhayes and others, 1972), off southwest Africa (Birch, 1979), off parts of southern California (Dietz and others, 1942), and on the Chatham Rise east of New

Zealand (Cullen, 1979). The ocean today is undersaturated with respect to apatite (Atlas, 1976, Atlas, oral communication reported in Burnett and Sheldon, 1979) owing to the low concentration of phosphorus and the formation of a complex ion of magnesium phosphate that effectively reduces the PO_4^{-3} ion concentration. Atlas' conclusions, as he points out, are based on pure sea-water and not on water similar to that near the bottom in areas of upwelling where dissolved organic matter that also can form complex ions with magnesium is present. Most evidence shows that phosphorus is not being removed significantly from the ocean today by chemical precipitation of phosphorite on the sea floor in areas of upwelling, even though minor amounts of phosphorus are being deposited as an integral part of fish debris and an adsorbed part of carbonaceous matter, carbonate sediments, metalliferous sediments and manganese nodules.

The past chemical character of the ocean with respect to phosphorus appears to have been different from that of today, implying a departure from the steady state composition assumed by many workers. One large past difference may have been in azoic Precambrian time when the low-oxygen, high-CO_2 atmosphere would have caused higher concentrations of dissolved CO_2 in the ocean than at present, which would tend to reduce the pH. If the ocean were acid, apatite would have been unstable. Maximum possible concentration of PO_4^{-3} ion in an acid ocean would have been controlled by the most insoluble of the acid phosphate minerals, which generally are more soluble than apatite. This argument assumes that the overall phosphate concentration of an ocean is generally controlled by the phosphate mineral phase in equilibrium with the ocean in areas of maximum solubility product of the appropriate ions, an assumption challenged by some workers. It follows from this argument that the phosphorus concentration of azoic Precambrian oceans before about 2,200 m.y. ago would have been much higher than it is today. In a lifeless ocean, biologic transport of phosphorus from surface water to deep water would not operate of course, and a biologically induced, deep water sink of phosphorus in the ocean would not exist. After life began, the pH of the Precambrian ocean increased due to removal of CO_2 from the atmosphere and ocean by biologic activity, and a point must have been reached where the water became alkaline and the solubility product of the ocean with respect to apatite was exceeded, possibly first in some particularly favorable areas. The earliest phosphorites to be deposited in the Precambrian ocean may owe their origin to this evolution of ocean chemistry. The Proterozoic apatitic stromatolitic phosphorites of China and India, which are thought to be primary precipitates induced by algal processes (Banerjee, 1978), may have been formed by this process, and such phosphorite may be more plentiful in rocks of this age in other parts of the world than is now realized.

The chemical character of the ocean later in the Proterozoic and in the Phanerozoic Eons also appears to have been different from that of today's ocean. Phosphorite appears from stratigraphic and petrographic evidence to have been deposited at the sediment-water interface. For example, in the Meade Peak phosphatic shale member of the Phosphoria Formation in southeastern Idaho, some phosphorite beds, a few tens of centimeters thick, are made up of true oolitic apatite grains and extend over a few thousand square kilometers. These phosphorite beds are interbedded with other thin, equally widespread beds of different types of phosphorite and carbonate rock and mudstone. The beds are laminated at all scales, from thin section, to hand specimen, to outcrop, to regional stratigraphic units; and it is difficult to conceive of them not being deposited at the sediment-water interface. Also in the Phosphoria Formation in Idaho widespread biostroms of phosphorite made up of shells of benthonic Orbiculoidea brachiopods are clearly sea-floor deposits, and pelletal phosphorite beds associated with them almost certainly are also sea-floor deposits. Pelletal phosphorite deposits in Jordan of Cretaceous age have great petrographic uniformity in a bed up to 12 meters thick and seem to be best explained by direct deposition on the sea-floor rather than by a process of reworking. All this argument is made against the suggested alternative origin (Cook, 1976; Y. Kolodny, oral communication reported in Burnett and Sheldon, 1979) that most bedded, marine phosphorites are deposited by winnowing of fine-grained sediments containing diagenetically deposited apatite pellets to form pure phosphorite. The argument is not that authigenic apatite deposition and winnowing doesn't occur, because much evidence shows that it does, but that it is neither the only process nor the dominant process of phosphorite formation. The evidence from the rocks themselves shows that most ancient phosphorite formed directly on the sea-floor.

The above arguments lead to the suggestion that 1) phosphorus composition of the ocean varied during geologic time and 2) there were times of high phosphorus concentration and significant phosphate primary sea-floor sedimentation and other times, including the present, of low phosphorus concentration and no significant phosphate sedimentation.

Episodicity of Marine Phosphorites

Several workers have suggested that phosphorite was deposited episodically during the Proterozoic and Phanerozoic Eons (Strakhov, 1969; Cook and McElhinny, 1979). In their recent summary, Cook and McElhinny (1979) assembled the evidence to show that major episodes of phosphogenesis occurred during the Miocene, Late Cretaceous to Eocene, Jurassic, Permian, Ordovician, Cambrian, late Proterozoic (Z) at 620 m.y., late Proterozoic (Z) at 700–800 m.y., middle Proterozoic (Y) and early Proterozoic (X) time. The paucity of phosphate in rocks of several other time intervals is equally as impressive as the abundance of phosphorite in the above time intervals. This includes Oligocene, Triassic, and Silurian times. The evidence for this episodicity seems large enough to overcome any argument of sampling errors due to vagaries of exposure of rocks of different ages.

Cook and McElhinny (1979) presented additional data showing episodes of iron ore and evaporite deposition and glacial and orogenic activity. They concluded that a correlation exists between iron ore and phosphorite deposition but that no consistent relationship exists between phosphorite deposition and the other events. They pointed out, however, that except during Mesozoic and early Tertiary time, a fairly good correlation exists between episodes of phosphorite deposition and glaciation.

Fischer and Arthur (1977) have advanced a general hypothesis to explain episodicity of many events in the geologic record of the pelagic realm for the last 100 m.y. They gave evidence for long episodes of warm, high-level, stable oceans alternating with shorter episodes of cold, low-level, rapidly circulating oceans. They postulated expanded ocean-wide oxygen minimum layers during the episodes of warm, high-level oceans. Following the model of Berger and Roth (1975), the Fischer and Arthur hypothesis states that in times of high-level warm seas, the increased residence time of deeper waters leads to an increase in their phosphate content, and possibly leads to apatite saturation. Upwelling during these times, while diminished, would deliver phosphorus-rich water to the shallow water sites of deposition. This idea is corroborated to some extent by the study of Burnett (1977), who analyzed the episodes of Quaternary phosphorite deposition with the sediments of the continental shelf of Peru and suggested a correlation between episodes of high sea level and phosphate deposition. On the other hand, the idea would seem to be in conflict with Cook and McElhinny's (1979) partial correlation of phosphogenesis and glaciation.

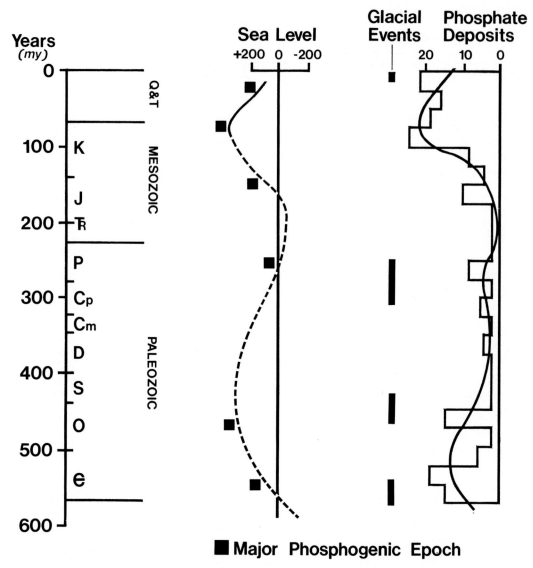

FIG. 1.—Phanerozoic phosphogenic and glacial epochs (Cook and McElhinny, 1979), and sea level changes (Tissot, 1979). Sea level curves dashed where less well known.

A comparison (fig. 1) of a general sea-level curve for the Phanerozoic (Tissot, 1979)[1] with a curve representing the major episodes of phosphogenesis shows that the Cambrian, Ordovician, Jurassic, Cretaceous to Eocene, and

[1] A general sea level curve of the Phanerozoic cannot be obtained from objective data. However, the percentage of continents covered by the ocean can be computed from facies maps, and a review of such analyses is given by Hallem (1978). The secular decrease during the Phanerozoic of marine inundation of the continents is hypothesized by Hallem to be due to plate tectonic

Miocene episodes of phosphogenesis occurred during the early Paleozoic and late Mesozoic to Tertiary sea-level maxima. Only the Permian episode of phosphogenesis occurred during a time of relatively low sea level. Times of low sea level corresponded with the episodes of decreased phosphate deposition in the Triassic, Early Jurassic, and Holocene.

processes, but the deviations from the secular change would contain the effects of eustatic sea level changes and give an approximate sea level curve. These deviations generally agree with Tissot's sea level curve.

Fischer and Arthur (1977) postulated a 32 m.y. cycle of high-level, warm seas and low-level, cool seas. The concept of minor cycles of comparable length superimposed on major cycles has been advanced for petroleum and coal by Tissot (1979). The same concept may be advanced for phosphate. As pointed out above, Burnett (1977) found a rough correlation between phosphorite deposition and high sea levels in the Quaternary phosphorite deposits on the Peruvian continental shelf. A cyclical relationship between phosphorite deposition and transgression and regression has been established for the Karatau sequence of Early Cambrian age of Kazakhstan, USSR (Eganov, 1979) and for the Phosphoria Formation of Permian age in the middle Rocky Mountains of the United States (Sheldon, 1963). Major phosphorite deposition in both of these units occurred during the transgressive and regressive phases of the cycle and not during either the high or low stillstands. Episodes of major as well as minor phosphogenesis may be due to second-order sea-level cycles imposed on the larger cycle.

HYPOTHESIS OF OCEANIC CIRCULATION AND PHOSPHORITE SEDIMENTATION

The following general hypothesis is advanced for consideration as one of several multiple-working hypotheses on marine phosphorite petrology.

After life began, phosphorus concentration would build up at deep levels in warm, high-level, stable oceans to values that would, at near-surface temperature, pressure, pH and high concentrations of organic matter, exceed the saturation concentration with respect to apatite. Vertical oceanic circulation would bring this phosphorus-rich water near the surface. This circulation could be accomplished primarily in two ways: 1) at times of high sea level by equatorial upwelling combined with circum-global equatorial currents (fig. 2), and 2) at the time of transition between high-level, warm seas and low-level, cold seas at the onset of intensified trade wind belt upwelling (fig. 3). As advanced by earlier workers (Kazakov, 1937; McKelvey and others, 1952) phosphorite would be deposited in either kind of upwelling where the solubility product of apatite was exceeded when the deeper water moved to shallower levels. Two processes would occur more or less simultaneously: 1) The deep, colder water would be depressurized and warmed and thus, its pH would rise, and 2) The nutrient-rich water on entering the photic zone would cause high biologic activity, which, in turn, would cause the formation of bottom waters rich in dissolved organic matter and even further enriched in total phosphorus owing to biogenic concentration (Gulbrandsen, 1969). During low sea-level stands, even during strong circulation, the deep-ocean phosphorus sink would have been depleted to the point that significant phosphorite sedimentation would have ceased.

Many problems seem to be explained by this general hypothesis, as discussed below.

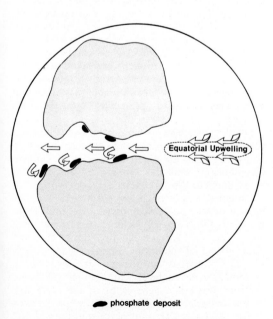

phosphate deposit

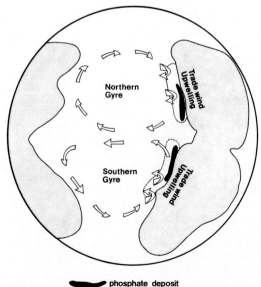

phosphate deposit

FIG. 2. —Idealized model of phosphate deposition due to equatorial upwelling.

FIG. 3.—Idealized model of phosphate deposition due to trade-wind-belt upwelling.

Relationship between Phosphogenesis and Glaciation

Cook and McElhinny (1979) showed partial relationship between glacial episodes and phosphogenesis, particularly for the Pliocene to Pleistocene, Permian, Ordovician and the late Proterozoic to Cambrian glacial episodes. The hypothesis suggested in the present paper relates episodes of trade wind belt phosphogenesis with glacial episodes, which are characterized by rapid circulation, low-level, cold oceans. For example, the late Miocene, Pliocene and Pleistocene glacial episode follows the middle Miocene episode of phosphogenesis. The Ross Sea of Antarctica was first fully iced over in the late Miocene (Brady and Martin, 1979), signaling the onset of the major Antarctic glaciation; the glaciation was accompanied by a lowering of sea level (Peck and others, 1979) and an increasing intensity of ocean circulation (Kaneps, 1979). As discussed below, phosphorites deposited during high-level, warm oceans at times of equitable world climate and no polar glaciation would be due primarily to equatorial upwelling and not to upwelling in the trade-wind belt.

Equatorial Phosphogenic Provinces

Ocean circulation gyres driven by the trade winds and westerly winds have strong divergent upwelling in the trade-wind belt on the eastern sides of the oceans; these gyres have been suggested as the mechanism for marine phosphogenesis (Kazakov, 1937; McKelvey and others, 1953; McKelvey, 1967). Although this mechanism may account for the phosphorites formed in the trade wind belts, it does not account for phosphorites formed in other phosphogenic provinces, the most important of which is the Tethyan Upper Cretaceous to lower Tertiary phosphogenic province of north Africa, the Middle East and northern South America (fig. 4). When the phosphorite was deposited, this province was at a paleolatitude of about 8°–15° N. The coriolis force is quite weak at such low latitudes, and the trade winds blew westward, parallel to the coast, making unlikely significant upwelling caused by the gyral circulation and the coriolis force alone. However, according to the equatorial-upwelling hypothesis, vertical mixing results from equatorial upwelling currents which are not driven by the coriolis force. Dynamic upwelling has been called upon earlier (McKelvey, 1967) to explain the east-west, low-latitude phosphogenic provinces, but this mechanism alone does not seem to give the required vertical mixing.

The insular phosphorites of the equatorial Pacific islands should in some way be related to marine sedimentary phosphorites. The insular

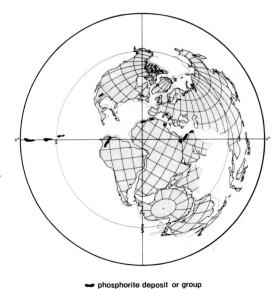

— phosphorite deposit or group
of seamounts with phosphorite on tops.

Fig. 4.—Phosphorite deposits of the Cretaceous and lower Tertiary periods. Continental reconstructions after Smith, Briden and Drewry, 1973.

phosphorites owe their origin to organic waste from equatorial plankton-fish-bird populations localized by equatorial upwelling (Hutchinson, 1950), and the marine phosphorites owe their origin to organic waste from plankton populations localized by upwelling. A relationship between the two kinds of phosphogenic provinces does exist in regions of trade-wind belt upwelling, where guano deposits on coastal islands form one of the phosphorus sediment sinks and sea-floor phosphorites form another. A similar relationship might be expected in areas of equatorial upwelling during episodes of phosphogenesis after sea birds evolved.

Some evidence exists for a relationship between seamount phosphorites and continental shelf phosphorites in the Late Cretaceous to Eocene phosphogenic episodes. Baturin (1978, Chapter 3) assembled the available data on worldwide phosphorite occurrence on seamounts. In the Pacific ocean, many seamounts in a zone from latitudes 17° N to 30° N and from longitudes 165° W to 150° E have on their upper surfaces phosphorites of submarine origin mixed with fossils of Cretaceous to Eocene age. More work is required to prove the ages of these phosphorites, but they are taken here to be of the same age as the contained fossils. Use of the procedures of Lancelot and Larson described in Larson and others (1975, p. 926) to determine the original positions of these deposits indicates that they were formed near the equator. Thus they give evidence of equatorial upwelling. These seamount phosphorites and the Gondwana Upper Cretaceous to Eocene Tethyan phosphorites formed in an equatorial phosphogenic province that nearly circled the globe (fig. 4). The seamount phosphorite formed in the zone of equatorial upwelling, and the northern Gondwana phosphorites formed where the phosphorus-rich waters flowed westward over the shallow continental shelf.

Relationship between Trade-Wind Upwelling and Equatorial Upwelling

Equatorial upwelling and trade-wind upwelling probably occurred simultaneously throughout geologic history, as they do now. Evidence for this simultaneous upwelling during a time of primarily equatorial phosphogenesis is the deposition of Cretaceous phosphorite of Mexico in the trade-wind upwelling belt of the north Pacific gyral at approximately the same time as the deposition of the Tethyan belt phosphorite, which was related to equatorial upwelling (fig. 4).

Perhaps the preferential distribution of large economic phosphorite deposits at lower latitudes within the trade-wind upwelling zones (Cook and McElhinny, 1979) was due to mixing of the phosphorus rich equatorial upwelling water with upwelling waters of the trade-wind circulation system. The Sechura phosphate deposit of Peru (Cheney and others, 1979) apparently occured at the juncture of the two current systems.

Other Types of Vertical Circulation

Other types of vertical circulation, in addition to equatorial and trade-wind-belt upwelling, probably occurred during epochs of phosphogenesis and caused deposition of phosphorite. The best example of additional vertical circulation systems operating along with equatorial and trade-wind-belt upwelling currents during an epoch of phosphogenesis is from the Miocene Epoch. In Miocene time in the trade-wind upwelling zones, deposition occurred in the USA and Mexico, Peru, offshore of southwestern Africa and offshore of northwestern Africa. Phosphorite was deposited during the Miocene Epoch in Indonesia (Hehuwat, 1975) perhaps in an equatorial upwelling zone. Other phosphorite deposition during the Miocene Epoch appears to have been due to different kinds of vertical circulation. The Miocene phosphorites of the southeastern United States, which presently are both onshore and offshore (Riggs, 1979), were due to some other type of vertical mixing combined perhaps with dynamic upwelling, and the Miocene phosphorite of the Chatham Rise east of New Zealand (Cullen, 1979) possibly was due

to yet another kind of circulation system. Although deposition during the Miocene drew on the deep ocean phosphorus sink that had been built up during the late Eocene and Oligocene Epochs after the Cretaceous to early Tertiary depletion of the deep ocean phosphorus sink, the circulation systems causing the phosphate deposition were varied.

It seems, however, that the most effective circulation systems insofar as phosphogenesis is concerned were equatorial upwelling during episodes of high-level warm oceans and trade-wind belt upwelling during episodes transitional from high-level, warm oceans to low-level, cold oceans. The effectiveness of the upwelling of either type depends on the interplay between deep-ocean richness of phosphorus and the intensity of upwelling; the effectiveness is not determined by the intensity of upwelling alone.

SUMMARY

A general hypothesis for deposition of marine phosphorite is summarized as follows:
Premises:
1. The deep ocean has constituted a major geochemical sink or reservoir for phosphorus since about 2,200 m.y. before present.
2. The phosphorus content of this sink builds up during periods of slow vertical mixing and declines during periods of rapid vertical mixing.
3. Vertical circulation cycles in the ocean correlate with cycles of high and low sea level.
4. Upward vertical mixing into shallow levels occurs primarily by equatorial upwelling and trade-wind-belt upwelling.
Hypothesis:
1. Episodes of phosphogenesis occur at the onset of episodes of vertical mixing after episodes of stability, during which the phosphorus content of the deep-ocean sink has built up to high levels.
2. The major phosphogenic episodes of the Cretaceous to early Tertiary are due to phosphorus withdrawal from the deep-ocean phosphorus sink primarily by equatorial upwelling at the time of high-level, warm seas.
3. The major phosphogenic episodes of the Cambrian, Ordovician and Permian Periods and the Miocene Epoch are due to phosphorus withdrawals from the deep-ocean phosphorus sink primarily by trade-wind-belt upwelling at the time of transition from the high-level, warm oceans to low-level, cold oceans; the transition relates to glacial episodes.
This general process of phosphogenesis began after the transition from the environment that existed 2,200 m.y. ago—an acidic ocean and an

oxygen-free atmosphere—to an environment of an alkaline ocean and an oxygen-rich atmosphere. A related but independent hypothesis is that during the transition period, a unique type of marine phosphogenesis resulted in deposition of stromatolitic phosphorite.

REFERENCES

ATLAS, E., 1975, Phosphate equilibria in sea water and interstitial waters: Ph.D. dissertation, 1975, Oregon State University, Dissert. Abs. Internat., v. 36, no. 7, p. 3285B.

BANERJEE, D. M., 1978, Chemical rhythmicity in the Precambrian laminated phosphatic stromatolites and its bearing on the origin of algal phosphorite; Indian Jour. of Earth Sci., v. 5, no. 1, p. 102–110.

BATURIN, G. I., 1971, Formation of phosphate sediments and water dynamics: Oceanology, v. 11, p. 372–376.

———, 1978, Phosphorites: Moscow, Nauka Press, 232 p., (in Russian).

BERGER, W. H. AND ROTH, P. H., 1975, Oceanic micropaleontology: progress and prospect: Rev. Geoph. and Space Physics, v. 13, no. 3, p. 561–635.

BIRCH, G. B., 1979, Phosphatic rocks on the western margin of South Africa: Jour. Sed. Petrology, v. 49, no. 1, p. 93–110.

BRADY, HOWARD AND MARTIN, HELENE, 1979, Ross Sea region in the Middle Miocene: a glimpse into the past: Science, v. 203, p. 437–438.

BURNETT, W. C., 1977, Geochemistry and origin of phosphorite deposits from off the coast of Peru and Chile: Geol. Soc. America Bull., v. 88, p. 813–823.

———, AND OAS, T. G., 1979, Environment of deposition of marine phosphate deposits off Peru and Chile, *in* Cook, P. J., and Shergold, J. H., eds., Proterozoic-Cambrian phosphorites, papers given at a UNESCO sponsored conference held in Australia in 1978: Canberra Publishing and Printing, p. 54–56.

———, AND SHELDON, R. P., eds., 1979, Report on the Marine Phosphatic Sediments Workshop: Honolulu, Hawaii, East-West Resource Systems Institute, East-West Center, 57 p.

BUSHINSKI, G. I., 1964, On shallow water origin of phosphorite sediments, *in* van Straaten, L.M.J.V., ed., Deltaic and shallow marine deposits: Amsterdam, Elsevier, p. 62–70.

CHENEY, T. M., McCLELLAN, G. H., AND MONTGOMERY, E. S., 1979, Sechura phosphate deposits, their stratigraphy, origin and composition: Econ. Geology, v. 74, no. 2, p. 232–259.

COOK, P. J., 1976, Sedimentary phosphate deposits, Chapter 11, *in* Wolf, K. H., ed., Handbook of strata-bound and stratiform ore deposits: New York, Elsevier, v. 7, p. 505–535.

———, AND McELHINNY, M. W., 1979, A reevaluation of the spatial and temporal distribution of sedimentary phosphate deposits in the light of plate tectonics: Econ. Geology, v. 74, no. 2, p. 315–330.

CULLEN, D. J., 1979, Submarine phosphorite deposits on Chatham Rise, east of New Zealand, *in* Cook, P. J., and Shergold, J. H., eds., Proterozoic-Cambrian phosphorites: Papers given at a UNESCO sponsored conference held in Australia in 1978: Canberra Publishing and Print., Australia, p. 54.

DIETZ, R. S., EMERY, K. O., AND SHEPARD, F. P., 1942, Phosphorite deposits on the seafloor off southern California: Geol. Soc. America Bull., v. 53, no. 6, p. 815–847.

EGANOV, E. A., 1979, The role of cyclic sedimentation in the formation of phosphorite deposits, *in* Cook, P. J. and Shergold, J. H., eds., Proterozoic-Cambrian phosphorites, papers given at UNESCO sponsored conference held in Australia in 1978: Canberra Publishing and Printing, Australia, p. 22–26.

FISCHER, A. G., AND ARTHUR, M. A., 1977, Secular variations in the pelagic realm: Soc. Econ. Paleontologist and Mineralogists Spec. Pub. 25, p. 19–50.

FROELICH, P. N., 1979, Marine phosphorus geochemistry: Kingston, R.I., Univ. of Rhode Island, unpublished Ph.D. dissert., University of Rhode Island.

GULBRANDSEN, R. A., 1969, Physical and chemical factors in the formation of marine apatite: Econ. Geology, v. 64, no. 4, p. 365–382.

HEHUWAT, F., 1975, Marine phosphorite deposits of Indonesia, *in* Proc. of the 12th session of the Committee for Co-ordination of Joint Prospecting for Mineral Resources in Asian Offshore Areas (CCOP), Economic and Social Commission for Asia and the Pacific, Bangkok, Thailand: Doc. 40, p. 282–286.

HALLEM, A., 1978, Secular changes in marine inundation of USSR and North America through the Phanerozoic: Nature, v. 269, no. 5631, p. 769–772.

HITE, R. J., 1976, Possible genetic relationships between evaporites, phosphorites, and iron-rich sediments [abs.]: Internat. Geol. Cong. 25th session, Sydney, v. 3, p. 835.

HUTCHINSON, G. E., 1950, The biogeochemistry of vertebrate excretion: Am. Mus. Nat. History Bull., v. 96, 554 p.

KANEPS, A. G., 1979, Gulf Stream: velocity fluctuations during the late Cenozoic: Science, v. 204, p. 297–301.

KAZAKOV, A. V., 1937, The phosphorite facies and the genesis of phosphorites, *in* Geological Investigations of Agricultural Ores: Trans. Sci. Inst. Fertilizers and Insecto-fungicides no. 142 (publ. for the 17th sess. Internat. Geol. Cong.), Leningrad, p. 95–113.

LARSON, R. L., MOBERLY, R., AND OTHERS, 1975, Initial Reports of the Deep Sea Drilling Project, vol. 32, Washington (U.S. Government Printing Office) 957 p.

MANSFIELD, G. R., 1940, The role of fluorine in phosphate deposition: Am. Jour. Sci., v. 238, no. 12, p. 833–879.

McKELVEY, V. E., SWANSON, R. W., AND SHELDON, R. P., 1953, The Permian phosphorite deposits of the western

United States, *in* Origine des gisements de phosphates de chaux: 19th Internat. Geol. Cong., Algiers, 1952, Comptes rendus, sec. 11, fasc. 11, p. 45–64.

——, 1967, Phosphate deposits: U.S. Geol. Survey Bull. 1252-D, p. D121.

MURRAY, JOHN, AND RENARD, A. F., 1891, Deep sea deposits, scientific results of the exploration voyage of H. M. S. Challenger, 1872–1876: London, Longmans, 525 p.

PECK, D. M., MISSIMER, T. M., SLATER, D. H., WISE, S. W., JR., AND O'DONNELL, T. H., 1979, Late Miocene glacial-eustatic lowering of sea level: evidence from the Jamiami Formation of south Florida: Geology, v. 7, no. 8, p. 285–288.

PEVEAR, D. R., 1966, The estuarine formation of United States Atlantic coastal plain phosphorite: Econ. Geol., v. 61, no. 2, p. 251–256.

RIGGS, S. R., 1979, Petrology of the Tertiary phosphorite system of Florida: Econ. Geol, v. 74, no. 2, p. 195–220.

SHELDON, R. P., 1964, Physical stratigraphy and mineral resources of Permian rocks in western Wyoming: U.S. Geol. Survey Prof. Paper 313-B, 269 p.

STRAKHOV, N. M., 1969, Principles of lithogenesis, 2: Consultants Bureau New York, N.Y., p. 235–261.

SUMMERHAYES, C. P., NUTTER, A. H., AND TOOMS, J. S., 1972, The distribution and origin of phosphate in sediments off northwest Africa: Sediment. Geol., v. 18, no. 1, p. 3–28.

TISSOT, B., 1979, Effects on prolific petroleum source rocks and major coal deposits caused by sea-level changes: Nature, v. 277, p. 463–465.

SEPM Special Publication No. 29, p. 249, November 1980

THE ORIGIN OF PHOSPHORITE DEPOSITS IN THE LIGHT OF OCCURRENCES OF RECENT SEA-FLOOR PHOSPHORITES
[extended abstract]

Y. KOLODNY
Department of Geology
The Hebrew University, Jerusalem, Israel

The question of the origin of sedimentary apatite concentrations can be approached from two directions:

On the one hand, it requires the understanding of the stability field of francolite and the kinetics of its crystallization. On the other hand, it is necessary to understand where, within the geo-chemical cycle of phosphorus, phosphorite is removed into the sedimentary column. Whereas it appears that the answer to the first question must rely heavily on experimental studies (see Atlas, 1975, Gulbrandsen, 1969), the second problem, the identification of environments of deposition of phosphorite, must primarily be solved by analysis of field data.

A major indicator, in this respect, is the repeated association of phosphorites with cherts (or diatomites) and organic rich shales. The trinity of P-Si-C which has been recognized as an association of elements related to biological activity, is further fingerprinted by a sharp ^{13}C depletion in carbonates of several of the well known deposits (Monterey Formation, Phosphoria Formation, Mishash Formation). It is concluded that the major phosphorus concentrating step is a biological one. The environment of apatite deposition, in which phosphorus is concentrated by organisms in areas of high productivity, is further identified by analysis of Recent phosphorite deposits (off Chile-Peru, off South-west Africa).

Both these localities are areas of present day upwelling. Upwelling, however, being often a necessary condition for high productivity is not sufficient for phosphorite formation; in most areas of present day upwelling phosphorites are not forming. In both localities, there is ample proof that a large part of the phosphate regeneration occurs not in the water body but rather in interstitial waters. It is from these waters that the first-stage apatite granules are formed. This diagenetic environment is reducing (measured Eh values reach -230 mv). The reducing nature of this environment is also demonstrated in several phosphorite deposits by a) presence of sulfides; b) occurrence of sea-water derived tetravalent uranium; c) a positive Eu anomaly on REE distribution plots in which the Ce depletion characteristic of deep sea-water generated sediments is weakened.

The final stage in phosphorite formation is that of mechanical enrichment and concentration of the diagenetically formed granules. This stage is characterized by oxidizing conditions. Whereas apatite *formed* diagenetically in stagnant basin sediments by phosphorus mobilization in interstitial waters, it was *concentrated* during periods of lower sea level stands in a high-energy environment.

This two stage scheme (originally proposed by Bushinskii [1966] and elaborated by Baturin [1971]) is in good accord with two geochemical observations:

a. Uranium occurs in two oxidation states. The U^{+4}/U^{+6} ratio probably reflects some complex function of a relation between the intensity of the first reducing stage and the secondary oxidizing reworking.

b. Sulfides in phosphorite bearing sediments coexist with sulfate in the apatite lattice. From $\delta^{34}S$ (Bliskovskiy et al., 1977) studies, this sulfate seems to be sea-water generated. Its introduction must have occurred at the later reworking stage.

Finally, the model of phosphorite formation, as deduced from the two Recent phosphorite forming environments, also explains one of the most striking textural features of fossil phosphorites—their clastic-conglomeratic appearance.

REFERENCES

ATLAS, E. L., 1975, Phosphate equilibria in seawater and interstitial waters: Ph.D. dissert., Corvallis, Oregon State Univ., 154 p.

BATURIN, G. N., 1971, Stages of phosphorite formation on the ocean floor: Nature Phys. Sci., v. 232, p. 61–62.

BLISKOVSKIY, V. Z., GRINENKO, V. A., MIGDISOV, L. I., AND SAVINA, L. I., 1977, Sulfur isotopic composition of the minerals of phosphorites: Geochem. Internat., v. 14, p. 148–155.

BUSHINSKII, G. I., 1966, The Origin of marine phosphorites: Lithology and Mineral Deposits, p. 292–311.

GULBRANDSEN, R. A., 1969, Physical and chemical factors in the formation of marine Apatite: Econ. Geol., v. 64, p. 365–382.